ADVANCING MATERIALS RESEARCH

National Academy of Engineering

National Academy of Sciences

with the participation of the
National Materials Advisory Board and the
Solid State Sciences Committee of the
National Research Council

Peter A. Psaras and H. Dale Langford, *editors*

Foreword by Frederick Seitz

NATIONAL ACADEMY PRESS
Washington, D.C. 1987

National Academy Press · 2101 Constitution Ave., NW · Washington, DC 20418

The National Academy of Sciences is a private organization chartered by the United States Congress in 1863 to advise the federal government on questions of science and technology. The National Academy of Engineering is a private organization established in 1964 to share in the chartered responsibilities of the National Academy of Sciences. The National Research Council was established in 1916 and is the operating division of the two Academies.

Funds for the program on Advancing Materials Research were provided by the National Science Foundation (Grant No. DMR-8511336), the Defense Advanced Research Projects Agency of the Department of Defense, the Department of Energy, the Andrew W. Mellon Foundation, Carnegie Corporation of New York, and the Technological Leadership Program of the National Academy of Engineering. A program initiative designed to lead to a funded project on this topic also led to the development of this report. The initiative was approved by the National Research Council Fund's Committee, whose members are the Presidents of the National Academy of Sciences, the National Academy of Engineering, and the Institute of Medicine.

The views expressed in this volume are those of the authors and are not presented as those of the sponsors.

Library of Congress Cataloging-in-Publication Data

Advancing materials research.

Based on presentations and discussions from a sympo-
sium held in Washington, D.C., 28–29 Oct. 1985.
  Bibliography: p.
  Includes index.
  1. Materials—Research—Congresses. I. Psaras,
Peter A. II. Langford, H. Dale. III. National Academy
of Engineering. IV. National Academy of Sciences (U.S.)
TA404.2.A39   1986   620.1′1   86-23656

ISBN 0-309-03697-6

ON THE COVER (left to right):
Top row: Potter in his workshop, from *The Progress of Man and Society,* John Trusler, 1791; Computed diffraction pattern for an ideal icosahedral quasicrystal; Bakelite billiard and cue balls, 1910, courtesy of Union Carbide Corporation. **Middle row:** Water wheel, from *The Iconographic Encyclopedia of Science, Literature, and Art,* 1851; Silicon wafer, courtesy of IBM Corporation; Corinthian capital, from *The Iconographic Encyclopedia.* **Bottom row:** Glass blower, from *The Progress of Man and Society;* Schematic of cross-linking in a polymer negative resist used in fabricating integrated circuits; Machine part, Jeff Zaraba/FOLIO.

First Printing, November 1986
Second Printing, July 1987
Third Printing, September 1988

ADVISORY COMMITTEE MEMBERS

---

*Cochairman, Advancing Materials Research Program

---

*Permanent affiliation: International Business Machines Corporation, Corporate Technical Institute, Thornwood, N.Y.

iv

Contents

Part 2
THE STATUS OF SELECTED SCIENTIFIC
AND TECHNICAL AREAS

Part 3
CURRENT TOPICS IN MATERIALS RESEARCH

Foreword

The field of materials research has an extended past as well as a long and promising future. As an area of human technical endeavor it is as old as *Homo faber*—the first member of our species to seek a stone or piece of wood to help accomplish a difficult task. The field came a long way as an empirical art in the hands of successive generations of individuals who sought to reach out ever further in helping their local societies develop a better physical relationship with the surrounding world. The edge of a stone sharpened by flaking was better for cutting or scraping than a typical natural stone. Flint and obsidian had great advantages over the more common fieldstone. A hafted stone hammer could be more effective in certain situations than a stone merely held in the hand. Copper, and particularly bronze, was less brittle and more malleable than stone. Moreover, it was learned that the metals could be melted and cast into form. Iron eventually proved better than bronze, and was much more available than copper and tin once one learned to reduce its ores with carbon, although it was probably first used in the relatively rare meteoric form—"skystone" to the ancients.

Perhaps what is most significant about materials research throughout its history is that, in parallel with the development of social organization and advances in the art of language, it tended to be a major limiting factor in determining the rate at which civilization could advance. The effectiveness of equipment of all kinds is conditioned in substantial part by the materials of which it is made. The nature and quality of materials in a device are as important as the ingenuity with which it is designed. Moreover, improvements in equipment have increased working efficiency and permitted greater freedom in society to promote both the expansion of population and the degree of specialization of those engaged in arts, crafts, and the management of social organization. In the past as at present, materials research became a major factor in setting the pace of civilization.

In the days before the formalization of modern science, the art of materials research was guided as much by mysticism or ritual magic as by logical reason. The metallurgist and the ceramicist were looked upon as practitioners of the black arts, as well as creators of indispensable products. Although they were neither of the nobility nor of the warrior or priestly classes, they gained a special position of veneration in society. The god of technology in Roman mythology—Vulcan—is a lame, swarthy genius who is among the least-favored of the gods. Yet, in recognition of his ingenuity and service, he is given as his wife Venus, the goddess of love and beauty. In medieval literature the processor of materials was looked upon as a close cousin of the alchemist.

Basic science in the modern sense first worked its way into materials research almost through the back door with the rise of the science of chemistry. This started some 200 years ago at the time of the first clear understanding of the nature of elements of which matter is composed. Actually, the process of wedding fields such as metallurgy and ceramics to science was slow, even though inevitable, because the development of useful materials depended fully as much on the art of fabrication as on the raw chemical composition of the product. This bifurcation in the technological base is reflected in more modern times by the emergence of the concept of "structure sensitivity" of materials—a concept that retained an aura of mysticism until the past few decades.

Nevertheless the die was cast. Materials research could not escape becoming a field of modern science even though nearly two centuries were required for the transition to become complete. It was helped along by applications of the optical microscope, x-ray and neutron diffraction, and the electron microscope—devices and techniques that became increasingly indispensable as new demands and new standards arose.

Interestingly enough, the purely scientific study of materials emerged in the last century as a result of the curiosity of chemists, physicists, and mineralogists and generated basic questions that have had a major impact on the evolution of the mainstream of modern science, particularly what is now called quantum physics. One thinks of the first observation of photoelectric emission from metal surfaces and of the deviations of specific heats of condensed matter at low temperatures from the values predicted by Dulong and Petit's law, or of the fundamental concern raised by such phenomena as the anomalous Hall effect and superconductivity regarding quantitative aspects of electron conduction in metals, insulators, and semiconductors. Alongside of this were, of course, scientific observations on material systems that were intriguing in their own right as part of the lore surrounding subsystems. Notable examples are the studies of slip bands and associated phenomena in single crystals of metals and salts, the observations of internal photoconductivity and photoluminescence in condensed systems, the discovery of the rectification of electric currents at interfaces between solids, and the study of the special elastic and plastic properties of what we now term polymeric materials.

The transition of materials research from a primarily empirical, technological endeavor to a truly scientific endeavor achieved its climax in the period following World War II. A large contingent of imaginative and talented young scientists from several disciplines joined in a concerted study of materials with the intention of leaving no area of investigation unexplored. They brought to bear high standards of precision and analysis in both experiment and theory. This movement has continued almost unabated. Whatever the initial impetus for the movement may have been, there is little doubt that it has been sustained at a substantial level in academic, industrial, and governmental laboratories on an international scale in significant part because of its influence on many areas of technology, including electronics, optics, ceramics, metallurgy, and plastics. In fact, much of the advanced exploratory research is now carried on as a normal part of the engineering disciplines. This includes fields such as chemical engineering, in which there is much interest in catalysts as well as the behavior of materials in severe environments.

It is interesting to note that some of the techniques that were exploited along the way to gain a deeper understanding of organic and inorganic materials systems are now finding extensive use in biochemistry and medicine. Not least among these techniques are x-ray diffraction, nuclear resonance, and laser technology.

The conference upon which this volume is based had a twofold goal: first, to commemorate the twenty-fifth anniversary of the Materials Research Laboratories in our country and, second, to demonstrate not only that the field is far from being exhausted but even more that the continued advance of the technological aspects of our complex civilization will inevitably be limited by advances in materials research. The field is and will remain one of the pacemakers that determine the nature and effectiveness of the devices we construct for the continued uplift of mankind.

The present volume, while reviewing history and accomplishments and describing developments at today's frontiers, also emphasizes the promises for the future. Some of these will emerge naturally as extensions of present work. Others will require new forms of instrumentation and the development of new techniques to optimize the use of such facilities. Here lies a challenge for our society.

As is clearly described in the introductory chapters by William O. Baker, Robert L. Sproull, and Lyle H. Schwartz, the Department of Defense deserves much credit for initiating the first series of Materials Research Laboratories in 1960. The department was influenced by a convincing and inspired report by Sproull and his colleagues and guided by the President's Scientific Advisory Committee on which Baker played a key role.

Moreover, we must not fail to recognize the important part played by the National Science Foundation a decade later when changing circumstances required that another agency assume the responsibility not only of accepting the sponsoring role, but of maintaining the standards and expanding the program as circumstances made possible.

It was my privilege to witness the germination and growth of the concept of the Materials Research Laboratories throughout the 1950s. It is a pleasure to emphasize here again the role played by John von Neumann, one of the most prescient scientists of our time. Had he not died prematurely (in 1957 at the age of 53), he would undoubtedly have initiated the laboratory system through his role as a commissioner in the Atomic Energy Commission and as an individual intensely interested in the application of research. His prescience was illustrated in many instances, not least in his early appreciation of the potentialities of the digital electronic computer and the transistor.

> FREDERICK SEITZ
> President Emeritus
> The Rockefeller University

Preface and Acknowledgments

Twenty-five years ago the Advanced Research Projects Agency of the Department of Defense established at several universities the first in a network of Materials Research Laboratories. A symposium entitled Advancing Materials Research was held in Washington, D.C., on 28–29 October 1985 in part to celebrate that anniversary. For planners of the event, however, the opportunity proved irresistible to undertake a project to explore broadly the status and prospects in materials research. The timing was especially significant. The twenty-fifth anniversary of the Materials Research Laboratories marks on the one hand the end of the first generation of a major national effort in materials research. On the other hand, it marks the entry into an era when materials research is advancing at an ever-increasing pace, generating both scientific and technological opportunities. This volume is based on the discussions and formal presentations at the symposium.

Anyone who scans these pages will be aware of the kinds of materials research carried out at university, industry, and government laboratories and leading to major advances in fields ranging from physics and chemistry to ceramics and metallurgy. Often the greatest excitement lies at the interfaces between fields or between basic science and engineering, and in fact we are now seeing a rapid diffusion of scientific advances in materials into new technology crucial to our well-being and security. Authors stress repeatedly that this flow of new technology requires a flow of talent nurtured through fundamental materials research. Evidence of the importance that members of the participating and sponsoring organizations attach to sustaining and extending materials research and training in the United States can be found in the chapters that follow.

The project was designed to achieve several goals. One was to look to the past for guidance to the future, and on that score we benefit from the perspective provided by those farsighted pioneers of 25 years ago, Frederick Seitz, William O. Baker, and Robert L. Sproull. Their combined contributions, and that of Lyle H. Schwartz, describe the birth of materials research in the United States and the status of the resulting educational experiment represented by the network of Materials Research Laboratories and other materials-oriented centers at universities throughout the country. Universities are naturally conservative institutions, slow to respond to new fields of study that affect time-honored disciplines. Thus, this experiment is still far from complete. Its success depends, as ever, on the development of academic programs that retain the strengths of individual disciplines yet afford the broad multidisciplinary perspective required in materials research and on the institutional infrastructure and external support mechanisms that underlie the effort.

A second goal of the project was for a representative group of practitioners to provide snapshots of some of the frontiers of materials research and to help map these areas by showing as many of their features as possible. Obviously a single symposium could not survey this diverse field in its entirety. The chapters in Part 2 of this volume survey recent developments and future directions in selected areas of materials science and engineering—polymers, ceramics, metals, catalysis, crystallography, mechanical and microstructural properties of materials, artificially structured materials, electronic and magnetic materials, materials chemistry and surface science, solid-state physics, and materials processing. The authors have projected the excitement, vigor, and open-endedness of research at the Materials Research Laboratories and other interdisciplinary laboratories in universities, industry, and government. Although any selection of authors and subjects in so diverse an enterprise must be somewhat arbitrary, these timely surveys reaffirm one's belief in the immense progress that multidisciplinary research is leading to, and they portray the breadth and depth of this flourishing field. All authors were encouraged to seek guidance from their peers; as a consequence, a rich, up-to-date selection of topics in materials research is presented.

A third goal was to explore present-day issues in the objectives, organization, administration, methods, and progress of materials research. Thus, Part 3 of this volume presents the views of members of panels drawn from the academic, governmental, and industrial communities. In a rapidly developing field such as materials, established methods for allocation of resources must be adapted to the needs of an emerging science and technology, and there is ample room for different points of view. The discussions in Part 3 reveal organizational challenges to the institutions involved in materials research. Yet, a common theme of these discussions is that collaboration among individual scientists and researchers from different disciplines holds the key to continued success in materials science and engineering.

In this context, the report of the Committee on the Survey of Materials Science and Engineering (COSMAT) in 1974 provided a frame of reference for the symposium. That landmark survey, carried out under the direction of Morris Cohen and William O. Baker, covered new ground in linking the scientific and technical branches of materials research with each other and with other fields of science and technology. We have tried to continue in that tradition, and note with satisfaction that the symposium served as a focal point for the current National Research Council survey of materials science and engineering. It is our hope and expectation that this book will be helpful during the next few years while a successor to the COSMAT report is being prepared under the leadership of Merton C. Flemings and Praveen Chaudhari.

The fourth and perhaps most important goal of the project, crystallized in the symposium itself, was to bring together the materials research community in the hope of developing greater consensus about its mission and needs. The community is diverse in its institutional and disciplinary bases. This diversity is the source of its richness and great scientific impact but also the cause for fragmentation that has made difficult the coherent articulation of its strengths and weaknesses. It was our hope that the symposium would enhance the cooperative spirit so much a part of the actual conduct of materials research and encourage dialogue between materials researchers and those in government and industry for whom materials are a key consideration. We are indebted to the speakers and the other participants for using the opportunity afforded by this symposium in this way.

We also acknowledge the contributions that many others have made to the success of the symposium and the completion of this book. Much of the early impetus for the effort came from Lyle H. Schwartz. We are grateful to Morris E. Fine for providing the right links with the National Academy of Sciences and the National Academy of Engineering and to Robert M. White and Frank Press for their enthusiastic and timely backing. Among the many members of the Advisory Committee who took key roles, we would like to single out William O. Baker, Herbert H. Johnson, John K. Hulm, J. David Litster, and Albert Narath. Strong support came from the National Science Foundation (NSF), the Advanced Research Projects Agency of the Department of Defense (DOD), and the Department of Energy (DOE). We particularly note the constructive roles of Erich Bloch, Lewis Nosanow, and Adriaan de Graaf for NSF; Leo Young, Benjamin Wilcox, and Richard Reynolds for DOD; and Donald Stevens and Louis Ianniello for DOE.

Numerous hands are required to go from an idea to a conference to a book, and in this regard we would like to thank Jesse H. Ausubel, Peter A. Psaras, Penelope J. Gibbs, and Loretta A. Sprissler of the National Academy of Engineering Program Office and H. Dale Langford, editor for the National Academy of Engineering. The offices of the Academy complex most concerned with materials, the National Materials Advisory Board (directed by

Klaus Zwilsky) and the Solid State Sciences Committee (tended by Donald C. Shapero), were most generous at several key points. Robert N. Smith and David Patterson ensured a remarkably smooth meeting program; Walter Boyne and Darlene Rose of the National Air and Space Museum proved gracious hosts for the MRLs' twenty-fifth birthday celebration at the museum. Pamela Steele designed the memorable artwork for the meeting and the book's cover, and James M. Gormley and Dorothy M. Sawicki provided experienced guidance in the publication process.

Finally, we would like to recognize Roman J. Wasilewski, who very much would have liked to be a part of this activity. Roman died on 3 February 1985. Those of us who knew him remember his fierce dedication to the cause of materials research. We take this opportunity to recall the great efforts he exerted on our behalf and to dedicate these proceedings to his memory.

THEODORE H. GEBALLE
Director, Center for Materials Research
Stanford University

DAVID WHITE
Director, Laboratory for Research
on the Structure of Matter, and
Professor of Chemistry, University of Pennsylvania

Part 1

HISTORICAL PERSPECTIVES

Advances in Materials
Research and Development

WILLIAM O. BAKER

The unprecedented progress of science and engineering in the second half of the twentieth century has advanced many worthy goals—beginning with the defense of freedom—and has fostered understanding of the world, its inhabitants, and the cosmos. In this context, materials research and development stands out—both as a twentieth-century phenomenon and as an endeavor that bridges the often-disparate objectives of understanding nature and of ensuring freedom.

This chapter describes, exemplifies, and analyzes various facets of the complex history and development of materials science and engineering both as a field of endeavor and as a national commitment that came into being in the late 1950s through the National Materials Program. Through this program, knowledge of matter has been augmented by new academic structures and by new connections of government and universities with industry and the national economy. A dominant theme throughout the chapter is the need for this nation to learn from and to apply the experiences of the national materials endeavor in addressing major scientific and technological issues in the coming decades.

The inception of the National Materials Program illustrates one of the first, and best, examples of leadership by a chief of state in twentieth-century science and engineering; it was generated by President Eisenhower through the White House Office of Science and Technology and Science Advisory Committee. And, of course, the enterprise has even deeper roots: the great science faculties of Britain and Germany began to see, from classical physics and chemistry, from the optics of Newton, the ionics of Faraday, the radiation of Röntgen, the atom of Thompson, Aston, and Bohr—and through the statistics and quantum mechanics in large assemblies of atoms and molecules—that solids and even liquids displayed some simplicities.

Still other origins of the materials science and engineering enterprise lay in the ways in which some industrial laboratories and government centers, such as those developing atomic energy, had been able to purify and modify crystals and glasses to achieve new public and commercial capabilities. (These developments range from isotope matrices for nuclear energy to transistors and solar cells, to space vehicles and their reentry nose cones and capsules, to synthetic polymers like polyethylene—which could be adapted to displace metals for sheathing cables—to nylon and its fiber correlates. Other derivatives of advances in materials science and engineering include modern telecommunications and computers.) The circumstances of the 1940s and 1950s also led to a less tangible development—a bold surmise from the White House Science Office, in its earliest days, that some fields in twentieth-century science and technology should promise enough scientific lure and luster to stimulate the keenest minds and to motivate the most creative thinkers; at the same time, knowledge achieved in such fields would be immediately useful for technical, public purposes and commercial needs.

In the late 1950s there was a very wide gulf between academic science and mathematics, as engendered by the great European traditions, and the engineering and technology of an inventive industrial era. This gap narrowed somewhat in a few urgent wartime projects such as the synthetic rubber program, which also supported the emerging proposition about coupling modern science and technology. Materials science and engineering could indeed bring together fundamental "knowledge for its own sake" and the compelling, restless demands of technology and manufacture. For we found with GR-S rubber, in the production of more than 700,000 tons of a new material within two years, that the sometime "odd couple" could be complementary and even reinforcing.

But no one had said yet that it should be possible for an independent, pluralistic government of a free nation to so modify tradition that it could stimulate industrial and academic materials research and development by request of the national leadership. With helpful but modest use of federal funds, it could only be hoped that a new chapter in the creation and use of new knowledge would be written. And yet that is what happened. The 1974 report of the National Academy of Sciences Committee on the Survey of Materials Science and Engineering (COSMAT) showed the profound impact on U.S. and even world resources that the National Materials Program has had.[1] Later studies, such as the analysis by Theodore H. Geballe on behalf of the National Science Foundation, and various related estimates of the intellectual appeal of condensed-matter science, have further established the existence of a worldwide conviction that new fundamentals of nature can now be discerned in condensed matter. Likewise we are seeing that the engineering and manufacture of commercial products as well as the systems for national security and public service are gaining crucially from basic findings about matter and its synthesis. The dreams of President Eisenhower's time are coming true.

And today, when we have returned to old arguments (for example, whether there should be a single department of science in Washington) and new challenges, when as a debtor nation we must compete vastly better against the products and innovations of a smartening world, it is wise to review our progress in materials science and engineering. We need to assess the national materials endeavor, and to reconsider its origins as a reference for future decisions. For in this and other fields, we should confer on what we ought to take care about as we face new and unexpected conditions on the planet. Accordingly, the experience with the National Materials Program continues to yield insights applicable to decisions about where we could and should go in the coming decades of pluralistic academic, governmental, and industrial science and technology. Noteworthy qualities of this program can be discerned in its beginnings, in its progress, and in the assumptions and premises underlying it.

ORIGINS OF NATIONWIDE SOLID-STATE SCIENCE
AND ENGINEERING

The impetus for developing a national program followed by some years the origins of materials research and development that took place in independent laboratories. The impetus for the program was found in a national opportunity for federal agencies concerned with weapons systems, rocket propulsion, nuclear reactors, spaceflight and reentry, as well as materials conservation and supply. Also, there had arisen postwar needs for a common base of research and development that could accommodate the needs of civilian services and industrial activity (through the National Bureau of Standards) and those of education and basic science (through the National Science Foundation).

Conviction of the values of a national program in materials science and engineering had already come from the surging growth in solid-state science and technology, largely in industrial laboratories from which came the transistor, the solar cell, new polymers, high-performance metals and alloys, and the rudimentary composites. This conviction intensified with the stirrings of interest in the far horizons of understanding condensed matter, for example, through the work of Eugene Wigner, Frederick Seitz, and William Conyers Herring in physics, and of C. P. Smyth in chemistry, at Princeton. Usable theory was forthcoming from Seitz's continued research at Carnegie Mellon and Illinois, from the wartime-stimulated interests and expert pedagogy of J. C. Slater at MIT, and from J. H. Van Vleck at Harvard.

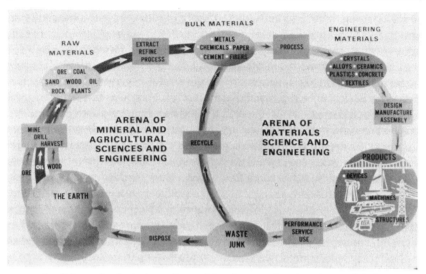

FIGURE 1 Schematic of relations of materials science and engineering to global resources and uses of matter. From the National Academy of Sciences.[1]

Solid-state work was not devoted to a single objective or goal, although, like the Manhattan Project, GR-S Program, Apollo Program, or National Cancer Plan, it assumed that science and engineering could work together in unprecedented intimacy. But further, science and engineering would *support* each other, as described in the COSMAT study (Figures 1 and 2).

When the time for federal focus came, the procedures of the National Materials Program (represented especially but not by any means exclusively in the university Materials Research Laboratories [see Schwartz, in this volume]), consisted of institutional unions of unprecedented scope. Yet those program efforts are the basis for the process that we would like to see extended widely in the times ahead. They have united academic and industrial scientists and engineers in joint actions, as foreseen in the Synthetic Rubber Program. They have united a community of users and makers of materials in industrial factories, government contract agencies (especially the Department of Defense), and the whole range of American industry from mining to molding. The program has united teaching and research in extraordinary ways through the interdisciplinary character of the effort. (The uniting of physics, chemistry, mathematics, mechanics, and other engineering fields in novel forms is a task yet uncompleted.) The materials work has united components and materials engineers with systems and electrical and mechanical engineers in unique ways. Here we have only to recall that materials science and engineering, whose early expression in the transistor and the solar cell would soon be succeeded by satellites, new intercontinental cable systems, and aircraft designs involving novel metals and alloys, now also supports super composites and digital computers and switches. Materials science and engineering provide light guides and composites for prosthetic parts in the human body, and ceramics for gas turbines. Thus, the materials era has dramatically advanced both design and performance engineering in a union not imaginable until only a decade or two ago.

I submit that materials science and engineering are already historic for these new combinations, which is the most important validation of that early surmise of the White House Science Office—that such unions, together with the nature of learning, would bring about an unprecedented speed of conversion of scientific discovery into technologic innovation and commercial and public production. This, too, has happened in electronics, now photonics, in rocketry, and in major refractory structures made of composites. We hope that it will extend into many other competitive and economically decisive domains, including automobiles, buildings, and public facilities.

I believe this strategy is the prescription this country needs for regaining primacy in international trade, in technology, in armaments, in learning, and in quality of living, because it contains sound guidance for the role of science and engineering in those larger and compelling national issues. At this time

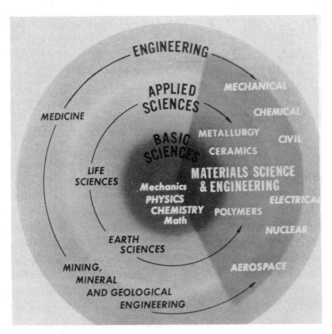

FIGURE 2 Interconnections of physical and life sciences related to engineering, showing the major role of solid matter.

in the advance of science and technology we must find larger values, which involve new ways of thinking and of working and of combining our institutions. That is exactly what we have been fortunate enough, in the era of solid-state science—of materials science and engineering—to do and to assess.

ISSUES EVOLVING FROM ENLARGED
MATERIALS TECHNOLOGY

Derivatives of the research and engineering concept embodied in the Interdisciplinary Laboratories (IDL)/Materials Research Laboratories (MRL) program continue to be instructive. Thus, George A. Keyworth II, President Reagan's Science Advisor and director of the Office of Science and Technology Policy, refers to the Engineering Research Centers organized by the National Science Foundation as ''the single most important thing that we've done as an Administration in increasing the efficiency and effectiveness of federal R&D dollars.''[2] He said the centers address a widely recognized need in various fields of science and technology:

Continued pushing of the frontiers in those fields was constrained by the difficulty of assembling multidisciplinary teams to work on the problems. Our universities are, justifiably and understandably, structured to pursue disciplinary research. On the other hand, we increasingly find ourselves as a nation confronting the solving of problems that have technically based solutions. We need to expose our young people to a problem-solving environment. . . . These Centers—I'd rather call them Science and Technology Centers—are multidisciplinary mechanisms by which chemists, physicists, neurobiologists, engineers, etc., can get together and solve exciting, intellectually demanding, real-world problems.[2]

These and other comments about the economic potential of the Engineering Research Centers are almost word-for-word descriptions of the original interdisciplinary laboratories of the National Materials Program. Thus, it is refreshing indeed to find such current agreement on the concept that has involved so significant a portion of our best academic talent.

The national commitment set in motion by President Eisenhower's call has other facets besides historic industrial and academic gains in materials science and engineering, both within and beyond the federal program. For instance, in the conservation and supplying of strategic materials, we have learned that national security depends heavily on integrated provision of processing and products coming from a host of minerals and related natural sources. We now have synthetic analogs for natural materials ranging from natural rubber to diamonds and platinum. This by no means suggests that we have efficient substitutes for all materials crucial to defense and a viable civilian economy. Rather, we have learned the degrees of alternatives that can be used and how to balance designs, processes, and basic materials properties with skills whose acquisition alone would justify the modest federal investments in all of our materials research and development.

Indeed, there are many dimensions to such a context. On the one hand, we respect the frustration of Richard A. Reynolds, new director of the Defense Sciences Office of the Defense Advanced Research Projects Agency (DARPA), regarding materials research priorities. Dr. Reynolds notes sparse funding of federal research on "growth of critical electronic materials," and says, "Furthermore, the United States is losing its international competitive edge with respect to the technology base necessary to support materials self-sufficiency in the manufacture of these man-made strategic materials."[3] In that case, his concerns could have extended beyond semiconductors and integrated-circuit ceramic substrates and the like. He has accurately perceived that the pervasiveness of materials science and engineering in our national and industrial programs does diffuse responsibility, as expected. And in this sense, the new academic centers for study of high-speed integrated circuits, quantum-well semiconductor systems discovered in industrial laboratories, and novel compositions of organic and ionic qualities have shown the need for major new characterization facilities such as synchrotron and neutron radiation sources. Hence others, mostly in industry, must take responsibility for the materials development and leadership that he is properly calling for.

But from another perspective, a recent book, entitled *Lost at the Frontier*,[4] presents one of the most stimulating and critical of many current commentaries about American science and engineering research and development. The senior author is a distinguished materials scientist and engineer, Rustum Roy. The book should remind us that the original precepts of the National Materials Program recognized the need to maintain progress in established fields, such as integrated circuits, ceramics, and other materials identified as priorities by Dr. Reynolds and DARPA. But these original precepts also heeded the larger issues raised in the critique by Shapley and Roy. These authors recognize astutely that the scientific and technical community also has wide responsibility to act with a degree of professionalism and intellectual performance concordant with the high calling from a chief of state, or from a supportive nation.

While messages such as those of Dr. Reynolds need to be considered—and we should note that many of his materials colleagues throughout the Department of Defense are also saying that more ought to be done—the issue is, What more should be done? What more must be done to enable materials science and engineering to fulfill new roles in contributing to the social and economic welfare of the nation? For this is what was intended in the White House initiatives. The National Materials Program was designed for the performance of science and technology in new ways. Industrial ingenuity, time-honored disciplines of academic discovery, the urgent technical requirements for national security, and the overriding need for human talents would be combined to meet the needs and potentialities of the twentieth century. The drafters of this program for the president in 1958 already knew that such expectations were justified and attainable. The practical origins of the solid-state era had already produced major gains from mutual feedback of technology and science in crystal growth, purification, semiconductor doping and synthesis, and adaptation of polymers as new structural and insulating materials.

For example, the development of high-frequency electronics for radar and microwaves had stimulated extensive and critical use of silicon and germanium point-contact diodes; the work of Scaff and his associates[5] and other studies at Purdue University and elsewhere had produced relatively satisfactory materials whose purity and quality could have been further refined by continued detailed pursuit of recognized technology. But the goal of 10^{15} or fewer foreign atoms per cubic centimeter in a single crystal was so far outside of that conventional pathway that it was spoken of only with a mixture of awe and humor. However, William G. Pfann, then a technologist involved in learning science, sensed that the phase rule worked in all directions. Through his zone-refining method, he achieved both the purity and perfection needed in semiconductor materials, thus opening simultaneously for academic and industrial application an epoch of purity and regularity in matter not two or three times but orders of magnitude greater than had been available. Similarly, investigators at the time saw in the chemical and petrochemical laboratories at Du Pont, Phillips Petroleum, and Union Carbide and in the academic work of Ziegler and co-workers and of Natta and Pasquon,[6] A. Morton at MIT, M. Morton at Akron, and others, that when appropriate characterization showed that the qualities required for polymers could be achieved in theory, chemical control could achieve those qualities in practice. For instance, by this pathway polyethylene could replace lead, which is both costly and ecologically sensitive, in the cables supplying electricity and communications around the world.

It should be recalled that these and a few other projects were also subjects of intense technical development in earlier decades. The new industrial tactic, which caused the change, was to combine science and engineering—to promote the interdisciplinary interactions of mechanics and chemistry, of physics and metallurgy. Pfann's work reduced the characteristic content of dislocations in metallic and semimetallic crystal surfaces from about 3.5 million per square centimeter to near zero. And on the way, the mechanical trauma of even 1,000 dislocations per square centimeter could be tracked. Even with the historic purity of less than 10^{17} carbon atoms per cubic centimeter of silicon, the solid showed more than five times the stress at yield that a typical "pure" specimen would show.

These and many other signals made clear that mobilization of a new national materials effort would affect vast technical capabilities. But even in the strength of matter, dominated by dislocation movements, challenge still lies ahead. A current study at the Battelle Memorial Institute finds that the fracture of matter and efforts to contain it now cost the United States no less than $119 billion per year. Even the appropriate basic categorizations of overload, brittle fracture, ductile rupture, fatigue, creep, creep rupture, stress corrosion, threading fatigue, thermal shock, buckling, and delamination require more specific scientific description than has yet been applied. The move toward automated manufacture and robotics processing of materials even accents the ignorance of these factors. As noted below, the appropriate control of dislocations may even provide new networks of conductivity and electronic and photonic responses in suitable crystals.

RECOGNITION OF NEW FRONTIERS

Along with these signals of need, there are signals of knowledge, perhaps as beckoning and as rich with meaning as those once heralding the solid-state and materials endeavors themselves. In polymers, we have long known, and technically and scientifically applied, the close coexistence of ordered and disordered phases. Indeed, a single chain can indulge in both, and many do. Whole classes of important materials, such as the Arnel fiber of Celanese Corporation, came from appropriate adjustment of lateral and longitudinal states of order, in that case, in cellulose triacetate. Annealing and heat treatment affecting such order are crucial factors in the performance of nearly all microcrystalline synthetic fibers, plastics, and films.

However, we have been rightly charmed by the beauty and utility of traditional crystallography. Only recently, computer-assisted study of aluminum alloyed with minor components of manganese, iron, and chromium has shown an icosahedral structure imputing 5-fold symmetry. This, of course, displaces atom groupings from the expected unit-cell behavior. On 29 July 1984, Japanese workers reported in the *Physical Review Letters* about a nickel-chromium alloy that in electron diffraction by small particles seems to exhibit a 12-fold symmetry. This they interpreted as a dodecagon, which indeed would conform to an intermediate structure between the disorder of glass and the regularity of a crystal. Reexamination of what were termed anomalous diffraction patterns of an aluminum-manganese-silicon alloy from AT&T Bell Laboratories offers a complementary example, where a unit cell would require thousands of atoms, but currently can best be interpreted as icosahedral arrays within such "unit cell." In India similar icosahedra seem to have been formed in magnesium-zinc-aluminum alloys by rapid cooling. There is also the report of a sheet structure with 10-fold symmetry within the sheet, but a periodic stacking of the sheets themselves.

The point is that conventional structure practices are not really sophisticated enough to deal with the growing diversity of materials science and engineering. Fortunately, this is being heeded by theorists such as P. J. Steinhardt and D. Levine at the University of Pennsylvania (the site of one of the three original Materials Research Laboratories). They have concentrated on the properties of a quasi-periodic translational order, with various degrees of orientational symmetry, leading to a total quasi-crystalline form such as octagonal orientation symmetry, in one of their recent models. At the National Bureau of Standards, Daniel S. Schechtman and his associates have studied an alloy of aluminum and manganese that seems to show some of this structure. Further significant examples of important new directions of study in materials science and engineering, which also reflect the initial concepts of the program, occur where bioscience intersects the study of condensed matter.

The National Materials Program in both its federal and independent forms is probably the only example of a major scientific frontier in which the initiative for study came from technologic and engineering efforts outside of academic centers. Yet the academic centers not only have provided the basic skills and training for the nonacademic work but also continue to organize knowledge and its validation in ways that will prepare for further discovery. The solid-state era in all its semiconducting, magnetic, and superconducting manifestations (the laser, light guides, extraordinary spectroscopy, and photonic circuitry) and polymer plastics, fibers, rubbers, and their growing interplay with the condensed biosystems in living tissue came from practical, usually commercially induced, although sometimes government-stimulated, ventures in their materials aspects. These materials factors are virtually central to the utility of the technical systems in modern life. Indeed, in the case of polymers and their products, they are the system.

The ventures that led to the solid-state era established a new degree of interaction between academic research and learning and certain industrial laboratories seeking commercially to extend human capabilities. This interaction is aided by public policy reflecting a willingness to involve a wide spectrum of independent citizens directly in government. It brings an originality and freshness of organization unknown in bureaucratic rigidities of nondemocratic or more traditional governing mechanisms.

Today, these interactions can go even further than before, as long as we pick the appropriate mutual goals. There are messages in the findings of H. Bock and R. Dammel at the University of Frankfort in work on pyrolysis of triazidosilane to get C_6H_5NSi (phenylsil isocyanide). J. Michl and G. Gross at Utah confirm and in fact have isolated the linear CNSi group. A familiar but significant footnote is attributed to Michl: "On warming, the product forms an insoluble polymer." Such comments about organic residues have marked the progress of macromolecular science and biotechnology!

ARRANGEMENTS FOR ONGOING ADVANCES

The special role of the National Materials Program, as represented in the Materials Research Laboratories (MRLs), provides dramatic evidence that there is operational and intellectual unity in materials science and engineering. This appears in the combination of science and engineering, in the combination of research and development, and in the combination of disciplines that are academically and professionally applied. As Schwartz (in this volume) shows, the MRLs themselves have notably enhanced, as well as embodied, this unity.

Beyond this, the national and international significance of advances in materials science and engineering is vast. The present microcosmos of MRLs, with about 400 faculty members remaining from a peak of 600 at the end of the ARPA era in 1971, is an important element in the macrocosmos of modern materials science and engineering. The extraordinary feature is how the purposes, goals, and inspiration of the national program of MRLs have been assimilated by, and reflected in, the large national endeavors.

Indeed, an epochal quality of the total system should be realized. Namely, our planet is mostly silicon, oxygen, and water, although silicates have a marvelous diversity of form. Obviously, materials science and engineering have exploited aspects of this diversity from the Stone Age to the present. But only in this half century have advances at the forefront of physical science and on the frontiers of technology and engineering been combined to bring out the qualities of silicon and its oxides that best serve human wants. These advances are familiar to us through such products as transistors, diodes, solar cells, computers, and all their derivatives. The advances are apparent in important synthetic polymers such as silicones as well as in the mortar and the substance of our buildings, cities, and roads. Moreover, we are seeing how science and engineering can reach far beyond the qualities of basic resources to achieve orders-of-magnitude advances in performance of the stuff of clay and continents.

The purification of silicon by means of Theurer's chemistry[7] and Pfann's zone refining have resulted in crucial derivatives, such as the production of silicon tetrachloride with less than 10 parts per million (ppm) of trichlorosilane and less than 5 parts per billion (ppb) of iron. Chemical conversion followed by oxidation within modified chemical vapor deposition is now used routinely to produce fibers of silicon containing less than 2 ppb of cobalt ions, less than 20 ppb of iron, less than 30 ppb of copper, and so on. The process is particularly effective also for epitaxial production of silicon films. Thus, the combination of modern chemical analysis, engineering processing, and the physics of characterizing matter has achieved in the oxide of silicon, a cosmic medium of the planet mixed with every other component of the stars, an unsurpassed purity.

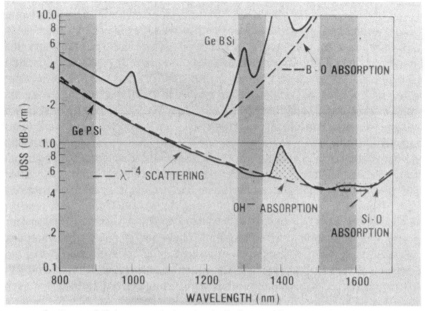

FIGURE 3 Loss of light transmission in decibels per kilometer of various factors in graded-index silica fibers, as a function of wavelength in nanometers. Hyperpure fibers have even half or a quarter of the absorption depicted.

In this pure state, silica transmits 1.2- to 1.6-micron-wavelength photons so well that there is an attenuation of less than 0.15 decibel per kilometer. However, silica-fiber light guides must stay pure, stable, and without significant hydration, since hydroxyl groups degrade their light-carrying ability (Figure 3). Therefore, through still other techniques of materials science and engineering, a composite is formed by deposition of selected and exquisitely controlled polymer films on the silica fiber as it is drawn. The resulting fibers, properly extruded and coated, have strengths far beyond the best fiberglass—a tenacity approaching 0.8 to 1 million pounds per square inch (psi) (Figure 4). Although still short of the 10.5 giganewtons per square meter (1.5 million psi) in a single, idealized silica solid, the tensile strength of modern optical fibers nevertheless approaches the ideal envisioned by Games Slater, the inventor of fiberglass. It is hardly surprising that the skills that make composites of silica with micron dimensions and overlayers of polymers lead one to composites in bulk. These materials are finding new uses in rockets, motor vehicles, boats, and houses.

But then, if our themes hold, the combinations of science and engineering intrinsic to materials programs and cultures should induce still other earth-matter advances. Carbon is ubiquitous, not just as 10^{16} atoms per cubic centimeter in hyperpure silicon, but as a chemical chameleon of the earth's materials. In various forms, carbon provides the major substance of life. In trees and plants its cellulosic form is the basis of tools and buildings, and carbon is the essence of most synthetic polymeric materials. It is the basis for combustible fuels, and, in its elementary form, it is even more spectacular as brightest diamond and darkest graphite.

How have the interaction of materials science and engineering and the intimate connections between research and application led to new carbon materials? The present response is polymer carbon, which can be pyrolyzed

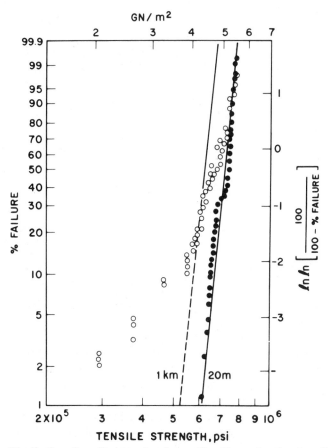

FIGURE 4 Distribution of tensile strengths of pure silica fibers, showing (in solid circles) precise control over 20-meter spans, with somewhat less consistency when characterized over kilometer spans.

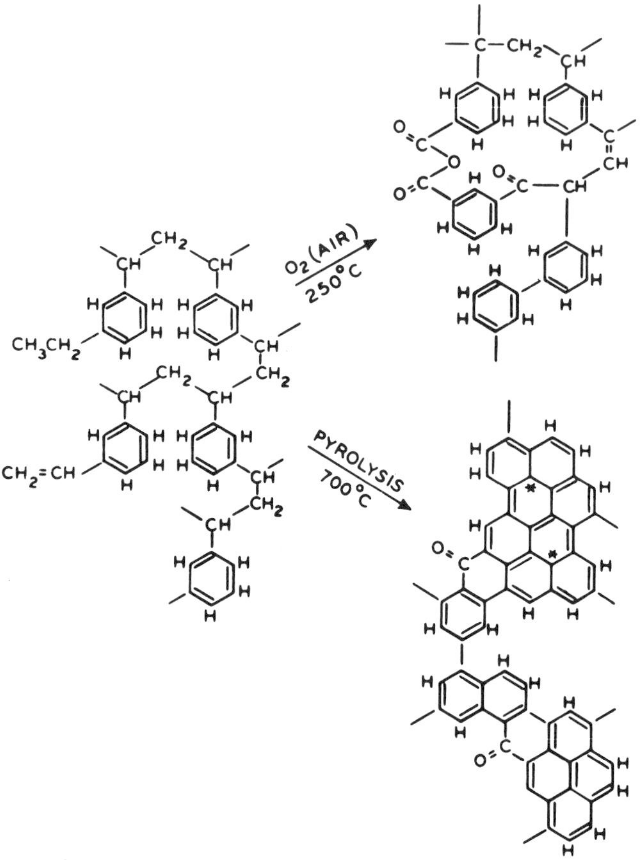

FIGURE 5 Representative effects of controlled oxidation and eventual pyrolysis on cross-linked hydrocarbon polymers, yielding refractory, and also very rigid, forms of polymer carbon. These can be used in composites of high strength and elastic modulus.

to various stages of cross-linked or polymer carbon conversion (Figure 5). The science of polymer carbon formation quickly produced fibers, and also spheres in which it was first studied, with a modulus of rigidity so high that it stirred thoughts of diamond structures. It also stimulated early experiments on how it would behave in place of the classic silicate or fiberglass reinforcement in matrices of casting polymer composites, where it has played a large role in structural uses. This composite evolution was already under way, quite apart from the original polymer carbon research. By 1947 the filament-wound glass composite rocket motor case had been successfully flown, and the associated industrial contractors supported the Navy's decision to use fiberglass motor cases for the Polaris missiles. Composites have since served in successive generations of rockets, reducing weight and providing strength and durability (Figure 6). Recently, makers of these composites have found that so-called graphite fiber, actually a polymer–carbon filament composite, outperforms other materials, including fiberglass composites. Using carbon filament instead of traditional metals for a rocket case can increase the range of a ballistic missile by about 600 miles (Figure 7). In the Trident II, for instance, polymer-fiber composites are used in motor parts, motor cases, and indeed throughout the missile system. Fiber strengths in the last few years have doubled and are expected to approach a million pounds per square inch even as the modulus of rigidity remains superlative.

Of course, the promise of future progress exists in systems other than those now known. In systems yielding polymer carbons, copolymers were originally identified with silicon and other elements. These can be converted to novel carbon ceramics, whose properties are beginning to be discussed in various parts of the materials community.

On yet another front, chemists and physicists interested in the process of polymer carbon formation recognized that extensive conjugation of the bonds occurs inside the polymer molecules. Accordingly, a wide span of electrical conductivity was produced. This phenomenon has led to practical applications in lightning arresters, resistor components, and various other devices. In turn, it has also engendered widespread study of other organic conductors such as the charge-transfer agents and their doped derivatives. By 1960, Herbert A. Pohl, then at Princeton University, had dealt extensively with doping of many of these conjugated structures. Thus, stage by stage, this

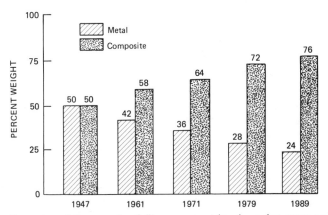

FIGURE 6 Examples of the growth of fibrous composites in rocket cases and motors, since mid century. From Hercules Corporation.

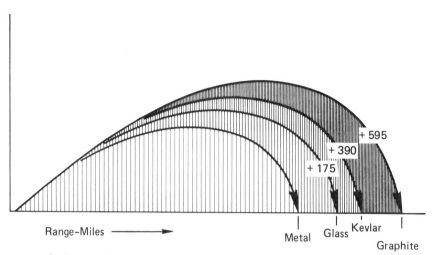

FIGURE 7   Increase in range of typical ballistic missiles through the use of polymer carbon composite materials, with attendant weight saving and efficiency. From Hercules Corporation.

admirable cumulative feature of materials science and engineering has expanded horizons in exceedingly diverse and long-unconnected areas of study, ranging from delicate microcircuitry to massive structures for power and transport.

SCIENTIFIC ADVANCES IN ATOMIC AND MOLECULAR STATE CHANGES

In a different context, other signals are arising. Hans Frauenfelder and E. Shyamsunder at the University of Illinois propose "protein quakes," in which macromolecular mechanical waves dissipate energy from the fission of myoglobin-iron when photochemically cut from carbon monoxide or oxygen molecules. Their postulates of glass-like relaxation converge with the widespectrum relaxation phenomena observed in polymers and identified decades ago with the single molecules themselves in ultrahigh-frequency shear and compressional studies.

Frontiers in materials science and engineering dynamics are steadily being added to the equilibrium and conventional chemical kinetic qualities, already providing productive links between basic science and materials technology. These findings bear heavily, of course, on the basic behavior of phase change, melting, and other processing properties. But again the new dimensions are striking, and again the interactions of technology, such as the annealing of semiconductor surfaces after ion implantation to restore order, as practiced by Soviet and Italian workers since 1977, have induced more scientific probes of pulsed laser heating. M. Downer, R. Fork, and C. Shank in AT&T's Holmdel Laboratories have been using 8-femtosecond pulses to generate an electron-hole plasma, which then shifts energy to lattice vibration. This phenomenon, in turn, has recently been studied using Raman scattering of photons. Findings indicated more than simple melting. J. VanVechten at IBM, and later, others, elaborated on the studies as the pulse times decreased to below the picosecond range. By the early 1980s a dozen or more distinguished solid-state and materials centers were pursuing this central question of the mechanism of melting. The femtosecond pulse frequency coupled with reflectivity studies currently demonstrates that a liquid is formed even in the presence of the plasma, and altogether new aspects of liquefaction are appearing.

PATTERNS FOR FURTHER ACTION—EXTENSIONS OF EARLY INITIATIVE

Diverse examples support the conclusion that the 25 years of detailed attention given to materials research and engineering through the National Materials Program has achieved an unprecedented and unsurpassed interaction of science and technology. This interaction appears in research and development in universities and industries and through conscientious government. Such communion has occurred in ways that permit us to build for the future and on a scale that other nations, intensifying their competition in traditional forms, have not yet adopted. Even the large government-industrial organizations supported by the Department of Defense, and to a lesser extent, the Department of Energy and NASA, for materials research and development are small in relation to the total national commitment in materials, as noted in the COSMAT report. Yet the sharing of knowledge from the federal stimulus is large and can be larger still. This is the special message of the National Materials Program.

It may be useful to recall the particular conditions that led to the National Materials Program and what was expected of it. Its current vitality was demonstrated at the 1985 fall meeting of the Materials Research Society (MRS) in Boston, where there were no fewer than 16 symposia, each representing a combination of other scientific society sponsors. The MRS itself played an invaluable professional role by sponsoring sessions on frontiers of materials research and on materials education. Indeed, the growth and quality of the MRS attest to the vigorous response of materials investigators and institutions to the call that went out in 1960 and give cause to believe that similar calls for scientific and technical achievement today could likewise be expected to succeed.

On the basis of 25 years of experience with the National Materials Program, let us finally look at the pertinent features that propelled it. We should imagine how the next challenges might be phrased if we expect such materials as the high-strength composite structures, unbreakable ceramics, continuous surfaces, and incorruptible metallics to realize their potentials.

The impetus for the National Materials Program was expressed in a short paper of 18 March 1958 from the White House Science Office (see Appendix to this chapter). That paper reflected the pressing interests of those times and also represented a certain coalition that included this author, as member of the President's Science Advisory Committee (PSAC), and a member of its staff. The paper underscored the need for information centers, which only now are being realized through the new general programs and publications of the MRS, and a few other professional societies, led especially by the American Chemical Society. There was even a paragraph on facilities, including a number of items that then cost no less than $20,000 each! It was said that both those items and buildings had to be supported.

At about the same time, in 1958, PSAC completed a report entitled *Strengthening American Science*.[8] It was not submitted to the President until December 1958, but its invention of the Federal Council for Science and Technology had been in planning during the latter half of that year. The report itself argued for more work on what was still classically known as "metals and materials." We cast doubt on a very fashionable and popular topic of those times, and one which has arisen repeatedly since. It is the notion of a separate set of institutes for materials science and engineering. Rather, the notion of university participation was forcefully injected into the thinking. Then, as the main outcome of the report, the Federal Council for Science and Technology was implemented on 13 March 1959 by an Executive Order of President Eisenhower. It was activated just two weeks later when James R. Killian, the first chairman of the Federal Council for Science and Technology and the first Special Assistant to the President for those functions, appointed a Coordinating Committee on Materials Research and Development, chaired by John W. Williams, Director of the Division of Research of the Atomic Energy Commission. We pursued the diligent, and by no means silent, doings of that body so that by 11 July 1960 we received an official communique from the Advanced Research Projects Agency of the Department of Defense (which we had designated as the responsible body) saying that "the Department of Defense portion of the Interdisciplinary Laboratory Program has been initiated."

Much of the operating philosophy, which was then accepted, had been summarized in our letter to Dr. Kelman of 10 June 1960. By July 16 the press had described the designation of the first three universities holding contracts for interdisciplinary materials research and development. The *New York Times* account of this action said, "The process by which this decision was reached illustrates the workings of the policy-making machinery built up in the past few years to coordinate the nation's scientific effort. It also illustrates the time that can elapse between a recognized need and action." Nevertheless, Cornell University, Northwestern University, and the University of Pennsylvania were moving into action. But files of that time reveal that in his formal notes, President Kennedy had further discussed the onset of the National Materials Program in the fall of 1961, when he appeared in Chapel Hill at the University of North Carolina.

All of these documents emphasize not only the multispecialty, or what we may call polybasic research features, but also a particular ethos of the National Materials Program. Some of this is summarized in a letter I wrote as a member of PSAC to Dr. Kelman on 10 June 1960:

> Much of this present federal support outside the National Science Foundation is paid for on the fictional premise that it yields a specific weapons system, irrigation plant, health measure, space vehicle, or the like. This not only deludes the public and the government administrator, but also degrades the university. . . .
>
> A properly coordinated materials program would not require narrow, synthetic, justifications of university study. There would be acceptable probability that the free choice of the investigator would nevertheless advance some phase of needed engineering or procurement. Likewise, there would be important relief of the pressures on individual professors to attach their own studies to the particular project that has the push and the cash at some moment, regardless of its long term scientific values. . . .
>
> It is not yet widely recognized that the materials research and development have a basic generality and thus new knowledge derived from them is almost immediately applicable to an extraordinary range of needs. In this situation, actions of the Federal Council for Science and Technology and specifically those of the Coordinating Committee can be of great value to the national efficiency and economy. Indeed, without such coordinating action it now appears difficult to see how there could be a followup of the original objectives of the Coordinating Committee noted in the minutes of April 8, 1959.[9]

That program is a major realization of the overall conclusion of the report *Strengthening American Science*. In this report we said, "The endless frontiers of science, now stretching to the stars, can provide rich opportunities for men to seek a common understanding of the natural forces which all men must obey, and which govern the world in which all men must live together."[8]

Advancing materials research and development takes a new but expected shape as we look forward to the next quarter century of materials science and engineering. We and others have recorded in scientific and technical detail the particular vanguard of innovation that we should seek and expect. But we can now add another dimension to the advance.

It is that new links among the traditional divisions of science and engineering can be formed to advance a domain of knowledge and practice, namely, solid-state science and materials technology. The resulting network can mobilize actions in education, industry, and government far beyond the size of the nucleating effort.

In contrast to major programs like the Manhattan Project, the Apollo Program, or the National Cancer Plan, this network does not represent collaboration for a specific goal or mission. Rather it is the generation of a technical capability that applies to nearly every feature of economics and public affairs.

The National Materials Program constitutes a precious American resource of more than a million people devoted to scientific and engineering research and development to advance materials science and technology. It responds to the national need put forward by President Eisenhower in the 1950s. It combines new and once-separate realms of learning and practice and is slowly recasting age-old academic habits. It is intrinsic in industrial and governmental programs to achieve automation of design and process. It is basic to the growth of new technical capabilities such as photonics, bioengineering support and repair of human organs, exploration of space and the oceans, and preservation of the environment. Most of all it is a worthy exercise of the mind.

A national program in materials science and engineering is a new venture in this century of science and technology. Today, almost everything mankind has tried to do with matter through the million years of human evolution can be done not just two or three times better but, through materials science and engineering, a thousand or a thousand thousand times better than we once thought possible.

NOTES

1. National Academy of Sciences, Committee on the Survey of Materials Science and Engineering, *Materials and Man's Needs,* Summary Report (National Academy of Sciences, Washington, D.C., 1974).
2. *Science and Government Report* **15** (18), 4 (1985).
3. R. A. Reynolds, Science **226** (4674), 494 (1984).
4. D. Shapley and R. Roy, *Lost at the Frontier* (ISI Press, Philadelphia, 1985).
5. J. H. Scaff and R. S. Ohl, Bell Sys. Tech. J. **26**, 1 (1947); J. H. Scaff, H. C. Theurer, and E. E. Schumacher, J. Metals Trans. AIME **185**, 383 (1949); W. G. Pfann and J. H. Scaff, *ibid.* 389 (1949).
6. K. Ziegler, E. Holzkamp, H. Breil, H. Martin, Angew. Chem. **67**, 541 (1955); G. Natta and I. Pasquon, Adv. Catal. **9**, 1 (1959).
7. H. C. Theurer, J. Electrochem. Soc. **107**, 29 (1960).
8. President's Science Advisory Committee, *Strengthening American Science* (U.S. Government Printing Office, Washington, D.C., 1958).
9. William O. Baker, letter to Robert Kelman, President's Science Advisory Committee, 10 June 1960 (unpublished).

Appendix

COORDINATING MATERIALS RESEARCH IN THE UNITED STATES

Background paper prepared by the staff of
The President's Science Advisory Committee
18 March 1958

Research and development in the field of materials is closely related to the missions and activities of a number of Federal agencies. Unique environmental conditions associated with rocket propulsion, nuclear reactors, space flight, and vehicle re-entry, have established the need for materials which are not currently available. There have been many clever engineering designs which have allowed some progress to be made but these designs have not diminished the urgent need for materials research and development. The use of ablation materials and heat-sinks have allowed progress in high temperature structures. The use of strip-wrap construction for rocket casings and the use of honeycomb structural panels have increased the strength to weight ratio for structures involved in space flight. Yet all of these have meant increases in complexity and cost which would not have been required if new and better materials already existed.

During the last decade significant advances have been made in the sciences of solids. The effect of impurities and surface conditions on physical properties has been partially established. Very pure materials have approached those predicted by calculations of binding energies. Samples of ceramics which are normally brittle have shown ductile properties when prepared under very closely controlled conditions. There is a general feeling, therefore, that such advances in science as these can lead to a technology of materials engineering quite different from the metallurgy, ceramics, and polymer technology of today. But to achieve this result it will be necessary to begin to relate the new fundamental knowledge of matter to the behavior of highly complex materials. This in turn will require scientists and engineers from many different disciplines—organic chemistry, physical chemistry, metallurgy, and solid-state physics—to associate their special knowledge and different points of view.

While problems of high temperature materials, and materials having a high strength to weight ratio, are very urgent matters for Federal agencies, they are of little significance in the civilian economy today. It thus becomes clear that the Federal Government will have to play a leading role in encouraging the research and development which is needed. Most of the agencies represented on the Federal Council have laboratories engaged in materials research and development, and also sponsor such work in universities and industry. A careful coordination of research and applied science programs among the various agencies can thus increase the effectiveness of the total program. In a situation characterized by a shortage of manpower well-grounded in solid state physics, physical chemistry and crystallography, one naturally turns to the university where funds produce not only the needed research but trained manpower as well. In various universities one finds the faculties engaged in planning interdepartmental efforts to establish a new materials science and engineering. One of their problems is the lack of buildings and equipment. There are many research tools such as electron microscopes, electron diffraction units, high temperature furnaces, and x-ray diffraction units, each of which represents a cost of approximately $20,000. In assisting the universities to do more research and to train more first-rate personnel some way must be found to provide support for interdepartmental and interdisciplinary groups, to provide funds for equipment and buildings, and to assure reasonable continuity of support. In addition, there is a need to define objectives which are suitable for the academic environment. It is extremely important that, whenever possible, engineering departments of universities be supported in the applied science aspects of materials in order that the basic work may have a practical significance as soon as possible.

It is also worthwhile to explore the possibility of an information center which would publish information on the latest research and development accomplishments which are of real significance. Such a center could also serve to coordinate the exchange of samples of known purity and physical properties.

The attention to university programs for research and education is of great importance but is only one step in a program to strengthen our national effort in materials. The many Government laboratories, private research institutes, and industrial laboratories also have significant roles to play. Perhaps the Federal Council can aid in planning a well-coordinated program based on the unique capabilities of these various laboratories and institutions, both public and private.

Materials Research Laboratories: The Early Years

ROBERT L. SPROULL

In examining the origins of the Materials Research Laboratories program in 1960, my purpose is not to evoke nostalgia for that time but to derive lessons for the present and the future by revisiting the program and its antecedents. I shall adopt the point of view that since we are looking back on events of 25 years ago, the proper unit of time is 25 years. Thus, my story starts on the science side, two "time constants" before 1960, in 1910.

THE SCIENTIFIC SETTING

By 1910, chemistry and metallurgy had already hailed many centuries of contributions to the understanding of materials and a transition from art to science that had recently been accelerated by the discovery of x rays. But the contribution from physics had been nearly zero; some descriptive "laws" like Dulong and Petit's law of specific heats and the Wiedemann-Franz ratio of thermal to electrical conductivity in metals were well known, but they papered over and concealed real understanding. Planck's introduction of the quantum theory in 1900 and Einstein's brilliant paper on the photoelectric effect in 1905 were only a gleam in the eye.

By one time constant later, in 1935, the seeds had been sown for a complete revolution in the understanding of matter. The clock really started running only in 1923, and, only four years later, the quantum mechanics developed by the giants Bohr, Schrödinger, Heisenberg, and others was being successfully and widely applied. Heitler and London used wave mechanics to describe the hydrogen molecule in 1927; Pauling extended the theory to molecules generally in the next eight years. Von Neumann introduced mathematical elegance at the same time. Sommerfeld and Bethe's monumental

Volume 24, Number 2, of the *Handbuch der Physik* appeared in 1933, full of rich ore that is still being mined. William Hume-Rothery's *The Metallic State* came out in 1931, and his seminal *The Structure of Metals and Alloys* was in manuscript by the end of our first period. A. H. Wilson, R. Peierls, Neville Mott, and many others rapidly advanced the science of the solid state.

I must recount two anecdotes from that period, both with profound implications for the rest of my story. The first concerns Robert Wichert Pohl, the Göttingen giant of experimental solid-state physics. He had borrowed a large diamond from a Berlin bank to measure the Hall effect in photoelectrons. But he, or more likely an assistant, had failed to secure the magnet pole pieces, and when the current was turned on, North and South made instant love at the expense of the brittle diamond. From this experience flowed his concentration on alkali halide crystals.

The second story concerns a very young 1932 graduate of Stanford University, Frederick Seitz. He went to Princeton to do graduate work with E. U. Condon. But Condon, who was then preparing the famous Condon and Shortley *Theory of Atomic Spectra*, advised him to work with Eugene Wigner instead; Condon remarked, "Solid-state physics is coming, and if you stay with me you'll just do calculations for my book."

I need spend little time on the second time constant, since the flowering of understanding and prediction during the period from 1935 to 1960 is well known. Chemistry adopted quantum mechanics with great effectiveness. Metallurgists were beginning to go far beyond their venerable concentration on the austenite-martensite transition. Even geologists were dusting off their hogbacks and cuestas and conducting synthetic mineralogy. Seitz's *The Modern Theory of Solids* in 1940 brought understanding to new heights and provided a common language for all workers in materials. William Shockley's theory of the p-n junction in 1949 and the realization of the junction transistor in 1951 produced immediate visions of a fantastic future for solid-state electronic devices. The complexity of so-called point defects was beginning to be appreciated, and dislocation theory was well advanced. New polymers and new alloys and metals like ductile titanium were being developed.

Thus, by 1960 the stage was set for spectacular advances in materials that would have profound effects on society. Physics was at last bringing something to the party, and metallurgists and chemists needed physicists, if only physicists would rise above their snobbery. Physicists needed chemists and metallurgists, since increasingly sophisticated experiments required detailed knowledge of chemical and physical imperfections and structures. Of even more consequence was the conviction that the design and creation of new materials, such as composites, high-temperature coatings, or catalysts, would require true collaboration among chemists, physicists, and engineers.

THE PROGRAM TAKES SHAPE

I now turn to the second element of the setting for 1960, the currents in and around Washington, and here I shall go back only one time constant, to 1935. The prewar defense establishment had been interested in mechanical properties of solids and in corrosion and coatings, and the Signal Corps contracted for work in vacuum-tube electronics, including work on that enduring mystery, the oxide-coated cathode. But our story really begins with three decisions reached in the months immediately following the war:

• Science and technology had much to contribute to national defense and prosperity and therefore could appropriately be supported by the federal government;
• The preparation of a new generation of scientists and engineers and much of federally supported research should be done in the same institutions, the research universities;
• The federal apparatus and process for this support through contracts (and later, grants) should be quite unlike the prewar "buying brooms" systems and should provide much more scope for the contractor's imagination and discovery and more harvesting by informal agency-contractor interactions rather than by fulfilling specifications.

The Office of Naval Research (ONR) was the immediate consequence, in late 1945 and early 1946, of these decisions, and it set the pattern for all the later agencies. Two elements of this pattern were especially important: (1) program managers who might be (and occasionally were) principal investigators, and principal investigators who might equally well be (and occasionally were) program managers; and (2) task statements in general terms, with maximum opportunity for creation and discovery. The other defense agencies, the Atomic Energy Commission (AEC), National Science Foundation (NSF), and National Aeronautics and Space Administration (NASA) warmly embraced this tradition.

Another consequence of the war was the Washington realization that the field of materials was far more complex and open-ended than it had appeared in 1935. The AEC had to contend with radiation-produced embrittlement and the Wigner disease (with the Szilard complications). The Department of Defense (DOD) had to contend with nose cones and a fascinating array of materials covered up by the nose cones, as well as the burgeoning opportunities in electronic and optical materials.

There were several Washington rays that converged in 1959–1960, but to begin with they were essentially independent, coming from AEC, ONR, the National Academy of Sciences (NAS), the White House, and DOD. One of the most important was the ray from AEC. The 1945 euphoria concerning the peaceful uses of atomic energy brought forth the innocent suggestion that electricity produced by fission reactors would soon be so cheap that it would not pay to meter it. (This suggestion, grossly uninformed about materials problems and their implication for Carnot efficiency, was on a par with the insertion by nuclear physicists of an anthracene crystal into one of the early synchrotrons to locate the beam by its fluorescence; it took weeks to clean up the gunk so that a reasonable vacuum could be maintained.) This extreme position was never seriously maintained by AEC, but realization of the compelling influence of materials limitations on nuclear reactor cost, efficiency, and safety was, let us say, slow to develop.

John von Neumann, who brought Hilbert space to bear on quantum mechanics, was especially upset that time and time again what he wanted to do was prevented by an inadequate science of materials. When he asked what limited the growth of that science, he was told, "Lack of people." And why not produce more capable people? "Lack of university facilities." He thus began pushing in the AEC General Advisory Committee (GAC) for a substantial program in sponsoring university facilities for materials research and graduate education. By the time he became ill and died in early 1957, Willard Libby had already effectively taken up the torch in the GAC. The AEC Metallurgy and Materials Branch Advisory Panel, of which Seitz was chairman, in its first report in 1956 called for new buildings and research facilities in universities for materials research and education. Although Edward Epremian, who was chief of AEC's Metallurgy and Materials Branch, recommended to the GAC that the AEC establish "Materials Research Institutes" at universities, the GAC would not commit the funds. After the launch of *Sputnik I* on 4 October 1957, however, this ray was revitalized by Donald K. Stevens, who succeeded Epremian in December 1957.

Another ray came from ONR with its Solid State Sciences Advisory Panel, a group affectionately known as the Navy's "chowder and marching society." Under the leadership of Seitz and Harvey Brooks, it had been studying Navy materials problems and helpfully visiting Navy laboratories since 1950. Its report on opportunities in solid-state science research appeared so soon before Sputnik that its authors were accused (jocularly, I hope) of being privy to Soviet secrets. Julius Harwood and others in ONR urged more materials work in universities.

A third ray was a National Academy of Sciences study sponsored by the Air Force in 1957.[1] This study, led by J. Herbert Hollomon, recommended in 1958 and 1959 the creation of a National Materials Laboratory. Opposition was quick and nearly universal, mostly because of the realization that such a move would only reassign people already in the field and would do nothing to enlarge the supply of trained scientists and engineers. It did, however, reinforce the need for action in materials research, and it documented advantages of interdisciplinary approaches.

A fourth ray emanated from the White House. James Killian was appointed Science Advisor to the President on 7 November 1957 and quickly organized the President's Scientific Advisory Committee (PSAC). Killian and PSAC member William O. Baker identified materials research and training as matters of top priority in the post-Sputnik environment. The Federal Council for Science and Technology, consisting of the heads of all the agencies involved in science and technology, was created as the administrative counterpart to PSAC. Its first and highly effective instrument was the Coordinating Committee on Materials Research and Development, made up of the materials heads in each agency, initially chaired by John H. Williams of AEC and later by Stevens.

A fifth ray started in the Department of Defense, encouraged by the White House interest. Herbert York, director of Defense Research and Engineering, Roy Johnson, director of the Advanced Research Projects Agency (ARPA) until November 1959, and John F. Kincaid of ARPA participated.

The focusing of these rays began in late 1958. A key meeting occurred when Libby, accompanied by Stevens, descended on York, buttressed by Kincaid. Stevens convinced York that his AEC investigations documented a great opportunity for the creation of interdisciplinary materials laboratories in universities and the universities' need for support for buildings. York asked Kincaid to evaluate Stevens's findings; Kincaid quickly agreed they were sound.

In the late winter and spring of 1959, Kincaid, Stevens, and others visited a number of research universities at which DOD and AEC work showed promise for development of interdisciplinary laboratories. This team again verified the need for space and modern research equipment and central facilities and the willingness on the part of the universities to take the risks of expansion if appropriate contracts could be worked out.

By early June of 1959, AEC had decided that its one-year contracting authority would not be sufficient for universities to commit space and borrow money to create facilities and to justify expansion by tenure-track professorial appointments. York agreed to DOD's taking the prime responsibility and assigned it to ARPA on 8 June 1959. DOD had the authority to write five-year contracts; the contracts were for four years, but an additional year was negotiated each year, so there were always at least three years ahead under the contracts. AEC never really left the program, however, and participated positively in the creation of facilities at Berkeley and Urbana and through individual research grants at what became ARPA Interdisciplinary Laboratories (IDLs). NASA joined later.

The selection of the first three laboratories proceeded through the academic year 1959–1960. Assisting Kincaid in ARPA was a group of consultants, including Morris Tanenbaum, G. J. Dienes, M. E. Hebb, J. Herbert Hollomon, and J. P. Howe. Charles Yost in the Air Force Office of Scientific

Research, Harwood, and others from the armed services also participated. All of the recent accomplishments of research and experience in educating Ph.D. students were considered, but the selection was not a prize for past performance; rather it was a judgment of the *promise* of a university for a significant expansion and a truly joint, cooperative attack on materials research across disciplines.

All of the rays finally came into focus with the first contracts in July 1960. (Coincidentally, 1960 was the year the most monumental real-light focusing of all time occurred in the first demonstration of the laser.) The three universities chosen by ARPA in 1960 were joined in later years by nine more ARPA contracts, three AEC contracts, and two NASA contracts. After a thoroughgoing review in 1971, the program, now called the Materials Research Laboratories program, was transferred to NSF in 1972.

Was this program a success? I believe it was a spectacular success, but I am probably one of the poorest possible evaluators. There is a theorem that says: "All education experiments are successful." The proof is simple: All education experiments are evaluated by their promoters. So, others must be asked for a dispassionate judgment. I do suggest, however, the way that the question "Success compared to what?" should be answered. The comparison should be with spending the same amounts on materials research by federal agencies through routine individual grants and contracts.

ASSESSING THE EXPERIENCE

Up to this point, I have given a quick look at the early history of the materials laboratories, announced their success, and acknowledged my negative credentials for making that announcement credible. There remains only to give my view as to why the program was successful and to draw any lessons we can from the experience. There is now renewed interest in Washington in "hyphenated" science, as evidenced by a recent report on new interdisciplinary research arrangements by the Government-University-Industry Research Roundtable and the Academy Industry Program of the National Academy of Sciences, National Academy of Engineering, and Institute of Medicine.[2] I believe the materials laboratories have much to teach us. I will therefore describe briefly what I believe to be the important features of this program, dividing them into features of the *field* of materials research, those *at the universities*, and those *in Washington*. Of course, the latter two are intimately connected and in many cases (e.g., building support) require looking at the same feature from two perspectives.

The important features of the field of materials research were, first, its immense variety and open-endedness. The preceding description of the situation in 1960 shows how intellectually auspicious it was. The second feature was the richness of connections among the disciplines, including not just chemistry, physics, and metallurgy, but mathematics, geology, and nearly all branches of engineering; and, of course, the connection throughout between theory and experiment. The third feature was the richness of applications across the vast area from consumer products to national defense. The Ph.D.s educated in the program had a marvelous choice of jobs, as near to or as far from immediately useful products as they chose. Since all product-oriented development is necessarily interdisciplinary, these young people were especially in demand for work, with direct benefits to society. The fourth feature was that most research projects in materials are of human scale, not requiring the huge team efforts associated with particle physics. Of course, cooperation and collaboration were essential. In later work in industry, exstudents might be part of sizable teams (on alloy development, for example), but Ph.D. research projects were naturally of human size, with maximum opportunity for individual initiative, for an individual's learning just how capable a scientist or engineer he could be.

The important features at each university were, first, that an umbrella contract provided for continuity of support and for the ability to buy large quanta of equipment and facilities. Second, a local director committed a substantial fraction of his career to making the program succeed. He could use the longevity of support to extract concessions from the university and departmental administrations. Third, the contract provided, in most cases, reimbursement over 10 years for the new construction required to do modern experimentation on materials. Fourth, the longevity of the contract induced the university to allocate to the project scarce and prime space in the middle of the campus, thereby establishing the maximum informal connections among disciplines. Fifth, central experimental facilities (such as those for electron microscopy or crystal growth) could have state-of-the-art equipment, even if it was very expensive, and they served as a mixing ground for students and faculty from several disciplines. Sixth, an executive committee composed of people with power and influence in the individual disciplines but oriented toward the success of the program helped the director over the rough spots with department chairmen, people who often were overly protective of their bishoprics and palatinates. Seventh, a contract was not given to an institution unless it had a strong disciplinary base on which to build. Interdisciplinary programs perched on weak disciplines are dangerous; interdisciplinary work already had a bad name on many campuses because of programs alleged to be interdisciplinary but without disciplines (on many campuses home economics was the example cited). Eighth, individual grants and contracts with federal agencies continued; most well-established principal investigators received the majority of their support from some other agency and might enjoy help from the program only in the central facilities or the building space. Thus, when the executive committee and director found that they had to say

"No" to a local high priest, it was not really "No" but only "No with the umbrella contract's money," and that made life easier.

This list may be incomplete, but perhaps more importantly it does not quite capture the flavor of the informal interaction among young and old, among electrical engineers and chemists, among administrators and bench scientists that was fostered by the umbrella contracts and was, in my view, at the heart of the success of the program. That ambience would have been different if research institutes had been built. I might illustrate this important point by mentioning Morris Tanenbaum's history of the development of hard superconductors, described in a report by the National Research Council's Materials Advisory Board at about the time of the birth of these laboratories.[3] Although Tanenbaum explained how the formal interdisciplinary nature of Bell Telephone Laboratories (BTL) "produced" this development, his text permits the conclusion that the most important part of BTL was the lunchroom! The unplanned interactions in various materials facilities in the midst of other campus activities played a key role in the success of the laboratories.

The important features of the program related to Washington were, first, in 1959–1960 and for a few years afterward, Washington was in an expansionist mood; initiatives were welcomed. Second, the flowing together of currents and conviction from NAS, PSAC, the Federal Council for Science and Technology, the Coordinating Committee on Materials Research and Development, and from AEC, DOD, and other agencies gave a solid, joint base to the program. Third, ARPA was a young agency with little doctrine and almost a passion for innovation; it held the profound conviction that the United States should never be only second best in any consequential technology. Fourth, ARPA was willing to write four-year contracts with a four-year renewal each year, thereby getting much more for the taxpayers' money than if it had insisted on year-by-year contracting. Further, ARPA gave convincing evidence that the program would last at least 10 years, and thereby induced universities to take the risks of borrowing money and building new facilities with a 10-year payback. Although several university presidents were very nervous about placing such confidence in the federal government, in the end all commitments were honored. Fifth, ARPA and other agencies exercised exemplary self-restraint in eschewing micromanagement; they left the allocation of funds to the local management, which resulted in enormous enhancement of efficiency and effectiveness. The work statement was extremely broad, speaking only to "the properties of materials," "fundamental relationships," and "theoretical and experimental studies in such fields as metallurgy, ceramic science, solid-state physics, chemistry, solid-state mechanics, surface phenomena, and polymer sciences." Sixth, the Bureau of the Budget and Capitol Hill were not as concerned about the details of programs as they are now. Seventh, the continuation of individual project support by the other agencies permitted these agencies to take justifiable pride in their part of the program and to connect it to agency missions.

These features of the Materials Research Laboratories program outlined above helped the program overcome oppositions and concerns, of which there were many. There was, of course, envy on the part of nonparticipating universities; only 3 of the 45 proposals in the first round were funded in 1960. The negative consequences were, of course, mitigated by subsequent rounds of ARPA, AEC, and NASA contracts and by a $6-million ARPA equipment grant program in 1960 and 1961, the funds going to the unsuccessful competitors. In Washington there was nervousness that the whole program was a packaging gimmick, getting wholesale what would not have been possible to get retail. On campuses, there was nervousness that "interdisciplinary" would become a buzzword that would dominate Washington allocation practice. Later, the Mansfield amendment (114 Cong. Rec. 29332 [1968]), which limited indirect costs that could be added to the base cost of a defense research grant on contract, played into the hands of those who equate "relevance" with "immediate applicability." The intended intimidation of program managers never quite came off, and only the most timid of universities gave credence to those who would have had one believe that the ARPA contracts were helping to napalm the Vietnamese. The program and its leaders were strong enough to shrug off these irritants.

Of course, not all of the features of the MRLs, especially the benign budgetary oversight by Congress and the executive branch, can be re-created for any program proposed today. However, the Materials Research Laboratories tell us that to the extent that these features can be adopted, a new program will be more auspicious.

Since the first Materials Research Laboratories were established, a generation of scientists and engineers has done its work. Some of these individuals have spent nearly their entire professional lives in these laboratories and have led spectacular careers in research and in the guidance of Ph.D. students. I am sure many would give a good deal of the credit to the early support from the ARPA program, to the central facilities, to the fine building, library, and connections with chemistry and metallurgy nourished by the program, and to the colleagues provided in part by the program. Of course, much is also due to their own imagination, energy, physical insight, drive, and generosity of spirit. Thus, although I do not suggest that I am competent to evaluate the materials laboratories, I do claim some part of the success of individuals as a success of the program.

ACKNOWLEDGMENT

I should like to thank D. K. Hess, R. E. Hughes, and D. K. Stevens for help in the preparation of this chapter.

NOTES

1. *A Report by the Committee on Materials Relating to Long-Range Scientific and Technical Trends of Interest to the Air Force* (National Academy of Sciences, Washington, D.C., 1958).
2. Government-University-Industry Research Roundtable and the Academy Industry Program, *New Alliances and Partnerships in American Science and Engineering* (National Academy Press, Washington, D.C., 1986).
3. M. Tanenbaum, in *Report of Ad Hoc Committee on Principles of Research-Engineering Interaction*, Materials Advisory Board, National Research Council, publication MAB-222-M (National Academy of Sciences, Washington, D.C., 1966), pp. J-1–J-59.

Materials Research Laboratories: Reviewing the First Twenty-Five Years

LYLE H. SCHWARTZ

Creativity is a singular effort. It is often said that no original idea has ever come from a committee. And yet, increasingly, group efforts are devoted to the solution of technical problems. Industrial research laboratories first, and then universities, turned to collaborative research teams that cross rigid departmental boundaries and use systems approaches to attack complex problems. The efforts leading to establishment of Materials Research Laboratories have been in the vanguard of this transition.

In 1960 the Advanced Research Projects Agency (ARPA) of the U.S. Department of Defense established the Interdisciplinary Laboratories (IDLs), later known as Materials Research Laboratories (MRLs). Their impact on materials research, on the universities in which they are housed, and on the very manner in which university research is organized has been profound and is still growing. The purpose of this chapter is to survey the brief but significant history of these laboratories, looking back to the time of their origin, tracing their evolution, and then summarizing some of their accomplishments.[1]

INTERDISCIPLINARY LABORATORIES

In the atmosphere of international competition symptomatic of the cold war and dramatized by the Soviet launching of *Sputnik I* in October 1957, an interagency Coordinating Committee on Materials Research and Development (CCMRD) was convened in 1958 at the urging of the U.S. Department of Defense (DOD). It was clear then as it is now that the national economy and security would depend increasingly on new technology, which in many cases would require new, more reliable materials. It was not as

TABLE 1   Year of Establishment and Termination of Interdisciplinary
Laboratories (IDLs)/Materials Research Laboratories (MRLs)

IDL/MRL University	Year Initiated	Year Terminated
Cornell	1960	
Pennsylvania	1960	
Northwestern	1960	
Brown	1961	
Chicago	1961	
Harvard	1961	
Maryland	1961	1977
MIT	1961	
North Carolina	1961	1978
Purdue	1961	*
Stanford	1961	
Illinois (Urbana)	1962 (with AEC)	
Carnegie Mellon	1973	*
Massachusetts (Amherst)	1973	
Pennsylvania State	1974	1980
Case Western Reserve	1974	*
Ohio State	1982	*

*Materials Research Laboratories at these institutions are being phased out. Materials Research Groups have recently been established at Carnegie Mellon University, Case Western Reserve University, Purdue University, the University of Michigan, Michigan State University, and the University of Texas at Austin.

clear then as it is today that a broad interdisciplinary education was necessary to make progress in materials research, but the farsighted members of the CCMRD did recognize that need. In 1959 they recommended the establishment of interdisciplinary laboratories for materials research to be built on university campuses to carry on research and to train graduate students. Their intention was to foster research in which the pertinent scientific and engineering disciplines would be brought to bear in a collective and cooperative manner on common problem areas in materials science.

The CCMRD recommendation was adopted by the Federal Council for Science and Technology and was assigned to ARPA in June 1959 for execution. During the next three years, 12 IDLs were established, as shown in Table 1. Coincidentally, the Atomic Energy Commission (now the Department of Energy [DOE]) supported analogous laboratories in three universities (University of California, Berkeley; University of Iowa; and University of Illinois), and the National Aeronautics and Space Administration followed with a smaller program. (Details of the events leading to the establishment of these various laboratories are presented in a 1960 address by William O. Baker.[2]) This presentation is limited to a discussion of the ARPA IDLs, which were renamed Materials Research Laboratories when the National Science Foundation (NSF) took over the program in 1972.

It is instructive to quote directly from the work statement in ARPA IDL contracts from 1960:

> The Contractor shall establish an *interdisciplinary materials research* program and shall furnish the necessary *personnel* and *facilities* for the conduct of research in the science of materials with the objective of furthering the *understanding of the factors which influence the properties of materials* and the *fundamental relationships which exist between composition and structure and the behavior of materials* [emphasis added].

In looking back, it should be recalled that in 1960 few academic departments at universities had sufficient breadth of coverage to justify the title "Materials Science," and none would even have considered the title "Materials Science and Engineering." Instead, there were many departments in which mining, process metallurgy, physical and mechanical metallurgy, and the physics of metals were the principal, and largely separate, areas of materials research. An occasional individual effort in ceramic engineering could be found, and polymer science, if available at all, was a topical course in advanced chemistry. Yet, 12 years later when the IDLs were transferred to NSF, materials science was a recognized discipline at many major research universities, and the change in emphasis in academia could be clearly demonstrated by the names selected by materials departments (see Table 2). The trend toward more general "materials" departments is continuing, as shown in the table.

TABLE 2 Trends in Titles of Materials Departments at U.S. Universities, 1964–1985

Department Title	Number of Departments, by Year		
	1964[a]	1970[b]	1985[b]
Minerals and Mining	9	7	5
Metallurgy	31	21	17
Materials	11	29	51
Other	18	21	17
Total	69	78	90

[a]Compiled from 1964–1970 *ASM Metallurgy/Materials Education Yearbook*, ed., J. P. Nielsen (American Society for Metals, Metals Park, Ohio).
[b]Compiled from 1985 *ASM Metallurgy/Materials Education Yearbook*, ed., K. Mukherjee (American Society for Metals, Metals Park, Ohio, 1985).

The establishment of the ARPA IDLs was the first attempt on U.S. university campuses to create a new style of research organization and to accelerate the processes of academic curricular change resulting from federal recognition of a specific national need. It was clear to the organizers of this experiment that this new mode for funding university research would require changes in the way universities do business—in particular, the traditional departmental organization would be threatened.

During the dramatic first years (see Sproull, in this volume), many of the IDL program goals were realized. Buildings were built, paid for by ARPA through a building use fee incorporated into the contract; interdisciplinary research facilities were established in these buildings, with sophisticated equipment operated by trained technicians and available to the entire materials community at the IDL. Graduate students were trained in large numbers and went on to populate the universities and federal and industrial laboratories, which were growing rapidly during this period. Research was carried out in myriad materials fields using federal funds assigned as block grants to the universities and administered locally.

A brief statistical view of the IDLs at their height is informative. In Fiscal Year 1969, for example, the funding for the IDL program reached its maximum—$18.97 million,[3] including $1.8 million in building use charges. In that same year a total of nearly 600 faculty members and 2,385 graduate students participated in the program, 360 doctoral degrees were awarded, and more than 2,000 papers by program participants were published. The research efforts of these students and faculty members were grouped into 134 "work units," or identifiable research project areas, and each participating university engaged in 6 to 20 such units. Significantly missing from the program at that time was the strong interactive team approach, which we now identify as a dominant feature of the Materials Research Laboratories and which would be left to the National Science Foundation to foster.

In the report *Materials and Man's Needs*, the National Academy of Sciences Committee on the Survey of Materials Science and Engineering (COSMAT) devoted extensive study to the materials centers (including all ARPA, AEC, and NASA block-funded institutions). The committee's list of successes for the materials center concept included the following:

• Drawing "attention to the emergence of coupled materials science and engineering as a new interdisciplinary focus of activity in a way which could not have been achieved otherwise."

• Demonstration "that block funding is perfectly feasible on a campus."

• Development of "excellent research groupings of faculty members, the building-up of a reputation and attraction for good students, and the training of first-rate materials scientists, physicists, chemists, and other professionals."

• Administrative efficiency achieved "through faculty saving their time in writing proposals and seeking support, and the agency officials likewise saving a great deal of administrative time.''

• ''A large number of students were trained in an excellent environment for advanced degrees.''[4]

Not surprisingly, the COSMAT report found some deficiencies in the program, the most important of which was the limited evidence of interdisciplinary effort as measured principally by the limited number of joint publications. (Of course, the number of joint publications should not be the only criterion in such an evaluation.) One could say of this period that the seeds for interdisciplinary cooperation had been sown but that the young plant needed cultivation. At its best, interdisciplinary activity at the IDLs consisted of the development of a community of scholars brought together by a block grant, which they administered jointly; of research facilities developed by expert disciplinarians but designed and operated in a manner conducive to shared use by students from other disciplines; of additions to faculties in related departments with expertise intended to complement existing strengths throughout the fields of materials research; and of seminar series and internal meetings organized expressly for educating colleagues in other departments. Without these beginnings, the next critical steps toward fully collaborative cross-disciplinarity could not have been achieved in the NSF program.

The COSMAT report was also critical of the effectiveness of the ARPA IDL effort to increase graduate education in materials research more rapidly than in other disciplines. It found that the number of M.S. and Ph.D. degrees granted in the traditional materials departments (Figure 1) grew at 12 to 13 percent per year through the 1960s, the same rate as that for the engineering field as a whole. It seems clear in retrospect that substantial government funding in many forms led to a general expansion of graduate education in all engineering fields. Instead of focusing on any failure of ARPA to do better in some quantitative sense in materials education than was done in other fields by other DOD agencies, DOE, and NASA, one should focus on the quality of the education received by the students. Both graduate and undergraduate students at the institutions where IDLs had been established benefited from the broad interdisciplinary view of materials research that entered the curriculum as faculties grew in size and diversity. By the early 1970s it was no longer uncommon at these schools to find ceramics (and even polymer science) taught as an integral part of the curriculum. Although the IDLs were not alone in this trend, they certainly led the way. Thus, much of the interdisciplinarity sought in the original CCMRD concept was realized through evolutionary changes in the traditional materials departments rather than by dramatic changes in interaction across university departmental lines. This cross-departmental interaction would come only with the group research concept introduced by NSF.

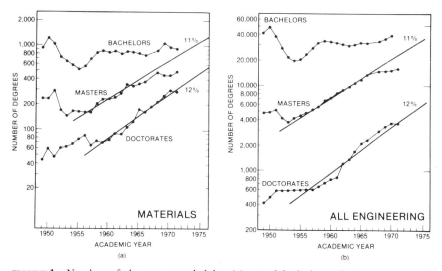

FIGURE 1 Number of degrees awarded by (a) materials-designated departments and (b) engineering departments in all fields (U.S. Engineering Council for Professional Development Schools), 1950–1970. (Percentages indicate average annual rate of growth during the 1960s.)[4]

TRANSFER OF IDLs TO NSF

The political complexities of the late 1960s led to reevaluation of the role of DOD in sponsoring non-mission-oriented research at universities. In 1970 it was decided that the appropriate agency to which responsibility for this program of research centers should be transferred was the National Science Foundation. However, the concepts of block funding, delegation of authority to local management, and shared experimental facilities differed markedly from those characterizing the traditional single-investigator, discipline-oriented mode of operation at NSF. After an extensive review of the program in 1971, NSF assumed responsibility for the IDLs in 1972, accepting the operational modes built into the program but adding a critical new component. As described in NSF's program policy statement, the laboratories—now renamed Materials Research Laboratories—would retain locally administered block (or "core") funding intended to "facilitate research in materials science and engineering which is either difficult or unfeasible to carry out under traditional funding of individual research." Most importantly, the new component added by NSF was that "scientific excellence is viewed as a necessary, but no longer sufficient, condition to qualify for MRL core support." In addition, the MRLs would be judged by their ability to foster "coherent, multidisciplinary and multi-investigator projects in major thrust areas requiring the expertise of two or more materials-related disciplines.'' These so-called thrust groups are the heart of the current core funding at MRLs; at their best they have achieved a transformation in the way materials research is done at universities and in the way graduate education proceeds.

The transfer of the MRLs to NSF required an organizational change and led to the establishment of the Materials Research Division, grouping the MRLs with programs that had concentrated on traditional materials departments as well as on areas of physics and chemistry clearly dealing with materials research.

At the time of its move from ARPA to NSF, the program included 600 faculty members at 12 universities. Of these faculty members, some 35 percent were physicists, 25 percent were chemists, 19 percent were metallurgists or members of materials science and engineering departments, 16 percent were from other engineering departments (mainly electrical), and the remaining 5 percent were from other fields. The transition from ARPA to NSF was rather complex, taking place over a two-year period; not all projects (or funds) were finally transferred. The total MRL budget for FY 1974 was $12.1 million, reduced from the $17.2 million for operations of the FY 1971 IDL budget. When the program was examined in 1975 by the MITRE Corporation on contract from the NSF,[5] the number of faculty members had been reduced to 532 and the distribution had shifted slightly from physics toward materials and engineering (Table 3). Inflation and limited NSF budgets in subsequent years led to further reduction in effort as measured in constant dollars (Figure 2) and a consequent further reduction in faculty to the 1985 level of 400. Furthermore, additions of new schools to the MRL program and phaseout of others led to the 1985 faculty distribution shown in Table 3. It is significant, and disturbing, that these trends seem counter to the increased emphasis on materials processing and chemistry in materials research. Balance in NSF funding is being achieved by other funding modes.

TABLE 3 Faculty Distribution in IDLs/MRLs, 1970, 1975, and 1985

Faculty	1970[a]	1975[b]	1985[c]
Materials science and engineering (includes metallurgy, geosciences, etc.)	19%	27%	35%
Physicists	35%	31%	35%
Chemists	25%	19%	17%
Other engineering	16%	23% }	12%
Other	5%	2% }	
Total number	600	532	400

[a]Note 1 of this chapter.
[b]Note 4.
[c]Note 6.

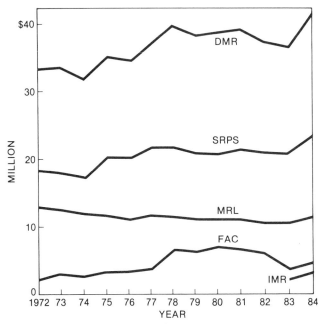

FIGURE 2   NSF-DMR budget, FY 1972–FY 1984, in constant 1982 dollars. DMR, Division of Materials Research; SRPS, single-investigator research project support; MRL, Materials Research Laboratories; FAC, national user facilities; IMR, instrumentation for materials research.

THRUST GROUPS

The formation of the interdisciplinary thrust groups referred to above varies among institutions. It often begins when several faculty members with common interests, challenged by the opportunity to attack complex problems and encouraged by the availability of a funding mode for group effort, come together for brainstorming. This exercise may be stimulated by an MRL director or may result from the efforts and ideas of a single faculty member, but it leads to the definition of a program area in which the university has substantial current or developing capability. As the research program concept is refined, other faculty members with complementary talents may be attracted to the group. In the formative years of the NSF MRL program, most projects proposed by well-conceived thrust groups were accepted, replacing single-investigator activity in the MRL.

By the mid-1970s, this new form of endeavor would compete with existing programs for limited core funding. New thrust groups are commonly given minimal (seed) funding to encourage continued effort and program refinement before full funding. The decision to fund is made by the MRL director in consultation with his advisory committee (and often with the further advice of an external visiting committee). Until 1985 the start-up of a major new thrust group activity began with a three-year grant from NSF after a site visit and further program evaluation. A recent change in NSF management procedure has opened the way for substantial redistribution of funds among MRLs, allowing for rapid response to new opportunities for research by thrust groups.

As the thrust group's activity develops, several forms of interaction may be found. For example, graduate students and postdoctoral associates who have the same faculty adviser usually work on common problems, some characterizing the structure of a given material, some studying its properties, others studying problems of theory. Group meetings permit interchange of information about progress as well as plans for the future. Major equipment facilities commonly are used for collaborative projects, and in other instances new, specialized laboratories are designed to support the research needs of the thrust group. At their best, thrust groups create an educational environment that differs radically from that of 25 years ago when each student associated almost exclusively with his adviser and peers. Thrust groups produce materials research unlike that carried out at universities even a decade ago when collaborative efforts by more than two investigators were difficult to stimulate and, once stimulated, difficult to fund.

SUMMARY OF MRL ACCOMPLISHMENTS

The current status of the MRL program may be summarized as follows. The NSF budget for the MRL program in FY 1985 was $27 million. MRL awards range from about $0.75 million to nearly $4 million, with the average award at about $2 million. About 60 percent of the budget is spent on thrust group research, 30 percent on facilities, and 10 percent on seed projects. The average number of faculty members participating in an MRL is about 30, with about 6 postdoctoral scholars, 25 graduate students, and 6 technicians. Since their inception in 1960, the MRLs have produced an estimated 3,000 Ph.D.s in materials research, funded primarily by block grants. Since 1972, when NSF took over the program, five new MRLs have been started and seven have been phased out (see Table 1).

In evaluating the research programs of the MRLs, issues of quality and character must be addressed. In its study of the MRL program, the MITRE Corporation evaluated quality using a complex peer review process. Reviewers compared publications of the faculty and students at the MRLs with those from peer non-MRL universities. Significant achievements identified and submitted to MITRE by MRLs were compared with those submitted from non-MRL "control" schools. The results of this analysis led the MITRE study group to conclude that the quality of research at the MRLs "is high with a greater number of major achievements at MRL's than at non-MRL institutions."[5]

The character of the research at MRLs is more difficult to describe. In the mid-1970s when data were being gathered for the MITRE study, only one graduate-student cycle (4 years) had passed since the introduction of the thrust group concept, and most thrust group efforts were only at their initiation stage. Now, 10 years later, the accomplishments of those thrust groups are the measure of the MRLs' character and effectiveness. The following list of research accomplishments of the MRLs was compiled in 1984 by Roman J. Wasilewski, head of NSF's MRL program for 10 years. His intention was to identify those developments that would be difficult or infeasible to achieve under traditional disciplinary project support.[1] The list omits numerous accomplishments of comparable caliber in which project support might just as readily have led to their success.

Organic Metals   The research field of organic metals opened as the result of the University of Pennsylvania group's early findings on tetrathiofulvalene-tetracyanoquinodimethane (TTF-TCNQ), which led to an unprecedented degree of collaboration between organic chemists and physicists. Most of the materials initially investigated were not new. Rather, it was the collaboration between researchers in synthesis chemistry and solid-state physics that led to exciting findings. The development of new, related materials followed quickly at the MRL at Northwestern University and elsewhere.

Ultralow Temperatures   Cornell University has pioneered in research in the millidegree range for over a decade. Support for this research had originally been requested from—and was declined by—a traditional disciplinary NSF program. The first disciplinary project support was in fact provided only several years after establishment of the MRL at Cornell—after the facilities and the technique had been developed and the first experimental observations of unexpected phase transitions were observed. Since then most of the low-temperature physics aspects of the program have been project-supported, while the parts of the research primarily concerned with phase transitions, which expanded rapidly to metallurgical transitions, remain core-supported.

Lower-Dimensionality Materials   The field of lower-dimensionality materials shows how rapidly progress can be achieved by cross-disciplinary involvement. Although materials like liquid crystals and intercalation compounds had long been known, they were of limited scientific interest for decades, viewed as curiosities with little scientific or technological potential. A collaborative MRL program combining research in synthesis and physics developed early at Harvard University and provided a major stimulus to the field. Similarly, MRL programs on intercalated compounds at MIT and the University of Pennsylvania and on molecularly stacked organic crystals at Northwestern University developed rapidly.

Surfaces and Interfaces With the current availability of sophisticated equipment and techniques, the area of surfaces and interfaces may be viewed as largely disciplinary and no longer requiring cross-disciplinary collaboration. Nevertheless, many of the original techniques, kinds of instrumentation, and approaches were adopted by groups at several of the MRLs. Areas in which major—and at times definitive—contributions came from the MRL surface science programs include the development of ultraviolet spectroscopy at the University of Pennsylvania and Cornell University (the Wisconsin Synchrotron Radiation Center was used); the application of synchrotron radiation to surface studies at Stanford University, where the MRL provided a significant input at the early stages; and the technique for spectroscopic analysis of adsorbed species at Purdue University. These contributions were primarily due to the close though seldom formalized collaboration between chemists and physicists and—equally significantly—between theorists and experimentalists.

Phase Transitions Although phase-transition phenomena have been of major interest to physicists over the last decade, the extension of the classical approaches to other than model materials was initiated at MRLs. The statistical mechanics approach to structural transitions in polyvinyl fluoride, successfully developed at Case Western Reserve University and already largely experimentally verified, has opened a new way of treating "real"—and quite complex—phase-transformation phenomena in polymeric materials. Theoretical calculations of the highly complex process of solidification in welding are now partly verified by research at Carnegie Mellon University and have similarly provided both a new approach and a potential for better control of this technologically important process. Studies of sol-gel (solution-to-gellation) transition across the transition temperature at Brown University and MIT, as well as the studies of spin glasses at the University of Chicago, all benefited markedly from the participation of cross-disciplinary expertise from the earliest stages of the programs.

New Materials According to the MITRE report, MRLs were unique in academia in 1975 in developing significant new materials, and they continue to dominate this field today. To mention only a few of these materials, nonlinear optical crystals of lithium niobate have been developed at Stanford University, and urea crystals at Cornell. Organic metals have been developed at the University of Pennsylvania and Northwestern University, block copolymers have been synthesized and studied at the University of Massachusetts, and highly reproducible fiber-polymer composites have been developed at Case Western Reserve University. Uniquely characterized transition metal oxides have been developed at Purdue University. All of these new materials represent sophistication in preparation and characterization of relatively common materials. Modulated materials with layer thicknesses varying from 5 to 50 angstroms are now almost routinely prepared at Northwestern University, Stanford University, and the University of Illinois. Quaternary and semimagnetic semiconductors are prepared at the University of Illinois and Purdue University, respectively. Submicron composite materials prepared at Cornell University for possible solar energy applications are some of the more novel, unorthodox materials originating at the MRLs. In each case of the preparation of a new material, the ultimate success demands a sustained collaboration of individuals with expertise in materials synthesis and characterization techniques at a level of sophistication seldom available in traditional disciplinary research.

To this list of accomplishments compiled by Wasilewski, I wish to add the following MRL programs:

• Mechanical behavior of metals fracture and high-strain-rate behavior (Brown University); fatigue and high-temperature behavior (Northwestern University and University of Pennsylvania); intergranular fracture (University of Pennsylvania)
• Fabrication of single-crystal optical fibers (Stanford University)
• Preparation, characterization, and understanding of amorphous materials (MIT, Harvard University, University of Pennsylvania, Stanford University, and the University of Chicago)
• Rapid solidification (MIT)
• Polymer science—dependence of crystallization properties on molecular weight (Northwestern University); high-modulus polyethylene (University of Massachusetts)
• New techniques for nondestructive testing (Stanford University)

The investment by ARPA and NSF in the IDL/MRL program has been substantial; ARPA contributed $158 million to the IDL program between 1960 and 1972, and NSF contributed $261 million to the MRL program between 1972 and 1985. The continued health of the program, the accomplishments in research and education, and the development of the MRL universities as major national resources have justified the continuation of the program in its evolved form.

To look only at the importance of the MRLs to the fields of materials research, however, is to miss some of their most profound effects. The IDLs were among the first examples of an interdisciplinary research center at their respective institutions. Their success and the perceived value of cross-disciplinary research set an example for other faculties and, perhaps even more importantly, for university administrations. Today's university register is incomplete without its list of study centers—in areas as diverse as information and technology, design, urban studies, robotics, environment, teaching, art, and history. There may be no cause and effect operating here, but it is certain that the IDL/MRL concept helped pave the way toward reorganization of the university research environment.

Significant in another area, the success of the MRL concept has encouraged new funding patterns by federal agencies. One can point to the significant research opportunity grants that have been made by the Office of Naval Research and those that have gone to the Centers for Super-Computers, the University/Industry Centers, the new Engineering Research Centers, and the new program for Materials Research Groups (MRGs) at NSF. The Engineering Research Centers share some of the same interdisciplinary goals for attacking complex problems that are the central theme of the MRLs. Of the first six Engineering Research Centers, two deal with materials—the Center for Composites Manufacturing Science and Engineering at the University of Delaware and Rutgers University, and the Center for Robotics Systems in Microelectronics at the University of California, Santa Barbara.

The Materials Research Groups, a new program in the Materials Research Division at NSF, create opportunities for multi-investigator efforts by individual thrust groups. In most cases, the universities awarded an MRG do not have an MRL, although MRGs have been established at Purdue, Carnegie Mellon, Pennsylvania State, and Case Western Reserve universities, where the MRLs have been or are being phased out (Table 1). MRGs should expand the variety of cross-disciplinary collaboration and further stimulate the trend toward interdisciplinary organization of the traditional materials departments. The following list of proposed areas of study in the first five MRGs shows the kinds of exciting new programs made possible by the MRG concept:

- Rensselaer Polytechnic Institute will investigate the various aspects of glass stability—chemical, mechanical, and microstructural—in order to understand the causes of glass degradation and provide a basis for developing more stable glasses.
- The Polytechnic Institute of New York will launch a program to gain a better understanding of chemical, physical, and processing effects on the aging of polymer blends, an important emerging class of materials.
- Pennsylvania State University will focus on the molecular engineering of new, chemically bonded ceramics. The materials will be consolidated without resorting to thermal diffusion, relying instead on chemical reactions at relatively low temperatures to cause the bonding.
- The University of Texas at Austin will seek answers to questions associated with the synthesis of new materials for photoelectrochemical devices and the underlying mechanisms of photochemical processes at interfaces.
- The California Institute of Technology will develop a program dealing with the motions of atoms and molecules at interfaces and their relationship to the synthesis and characterization of new materials.

The MRGs should be viewed as a logical intermediate stage between the traditional single-investigator research programs and the MRLs. Taken together, the MRLs and MRGs represent an increasing fraction of the budget of the NSF Materials Research Division and demonstrate a recognition of the trend toward greater cross-departmental interaction in materials research. Furthermore, as the project titles indicate, these Materials Research Groups, along with the new Engineering Research Centers, will bring more chemistry and engineering into the NSF group research program in materials.

The concept of block funding was originally viewed as an experiment. The experiment led to radical measures intended to eliminate barriers to the solution of complex problems in the study of materials. It is fair to conclude, 25 years later, that the experiment was successful and that materials science has fared much better than it might have otherwise.

NOTES

1. My own personal experiences strongly color my remarks, as I have grown up professionally at Northwestern University (which housed one of the first three IDLs, along with Cornell University and the University of Pennsylvania), and was privileged to serve as the director of the Materials Research Center at Northwestern before assuming my present position as director of the Institute for Materials Science and Engineering at the National Bureau of Standards.

   I am particularly indebted to the late Roman J. Wasilewski for the detailed historical perspective provided in his final report to the National Science Foundation (NSF) [R. J. Wasilewski, Outline of MRL Program. Internal NSF Memorandum to Division Director, Materials Research Division, National Science Foundation, Dec. 22, 1981] and in a 1984 unpublished manuscript dealing with the development of the Materials Research Laboratory program. Ro Wasilewski, who died on 3 February 1985, headed the Materials Research Laboratory Section at NSF for 10 years from the time of the transfer of the IDLs to NSF in 1972. Much of what is good about the MRLs can be attributed to his farsighted management of the program.

2. W. O. Baker, "The National Role of Materials Research and Development," in *Properties of Crystalline Solids*, Special Technical Publication No. 283, American Society for Testing and Materials, 1960, pp. 1–7.

3. R. A. Huggins, Overview of Advanced Research Projects Agency Interdisciplinary Research Laboratories as of June 30, 1970. Advanced Research Projects Agency, U.S. Department of Defense.

4. National Academy of Sciences, Committee on the Survey of Materials Science and Engineering (COSMAT), *Materials and Man's Needs: Materials Science and Engineering*, Vol. III (National Academy of Sciences, Washington, D.C., 1975), pp. 7-209–7-210.

5. J. G. Ling and M. A. Hand, "Federal Funding in Materials Research," (summary of the findings of the MITRE report). Science **209**, 1203 (1980); Technical Report 7764 (MITRE Corp., Bedford, Mass., Sept. 1978).

6. K. Mukherjee, ed., *ASM Metallurgy/Materials Education Yearbook*, American Society for Metals, Metals Park, Ohio, 1985.

Part 2

THE STATUS OF SELECTED
SCIENTIFIC AND TECHNICAL AREAS

Progress and Prospects
in Metallurgical Research

MORRIS COHEN

The idea of interrelationships among processing, structure, property, and performance in materials—a concept that now forms the backbone of modern materials science and engineering[1]—began to take shape in metallurgy well over a century ago with the advent of the metallographic microscope.[2] Processing, properties, and performance of metals and alloys had been known to mankind in one way or another for millennia, but the dawn of metallurgical *science* as we view it today might well be identified with the emergence of *microstructure*. That scientific event forged a connecting link to the practice of metallurgical engineering and technology, and all these elements progressively coalesced into what has become the discipline of metallurgy.

Accordingly, to highlight some of the significant accomplishments and anticipations of metallurgical research, we shall regard metallurgy as the science, engineering, and technology of metallic materials. In other terms, it covers the study, production, manipulation, and use of metals and alloys; it is the part of materials science and engineering that not only inquires into the nature of metallic materials but also attempts to harness such knowledge for societal purposes.

The following summary reflects the diverse inputs of some 80 contributors in metallurgical research whose multifaceted cooperation in this task is gratefully acknowledged. To the extent possible, the numerous suggestions and viewpoints have been unilaterally blended into topical themes, specifically selected because of their promise for new ferment in metallurgical research.

It should be emphasized at the outset that virtually all phenomena in metallurgy are incompletely understood, but this is likewise the case for most aspects of any science or technology. Indeed, arguments can be made for needing further research and insight on just about any identifiable subject in materials science and engineering. Nevertheless, some gaps in metallurgical knowledge are long-standing and costly to society. For example, the damage from metal corrosion and other types of failure in service amounts to more than $200 billion per year in 1982 dollars,[3] a loss that is commensurate with the annual federal deficit! One may certainly wonder why the nation puts up with this appalling extravagance. The probable answer is that metals, as reflected in Figure 1,[4] exhibit combined ranges of properties not enjoyed by other classes of materials (in stiffness, strength, toughness, and thermal

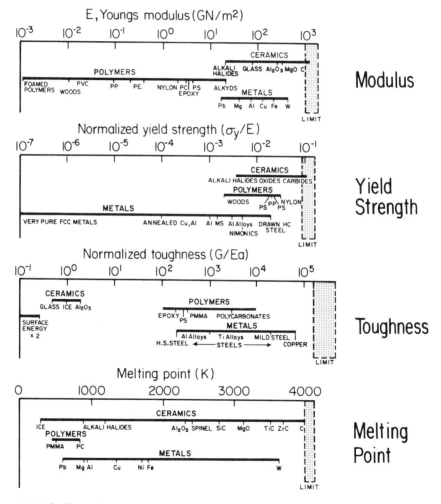

FIGURE 1 Some important properties of engineering materials, arranged to compare metals, ceramics, and polymers. For the indicated normalized toughness, G is in units of J/m^2, E is Young's modulus in corresponding units, and a is the atomic radius. From Ashby.[4]

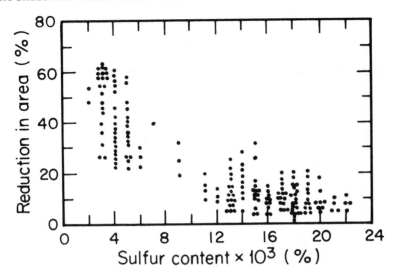

FIGURE 2 Relationship between through-thickness ductility of steel plate and the sulfur content. From Billingham.[5] Reprinted with permission.

characteristics, as well as in economic availability) that make them incredibly useful to humanity. In a similar vein, society seems to "accept" the loss of some 50,000 lives per year on U.S. highways because automobiles are so useful. Metals, like automobiles, have become engrained in our way of life; neither should be taken for granted.

PROCESSING

Every step in the materials cycle involves processing. In metallurgy, processing comprises all operations that produce, shape, and control the properties of metallic materials to make them perform effectively in service. Metal processing ranges from large scale, as in steel production and refining, to small scale, as in thin-film formation.

Steel Refining

Advances in steel refining, particularly through ladle metallurgy involving the injection of calcium, rare earths, and fluxes as well as vacuum degassing, have led to remarkable improvements in compositional control and steel cleanliness. Figure 2 shows the pronounced increase in through-thickness ductility of plate steels that results from the reduction of sulfur content and, hence, of sulfide inclusions.[5] This development, growing out of investigations on the multicomponent thermodynamics of sulfur in liquid steel, has spawned the reliable use in pipeline steels and oil-drilling rigs of heavy sections resistant to laminar tearing. The achievement of such metallurgical control in liquid steel is all the more prodigious when one considers the 100- to 200-ton scale of the ladle-refining operations.

Of comparable importance is the potential removal of phosphorus. Rare-earth additions have promise in this respect[6] and deserve the kind of research attention that has been given to calcium in its affinity for sulfur. Phosphorus increases the sensitivity of high-strength steels to embrittlement, and its elimination would constitute a major advance in ferrous metallurgy.

Controlled Rolling of Steel

An example of solid-state processing that has reached commercial scale in steelmaking is the controlled rolling of steels that are microalloyed with relatively stable carbide- and nitride-forming elements such as niobium, vanadium, and titanium. Here, the precipitation of carbonitride particles is induced by plastic deformation of the austenitic phase during the rolling schedule, and recrystallization of the austenite is then inhibited because the grain boundaries are pinned by the precipitated particles. Further rolling to low finishing temperatures (but still substantially in the austenitic range) leads to a flattening of the austenitic grains, the thin dimension of which contributes to a very fine-grained ferritic structure on further cooling.

The resulting grain refinement, thus attained without the expense of separate heat treatment, contributes both strengthening and toughening, as shown in Figures 3 and 4.[7,8] This kind of double benefit in structure-property relations is an unusual circumstance in alloy systems, and it forms the basis of the high-strength, low-alloy (HSLA) steels that have been developed during the past quarter century. An additional advantage of these steels is that their beneficial properties are obtainable with low carbon contents and therefore are compatible with excellent welding characteristics for construction purposes. One measure of the technological success of HSLA steels is their increasing utilization in automobiles, despite the general downsizing for fuel efficiency. According to Figure 5, the amount of HSLA steel used per vehicle has been increasing even more rapidly than the lower-density aluminum alloys, plastics, and composites.[9]

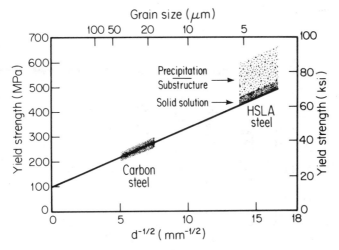

FIGURE 3 Strengthening of low-carbon steel with decreasing ferritic grain size (Hall-Petch relationship). Additional strengthening contributions are illustrated schematically for solid-solution, substructural, and precipitation effects. From Baird and Preston.[7] Reprinted with permission.

Rapid Solidification Processing

The pioneering publications of Pond[10] in 1958 and Klement, Willens, and Duwez[11] in 1960 ushered in a dynamic era of research and development on rapid solidification processing (RSP). The major part of this research has been directed to metallic materials, although the phenomena at play are

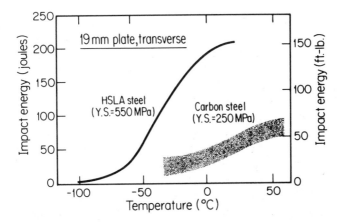

FIGURE 4 Toughness (Charpy impact test) of two low-carbon steels versus test temperature; comparison of plain-carbon hot-rolled steel with microalloyed controlled-rolled steel. From Hansen.[8]

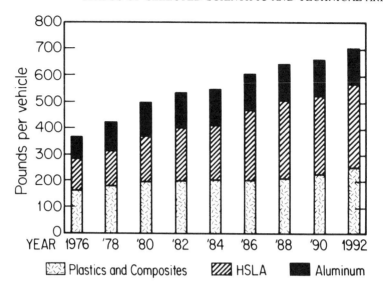

FIGURE 5   Increasing automobile use (actual and projected) of certain materials, including high-strength, low-alloy steels, in the United States, despite the overall trend toward downsizing. From Materials Modeling Associates.[9]

operative in other classes of materials as well. Cooling rates up to 10^9 K/s have been reported, but most of the basic effects are observed with cooling rates of 10^4 to 10^6 K/s attained by splat quenching, melt spinning, planar-flow casting, atomized droplet solidification, or self-quenching after surface melting. The corresponding solidification rates, in terms of liquid-solid interfacial velocities, can range up to tens of meters per second, in contrast to about 1 cm/s for a typical mold casting. The microstructures resulting from RSP are characterized by enhanced compositional uniformity, refinement of the microconstituents, high degrees of supersaturation, and retention of metastable phases including metallic glasses. The aluminum-manganese phase with anomalous fivefold symmetry[12] (see Cahn and Gratias, in this volume) is a startling example of metastability brought to light by RSP. The existence of such a pentagonal structure is distinctly forbidden by long-standing crystallographic theory, thus posing a fundamental dilemma. One rationalization is to regard the strange structure as quasi-periodic instead of truly periodic.

The retention of metastable glassy states in certain alloy systems by RSP offers a classic example of a novel processing method that has paved the way to new regimes of structure, property, and performance relationships. For melt compositions whose glass transition temperatures are about half the respective melting points, a cooling rate of approximately 10^6 K/s is sufficient to avoid crystal nucleation and thus allow glass formation. Metallic glasses are typically high in strength but are not ''glass-brittle.'' They tend to undergo localized shear (due to lack of strain hardening) when stressed beyond the yield strength, and thus they resist fracture even though they are not generally deformable like crystalline alloys. The metallic glasses based on metal (Fe, Ni, Co) and metalloid (B, Si, P, C) combinations are of special interest in view of their markedly low magnetic losses, and the processing is potentially inexpensive because of direct casting of the alloy liquid to final strip form. The technological impact of this metal-processing development is discussed below in the section on magnetic alloys.

The extensive refinement of dendritic structures caused by increased cooling rate or growth velocity during the solidification of crystalline alloys is shown by Figure 6.[13] The reduction in dendritic-arm spacing not only improves the as-cast strength and ductility[14] but also promotes compositional uniformity by decreasing the diffusion distances between the regions of microsegregation formed by solute buildup in the last pockets of liquid to solidify between the dendritic arms. Such compositional uniformity is advantageous in raising the incipient melting temperature of alloys intended for high-temperature service, as in the case of superalloys. At the same time, second phases that are likely to precipitate in the microsegregated regions tend to be finer in size and more uniformly distributed because of the rapid solidification. These second phases often appear as intermetallic compounds or nonmetallic inclusions that are embrittling when present in coarse or segregated form but that can be desirable when finely divided and well dispersed.

A beneficial consequence of uniform dispersions is that they pin grain boundaries of the matrix phase and thus inhibit grain growth, as shown in Figure 7.[15] The effectiveness of this phenomenon is an inverse function of d/f_v, where d is the average diameter of the precipitated particles and f_v is their volume fraction. This means that for the grain boundary pinning to persist at very high temperatures, the distributed phase must be sufficiently

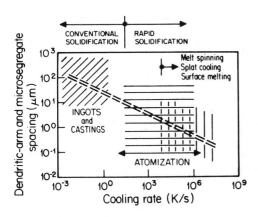

FIGURE 6 Dendritic-arm and microsegregate spacing in as-cast aluminum alloy microstructures as a function of cooling rate from the liquid state. From Cohen, Kear, and Mehrabian.[13] Reprinted with permission.

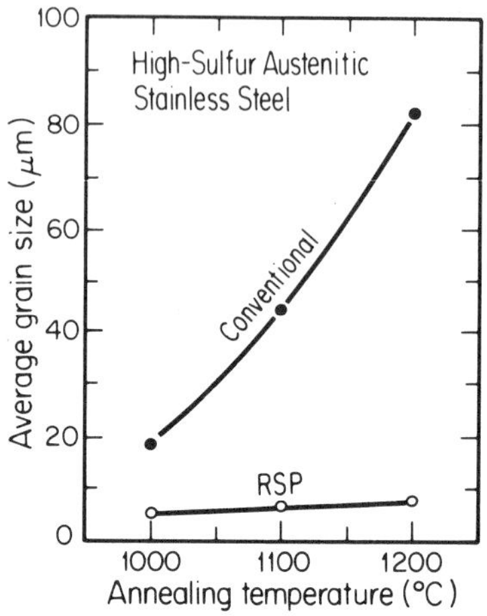

FIGURE 7   Grain growth characteristics of high-sulfur austenitic stainless steel after conventional processing versus rapid solidification processing. The latter was produced by centrifugal atomizing and subsequent consolidation by hot extrusion. From Kelly and Vander Sande.[15] Reprinted with permission.

stable (minimal solubility in the matrix phase) to resist Ostwald ripening. Such phases are generally more soluble in the *liquid* state (e.g., oxides, silicates, and oxysulfides in liquid steel) and are then amenable to uniform dispersal as fine precipitates in the *solid* state by RSP. The resulting resistance to grain growth permits the consolidation of rapidly solidified particulates and subsequent heat treatment to be carried out at relatively high temperatures without undue grain coarsening. Moreover, with larger-volume fractions of stable second phases, including appropriate intermetallic compounds, dispersion strengthening can be achieved and maintained at elevated temperatures.

An example of second-phase refinement by RSP is shown in Figure 8.[16] Here the addition of 10 weight percent beryllium to a commercial aluminum-copper alloy leads to extremely coarse second phases upon normal ingot solidification, whereas RSP produces a very fine dispersion of the second phases. In this instance, as much as 10 weight percent beryllium can be dissolved in the liquid alloy and then precipitated by rapid solidification as a finely distributed beryllium-containing compound (approximately Be_3Cu) in the solid alloy, with the maximum equilibrium solubility of the beryllium in solid aluminum being only about 0.03 weight percent. The corresponding improvements in strength and ductility given in the caption of Figure 8 are also worthy of note. The large beryllium addition made possible by RSP is of further potential value because it increases the stiffness and decreases the density of aluminum-base alloys.[16]

Figure 9 compares the high-temperature strength of RSP aluminum alloys with that of conventionally processed high-strength aluminum alloys.[17] For these studies, the compositions of the RSP alloys were specially developed

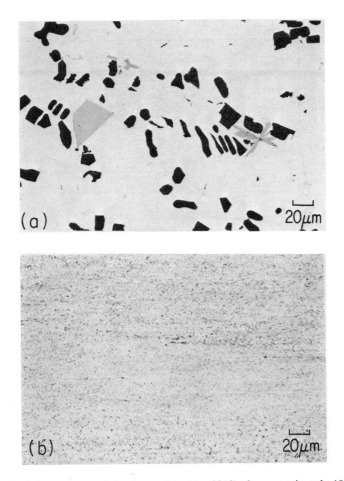

FIGURE 8 Microstructure of aluminum alloy (No. 2219) plus approximately 10 wt % beryllium (a) after normal casting and hot extrusion (yield strength 43.3 ksi, tensile elongation 1.7 percent), and (b) after RSP by melt spinning and hot extrusion (yield strength 43.3 ksi, tensile elongation 15 percent). From Vidoz et al.[16] Reprinted with permission.

to take advantage of RSP; the intermetallic phases involved would be much too coarse and embrittling if they were to form during regular solidification. The strength retention exhibited by the RSP alloys at elevated temperatures is quite striking and is beginning to match or exceed the density-compensated strength of titanium alloys over the temperature range studied. Surely the time is now ripe to apply RSP to titanium alloys and possibly even to niobium-base alloys.

The RSP aluminum alloys are also unusually resistant to corrosion, ac-

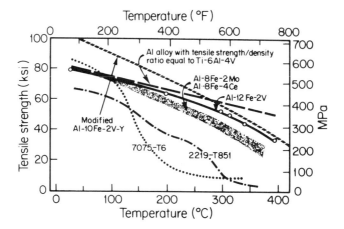

FIGURE 9   High-temperature strength of rapidly solidified A1-Fe-X alloys, compared to two conventionally processed high-strength aluminum alloys. Dashed line indicates strength required of aluminum alloys to have the same density-compensated strength as a commercial titanium alloy. From Adam and Lewis.[17] Reprinted with permission.

cording to the salt-fog data in Figure 10.[17] The observed weight losses are primarily due to pitting, signifying that a novel phenomenon may be inhibiting the pitting attack. Conceivably, in the RSP aluminum alloys, the pitting sites are sufficiently close together that the localized galvanic cells tend to shield one another. The alloy chemistry per se may also be playing an important role that would not otherwise be revealed except for the compositional uniformity contributed by rapid solidification.

In any event, the operative phenomena are worthy of deep study, consid-

FIGURE 10   Weight loss in saline corrosion test of rapidly solidified A1-Fe-Zr-V alloys compared to three conventionally processed aluminum alloys. From Adam and Lewis.[17] Reprinted with permission.

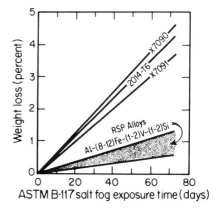

ering their extraordinary chemical effects and prospective benefits for engineering applications. Even more enticing is that RSP magnesium alloys also display enhanced resistance to corrosion[18] but again the fundamentals are not yet clear.

No less graphic is the effect of RSP on the oxidation resistance of high-temperature alloys, including superalloys; the oxide scales that normally develop on such alloys then become more adherent and protective. With RSP stainless steels,[19] the fine grain size provides extra paths for chromium atoms to reach the surface quickly and so maintain a chromium oxide layer. If the chromium supply from the base metal is deficient, iron oxide begins to form in the outer scale and renders it less protective. Because of the grain-boundary diffusion mechanism, oxide phases form to some extent at the outer grain-boundary junctures in continuity with the surface oxide layer, perhaps helping to lock the scale to the base alloy. There are also indications that finely dispersed stable phases, such as hafnium and yttrium oxides or sulfides, may participate in the oxidation resistance. Although adequate understanding of the relevant phenomena is still lacking, the effects can be dramatic. Figure 11[20] shows the results of a severe, cyclic oxidation test on two RSP superalloy specimens, with and without the addition of yttrium. It is obvious here that a fertile field of basic research on oxide-scale formation lies ahead, with far-reaching technological implications.

The second-phase precipitates in RSP alloys can be refined even further if the rapid solidification occurs under conditions of solute trapping—i.e., when the interfacial velocity is fast enough (whether by supercooling or by sufficiently rapid heat extraction) to prevent equilibrium partitioning between the liquid and the solid at the growth front. If precipitation is then allowed to take place from the resulting highly supersaturated *solid* solution rather than during the prior solidification process, the particles can be a factor of 10 smaller than in the absence of solute trapping. As indicated by Figure 12,[21] solute trapping ($k > k_0$) sets in when the interfacial velocity reaches within an order of magnitude of the diffusive velocity (D_L/λ, where D_L is the solute diffusivity in the liquid phase and λ is the diffusion jump distance). The solute trapping becomes substantially complete ($k \cong 1$) when the interfacial velocity reaches about an order of magnitude greater than the diffusive velocity. It is evident, then, that one of the future thrusts of RSP research lies in the direction of hitherto unexplored alloy systems and compositional regimes that can be accessed by faster solidification rates, thereby opening up new ranges of structure-property relationships. In this approach, the formation of exotic metastable phases (such as the aforementioned metallic glasses and the "forbidden" fivefold structure in the aluminum-manganese system) should become more common in view of the suppressed equilibrium reactions and the greater opportunities for less stable phases to compete in the kinetics of nucleation and growth. Although the emergence and nature

FIGURE 11 Rapidly solidified Ni-Al-Cr-W superalloy specimens with (left) and without (right) yttrium additions, after a cyclic oxidation test consisting of 300 one-hour heatings in air at 1150°C. From Cox.[20]

of such phases cannot be predicted yet, one can confidently anticipate that surprises will continue to arise out of this netherworld of metastability.

Ion Implantation and Beam Processing

The advent of processing methods based on the injection of accelerated ions (10 to 500 keV) into solid metals and alloys is leading to a new world

FIGURE 12 Variations of interfacial partition ratio, k, with growth velocity, v, normalized to the diffusive velocity, D_L/λ, where D_L = liquid diffusivity and λ = diffusion jump distance; k_0 = equilibrium partition coefficient. From Boettinger, Coriell, and Sekerka.[21] Reprinted with permission.

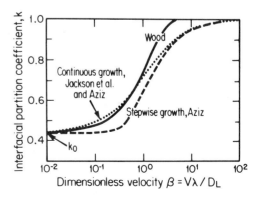

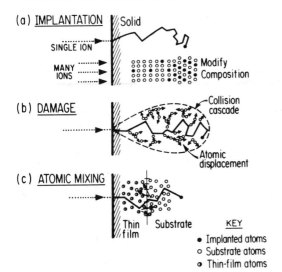

FIGURE 13 Schematic representation of (a) ion implantation, (b) structural damage, and (c) atomic mixing resulting from energetic ion beams. From Williams and Poate.[22] Reprinted with permission.

of metallurgy through the modification of near-surface properties. Figure 13[22] shows a schematic representation of compositional changes and lattice damages resulting from ion implantation and atomic mixing. The latter process, shown here for atomic interchanges between a thin film and its substrate, can be brought about by the ion beam itself or, alternatively, by a laser beam. Extended solid solutions up to 10 atomic percent of almost any kind of atom in any base metal can be achieved to depths of hundreds of atomic layers. The effective quenching rates are estimated to range up to 10^{14} K/s. Ion implantation and laser-beam mixing are compared in Table 1.[23]

Although many alloy systems and compositional variations have been investigated by these surface-modification methods, at least to some extent,[24] much of the research impetus has been directed to semiconductor and electronic materials. On the other hand, the metallurgical community has shown particular interest in potential applications requiring resistance to surface-initiated deterioration in service, such as wear, corrosion, erosion, and fatigue failure of high-performance alloys.[25] Undoubtedly there will be considerable effort to exploit these intriguing possibilities for tools, dies, bearings, nozzles, orthopedic implants, and numerous other industrial components.

However, in parallel with these prospective applications, ion implantation and beam mixing deserve more attention in metallurgical research as pathways for attaining new microstructural states that have not been reached before. The opportunities for extreme supersaturations and metastable-phase

TABLE 1   Comparison of Ion Implantation and Laser Processing as Surface-Modification Techniques

Property Compared	Ion Implantation	Laser Processing
Modification process	Ion bombardment, collisions with substrate	Rapid melting followed by rapid solidification
Effect on surface topography	No change in sample appearance and dimensions	Characteristic ripples or chevron patterns
Typical depth of modified region	100 Å to 1,000 Å (0.1 μm)	10 μm to 100 μm (0.1 mm) (larger for coatings)
Effect on metallurgical microstructure	Usually forms solid solution with no change in grain size; under certain conditions, can get second phases or metastable phases	Usually epitaxial resolidification, with possible refinement of subgrain microstructure
Surface cleanliness	Good—clean vacuum conditions	Variable—gas shield used, but some surface contamination and oxidation
Typical sample size (for research purposes)	1 to 10 sq. in.	1 to 10 sq. in.

SOURCE: McCafferty et al.[23]

formation in the ion-bombarded surface layers are virtually limitless. Furthermore, high-resolution, high-sensitivity microanalytical techniques for probing such states of matter and their transformation products are now available. The following accounts of experiments illustrate some novel research approaches for taking advantage of ion implantation and beam mixing.

The curves in Figure 14 show the yttrium-concentration/depth profiles in a cobalt–45 atomic percent chromium alloy after low (2×10^{14} Y/cm^2) and high (2×10^{16} Y/cm^2) dosages of yttrium ion implantation, followed by an oxidation exposure of both specimens at 1273 K to produce a chromium oxide scale.[26] The fact that the implanted yttrium concentration peaks near the gas/oxide surface in the specimen having the higher yttrium dosage, whereas it peaks near the oxide/alloy interface in the specimen having the lower yttrium dosage, indicates that the scale growth mechanism is fundamentally different in the two cases. This difference signifies that the yttrium-concentration profiles are acting as Kirkendall markers during the scale growth process and demonstrates that the diffusion flux in the higher-dose specimen is carried mainly by the O^{2-} ions passing through the scale from the outer surface of the oxide to the inner oxide/alloy interface, whereas in the lower-dose specimen the diffusion flux is carried mainly by the Cr^{3+} ions passing through the scale in the opposite direction. Correspondingly, there is a profound contrast in the oxidation rates of the two specimens, as shown in Figure

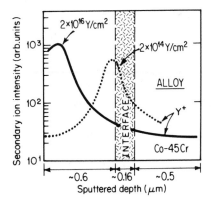

FIGURE 14 Yttrium-concentration/depth profiles in a cobalt–45 atomic percent chromium alloy after low (2 × 10^{14} Y/cm^2) and high (2 × 10^{16} Y/cm^2) dosages of yttrium ion implantation at 70 keV, followed by oxidation in 1 atm oxygen at 1273 K. From Przybylski.[26] Reprinted with permission.

15;[26] the higher-dose specimen (whose oxidation is controlled by O^{2-} diffusion) is much more resistant to oxidation than is the lower-dose specimen (whose oxidation is controlled by Cr^{3+} diffusion). Another surprising observation is that microanalytical measurements (by energy-dispersive x-ray analysis) demonstrates that the yttrium *in the scale* is located almost exclusively in the oxide grain boundaries without detectable presence of second phases.[27] It is tempting to speculate that, in the higher-dose specimens, the implanted yttrium is present in sufficient concentration along the oxide grain boundaries to inhibit the Cr^{3+} ion diffusion that would otherwise select these short-circuiting paths, and so the rate-controlling oxidation mechanism is then shifted to the slower O^{2-} diffusion.

Clearly, there are new challenges in these findings, not only from the standpoint of ion implantation research per se, but also as a technique for understanding and using the potent oxidation resistance contributed by small percentages of elements like yttrium in high-temperature alloys.

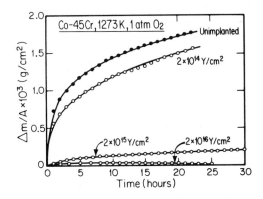

FIGURE 15 Isothermal oxidation kinetics of a cobalt–45 atomic percent chromium alloy after various dosages of yttrium ion implantation at 70 keV. From Przybylski.[26] Reprinted with permission.

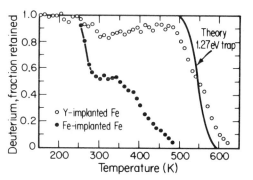

FIGURE 16   Release of deuterium (injected with 10^{16} D/cm² dosage at 15 keV) from traps in Fe-implanted iron and in Y-implanted (4 × 10^{16} Y/cm² dosage at 190 keV) iron as a function of increasing temperature. From Myers.[28] Reprinted with permission.

The lattice defects introduced by ion implantation can trap hydrogen, a circumstance that suggests a method for reducing or controlling hydrogen embrittlement in steel. Research along these lines should have great appeal in ferrous metallurgy because the efficacy of high-strength steels is frequently undermined by the detrimental effects of trace amounts of dissolved hydrogen, such as may be picked up even superficially from a moist environment. It has been discovered that such defect traps become very potent when iron is ion-implanted with yttrium. Experiments on the temperature-dependent release of deuterium from defect traps in yttrium-implanted and in iron-implanted iron specimens are compared in Figure 16.[28] It is evident that the deuterium is much more tightly bound to the yttrium-implanted traps than to the iron-implanted traps. The question that immediately arises is whether hydrogen embrittlement in hardened steel might well be ameliorated by ion implantation with yttrium or similar ions; it is a possibility that warrants high-priority study.

Ion- or laser-beam mixing, referred to earlier, can interchange atoms between a surface film and its substrate, often forming a new phase by "skin melting" and rapid solidification. It is conceivable that this mixing process could be made more efficient, and more varied morphologically, if the specimen itself were to consist of a very fine dispersion embedded in the matrix phase, prepared in the first place by RSP. Pulsed-beam mixing under these conditions could lead to further microstructural refinement or the formation of hitherto-unknown metastable phases. This type of surface treatment deserves detailed exploration. Unique mechanical behavior (as well as the corrosion and oxidation resistance described previously) may be expected from still finer structures; this is discussed more specifically in a later section on microstructural refinement.

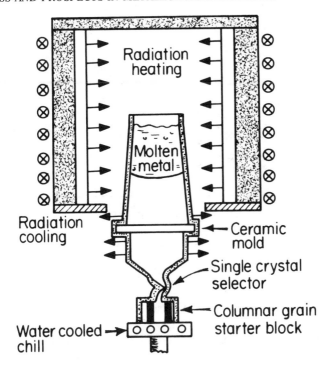

FIGURE 17   Single-crystal solidification process for casting superalloy turbine blades to eliminate grain boundaries. From Gell, Duhl, and Giamei.[30] Reprinted with permission.

Single-Crystal Processing

The use of single crystals in metallurgical research and in microelectronic devices is well known, but it was only in 1982 that monocrystalline alloys first entered service as a critical *structural* component. It was a high-technology application in every sense of the word, following two decades of research and development on cast superalloy turbine blades.[29,30] As a result, single-crystal gas-turbine blades are now performing advantageously in both commercial and military aircraft engines.[30]

There are high-temperature applications in which the grain boundaries and random grain orientations of polycrystalline superalloys are undesirable, in part because of thermal fatigue failure and creep rupture along such interfaces. This motivated the development of directional solidification during the 1970s to produce columnar grains with controlled orientation and with grain boundaries parallel to the main stress direction. The next major step was to eliminate the grain boundaries entirely; this was made possible and practical by the single-crystal casting process shown schematically in Figure 17.[30] The helical

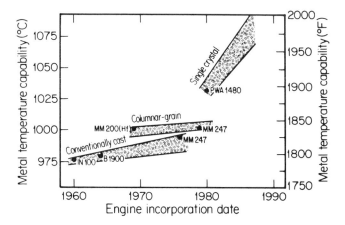

FIGURE 18   Progress in temperature capability of nickel-base superalloys, due to compositional and process innovations. From Gell and Duhl.[31] Reprinted with permission.

channel above the water-cooled solidification "starter block" permits only a single growing grain to pass through, normally with a $\langle 001 \rangle$ crystallographic direction advancing parallel to the longitudinal axis of the turbine blade. However, seeding also permits the selection of other orientations for the study of anisotropic properties.

Ordinarily, the optimal composition of superalloys is complicated by a menu of alloying elements to help stabilize the grain boundaries at elevated temperatures. Since this is not necessary with monocrystals, the compositional variations can be focused on property control of the base alloy—e.g., improvement of creep strength as a function of temperature. The progress along these lines has been truly remarkable. Figure 18[31] indicates that the single-crystal processing of superalloy turbine blades has led to a quantum jump in high-temperature operating capability, and the way is now open to substantial further improvements, with corresponding benefits in engine performance and fuel efficiency.

MICROSTRUCTURAL REFINEMENT

Strength and Toughness

Notwithstanding the sharp advance in gas turbine technology resulting from the single-crystal processing of turbine blades, other metallurgical fronts will see a strong push toward finer and finer microstructures, both in grain size of the matrix phase and in particle size of the embedded precipitates. This is one of the promising aspects of RSP, as described earlier. Extending the range of structure-property relationships through microstructural refinement now constitutes a frontier of metallurgical research reaching down into the nanometer regime.

Dispersed precipitates are effective in obstructing dislocation motion and, hence, in raising the strength of alloys, but such precipitates can also be detrimental to toughness because of void initiation, which promotes shear localization and fracture. It has been estimated,[32] however, that particles smaller than about 20 nm should be subcritical in size relative to void nucleation, whereas particles larger than about 1 nm should be capable of resisting dislocation motion. Thus, a "window of opportunity" exists in this size range for optimum dispersion strengthening and toughening. A further contribution to strength and toughness is obtainable from grain refinement of the matrix phase; in fact, no limit has yet been established in these favorable trends with diminishing grain size. Consequently, they should be exploited, or at least tested, by processing methods now available.

These guidelines have recently been adopted in a comprehensive initiative to increase the fracture toughness of ultrahigh-strength martensitic steels and, at the same time, to test the theoretical and practical limits of the relevant structure-property relationships due to microstructural refinement.[33] In view of the obvious technological impact of such high-performance steels, several university, governmental, and industrial laboratories are now participating in this research endeavor.

Superplasticity

Fine-grained microstructures can be advantageous for plastic-forming operations at elevated temperatures by inducing superplasticity. With rising temperature, grain boundaries in alloy systems tend to lose their strengthening capability and participate in new modes of plastic deformation. If grain growth can be inhibited to maintain a sufficiently fine grain size, typically through the presence of a second phase, as discussed earlier, extensive plasticity may be encountered—e.g., several hundred percent elongation in a tensile test.

Figure 19 summarizes the essential mechanical behavior characteristics of superplasticity.[34] High strain-rate sensitivity (m) is required to achieve stable necking-free elongation, and this condition is favored by an optimum strain rate (usually rather slow), which can be increased with decreasing grain size and with increasing temperature (if grain growth is inhibited). An impressive example of superplastic forming is shown in Figure 20, which illustrates the closed-die forging of a superalloy gas-turbine wheel, with integral blades, in only two steps from a hot-extruded billet of RSP powders.[20] Many other industrial shaping operations based on superplasticity are now in commercial practice.[35]

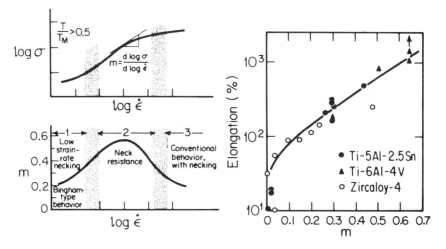

FIGURE 19   Mechanical behavior characteristics involved in superplasticity, showing relationships between strain rate, strain-rate sensitivity, and tensile elongation. From Backofen.[34] Reprinted with permission.

Microstructural models to account for superplastic behavior commonly involve diffusion-aided grain-neighbor switching in the overall process of contributing large macroscopic displacements while generally tending to maintain a steady-state grain size and shape. One such model is idealized in Figure 21.[36] Clearly, the grain boundaries play a crucial role in superplasticity, hence the necessity for a small, stable grain size. Accordingly, the aforementioned thrust toward greater microstructural refinement should lead

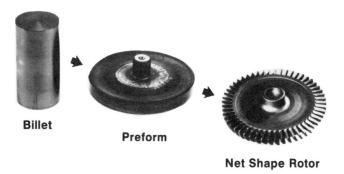

Billet

Preform

Net Shape Rotor

FIGURE 20   Superplastic forming of a superalloy gas-turbine rotor with integral blades in two steps from a hot-extruded billet of rapidly solidified (centrifugally atomized) powders. From Cox.[20]

Strain: 0   0.275   0.55

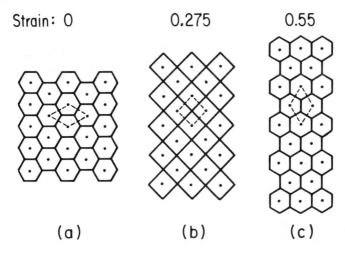

(a)   (b)   (c)

FIGURE 21 Model of superplasticity: schematic representation of grain-neighbor switching on a microscale that results in large-scale displacements. Steps from (a) to (b) and from (b) to (c) require the same transport of matter by diffusion and involve equal displacements of the grain centers. From Ashby et al.[36] Reprinted with permission.

to ease of deformation processing at high temperatures as well as to improved mechanical properties at low temperatures—an extremely attractive prospect indeed.

Nanocrystalline Metals

Extending microstructural refinement down to the range of nanostructures has been made feasible by evaporation and fine-particle condensation techniques, as shown schematically in Figure 22.[37] Evaporation from the molten metal, or from a number of separate melts, is conducted in an inert gas at low pressure, and the resulting powders (condensed on a cold finger at the liquid nitrogen temperature) have an average particle size of several nanometers. The powders can then be examined as such or after being cold-pressed into bulk form.

When the compacted specimen grain size is about 5 nm, there are approximately 10^{19} cm^{-3} boundaries between adjacent grains, and the crystalline and interfacial "phases" have nearly the same volume fraction, assuming a grain boundary thickness of 1 to 2 nm (Figure 23). Observations by x-ray diffraction, Mössbauer spectroscopy, and positron annihilation on compacted nanocrystalline iron indicate that the arrangement of atoms at the grain boundaries is gas-like, rather than crystalline or glass-like; the grain boundary structure appears to have no short-range order when integrated over the

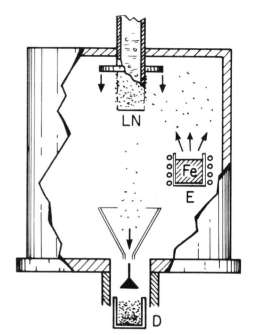

FIGURE 22 Evaporation and condensation chamber for producing nanoscale powders, which can then be compacted into nanocrystalline bulk specimens: E = evaporation crucible; LN = liquid nitrogen cold finger for condensing powder; D = device for compacting powder. From Birringer, Herr, and Gleiter.[37]

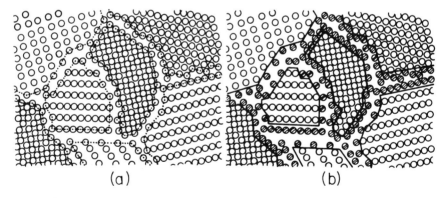

FIGURE 23 Hard-sphere representation of cross section through a polycrystalline aggregate. In (a), all atoms (open circles) are allocated to crystalline grains as outlined by the dotted lines. In (b), the cross-hatched circles represent atoms allocated to the grain boundary regions between neighboring grains. When the grain size is approximately 5 nm, the grain boundary volume is about equal to the crystalline volume. From Birringer, Herr, and Gleiter.[37]

TABLE 2 Properties of Nanocrystalline Metals Compared to the Normal Crystal and Glassy States

Property	Units	Metal	Crystal	Glass	Nanocrystal
Thermal expansion	10^{-6} K^{-1}	Cu	17	18 (+6%)	31 (+80%)
Saturation magnetization (4 K)	emu/g	Fe	222	~215 (−3%)	~130 (−40%)
Magnetic susceptibility	10^{-6} emu/gOe	Sb	−1	−0.03 (liquid)	+20 (+2000%)
Density	g/cm³	Fe	7.9	7.5 (−5%)	6 (−25%)
Fracture stress	kgf/mm²	Fe + 1.8 wt % C	50		600 (+1000%)
Specific heat (130 to 340 K)	J/kg	Fe	0.42	0.45 (+7%)	0.65 (+55%)
Activation energy for self-diffusion	kcal/mol	Ag Au	35.8 34.8		16 (−55%) 19 (−45%)
Critical temperature for superconductivity	K	Al	1.2		3.2 (+165%)

NOTE: Percentage differences shown in parentheses are relative to the normal crystalline state.

SOURCE: Birringer, Herr, and Gleiter.[37]

enormous number of adjacent-crystal pairs and their respective orientations. Nanocrystalline, glassy, and normal crystalline properties of various metals are compared in Table 2.[37]

By and large, properties that differ by less than 10 percent between the crystalline and glassy states will differ very much more from those of the nanocrystalline state. The phonon-dependent thermal-expansion and specific-heat differences in Table 2 have been interpreted to signify that the grain boundary structure in nanocrystalline metals constitutes a novel state of matter in solids. On the other hand, the remarkable strength of the nanocrystalline iron-carbon alloy is reasonably commensurate with the Hall-Petch strengthening to be expected from grain refinement alone; in fact, this magnitude of strengthening is also found with pure nanocrystalline iron.[38] The 1.8 weight percent carbon in the iron-carbon alloy shown in Table 2 is presumably present as nanocrystals of carbon—i.e., not atomically dissolved in the iron. Such "alloy mixtures" deserve detailed investigation of their structural changes on heating as well as their physical, chemical, and mechanical properties. Experiments along these lines, reaching into the nanoscale grain-size regime and generating a correspondingly high concentration of grain boundary material, represent a new research frontier not only for metals and alloys but for other classes of materials as well. Moreover, the evaporation and condensation method for accessing ultrafine grain sizes in complex alloy systems has the unique feature of not depending on mutual solubility in the liquid state to carry out the alloying.

Modulated Structures

A different type of microstructural refinement is displayed by multilayered or modulated structures, and the resulting properties are most intriguing. In the solid-state community, the terms "artificially structured materials" and "strained-layer superlattices" have been adopted, particularly when semiconducting, optical, and magnetic phenomena are of primary interest. This field has been reviewed quite comprehensively in a recent report of the Solid State Sciences Committee of the National Research Council.[39] For present purposes, however, we shall focus on the mechanical behavior of metallic systems, in line with the metallurgical emphasis of this chapter.

A number of vapor-deposited compositionally modulated alloy systems (e.g., copper-nickel, gold-nickel, copper-palladium, and silver-palladium) exhibit the strange elastic characteristics shown in Figure 24.[40] The biaxial modulus plotted against the wavelength of layered Cu-Ni specimens is determined from a miniature bulge test and is found to peak sharply at a wavelength of about 20 angstroms.[40] This "supermodulus effect" represents a phenomenal increase in stiffness, amounting to a factor of 2 to 4 over that of a homogeneous Cu-Ni alloy, and indicates that a significant change compared to stiffness in bulk materials has taken place.

FIGURE 24   Biaxial modulus versus wavelength of compositional modulations having approximately equal layers of vapor-deposited copper and nickel with {111} texture. From Tsakalakos and Hilliard.[40] Reprinted with permission.

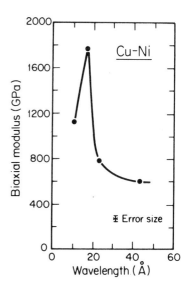

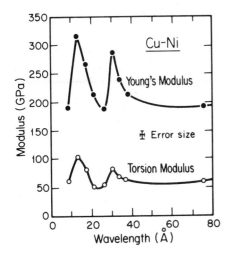

FIGURE 25 Young's modulus and torsion modulus versus wavelength of compositional modulations having approximately equal layers of vapor-deposited copper and nickel with {111} texture. From Baral, Ketterson, and Hilliard.[43] Reprinted with permission.

As yet, we have no generally satisfactory theory for this unexpected enhancement in stiffness. One suggestion attributes the effect to coherency strains of approximately a few percent owing to lattice matching between the alternating layers,[41] but thus far the supermodulus behavior has been observed only with alloy systems in which one of the components is a transition metal. For example, the modulus effect is not seen with compositionally layered copper-gold alloys.[42] Another explanation is electronic in nature, namely, that the periodicity of the modulated structure introduces a Brillouin zone which happens to contact a flat portion of the Fermi surface when the layered wavelength is optimal.[40] This circumstance is thought to produce a stable energy configuration, which then contributes a large measure of resistance to imposed elastic deformation.

However, more recently, separate elastic moduli (Young's, flexural, and torsion) have been measured on multilayered Cu-Ni specimens having the same average composition and the same wavelength range as for the biaxial modulus measurements in Figure 24. It is surprising to find that the newer results in Figure 25 show *two* distinct peaks—at 12 and 28 angstroms—as a function of modulation wavelength.[43] The elasticity interrelationships are such that the double peaks in Figure 25 are consistent with the single-peak biaxial measurements in Figure 24, but now a proper theory of the supermodulus effect must account for sharp enhancements in elastic constants at two optimal wavelengths. Obviously, a bizarre aspect of metal science has emerged here, with fertile opportunities for interactive experimental and theoretical research toward a deeper insight into the basic nature of the metallic state.

Modulated structures arising from the spinodal decomposition of unstable solid solutions are well known, but a relatively new finding is that virgin iron-carbon martensites also decompose spinodally into modulated structures of coherent high- and low-carbon interstitial solid solutions. This happens on aging, even below room temperature, before there is any evidence of the usual carbide precipitation sequences that occur later during tempering. As indicated in Figure 26,[44] the carbon content of the high-carbon regions increases progressively (by uphill diffusion) and levels off at approximately 11 atomic percent. (This carbon content corresponds to the composition Fe_8C, which has not yet been established as a carbide phase, but the analogous compound $Fe_{16}N_2$ is known.) The wavelength of the modulations starts at about 20 angstroms and then undergoes coarsening. During the latter stage,

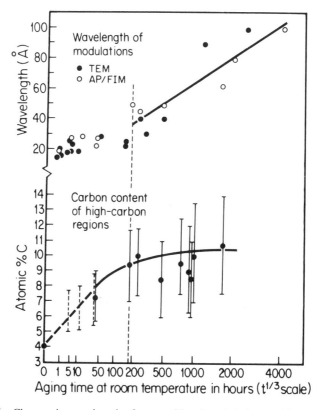

FIGURE 26   Changes in wavelength of compositional modulations and in carbon content of the associated high-carbon regions in Fe–15Ni–1C martensite on aging at room temperature, as measured by transmission electron microscopy and atom probe/field-ion microscopy. From Taylor and Smith.[44]

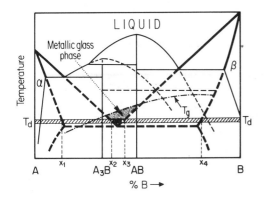

FIGURE 27 Isothermal formation of a metastable metallic glass by interdiffusion at temperature T_d between two crystalline phases A and B when the stable phases A_3B and AB do not nucleate. T_g = glass transition temperature. From Perepezko.[47]

the carbon content of the low-carbon regions becomes virtually nil, and in view of the coherency between the high- and low-carbon modulations, the elastic strains may reach the incredible level of 17 percent. It has not been realized before that such layered structures and the attendant coherency strains might be playing a substantial role in the classic strengthening of iron-carbon martensites—a matter of vast industrial importance. This long-standing challenge in ferrous metallurgy has defied all theories of steel hardening over the years, but now the existence of fine-scale compositional modulations offers a new outlook for a reinvigorated theoretical attack on the problem.

The use of layered structures for interdiffusion measurements is well known[45] and need not be reviewed here. However, there is one related phenomenon that warrants particular attention as a technique for synthesizing bulk metallic glasses.[46] In particular, the hypothetical alloy system shown in Figure 27 can form metastable intermediate phases if the more stable intermediate phases are sufficiently slow to nucleate during interdiffusion between layers of the pure metals A and B.[47] In such a case, one of the metastable phases may be a liquid, and, if the interdiffusion temperature happens to lie below the glass transition temperature of the supercooled liquid, a metallic glass will then form at the expense of the crystalline A and B components, starting at each A/B interface in the multilayered specimen, as in Figure 28.[46] Examples of alloy systems that behave in this way are gold-lanthanum, nickel-hafnium, and cobalt-zirconium; in each instance, the first component is a "fast diffuser" whereas the second is a "slow diffuser." Apparently, this condition tends to inhibit the nucleation of crystalline phases while favoring the rapid formation and thickening of a glassy phase.[47]

In a real sense under these circumstances, the two crystalline metals A and B dissolve in, or melt into, the growing glassy phase, notwithstanding the relatively low interdiffusion temperature involved. This process can result in the production of homogeneous glassy alloys for the kinds of bulk property measurements and test purposes that have not been feasible before. It is also

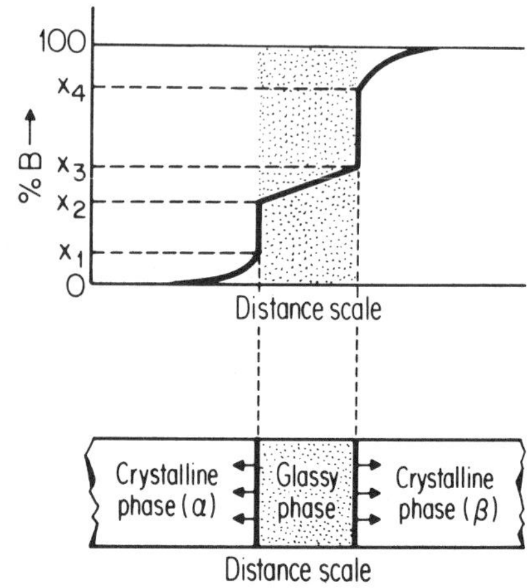

FIGURE 28   Schematic representation of metallic glass interdiffusion layer growing isothermally between crystalline A-rich and B-rich phases, corresponding to metastable equilibrium relationships at temperatures T_d in Figure 27. From Schwarz and Johnson.[46] Reprinted with permission.

evident that, in such metallic systems, bulk glasses can likewise be synthesized from compacted *powders* of the component metals, thus greatly facilitating appropriate specimen preparation. One can easily visualize new directions of research activity emerging from these recent studies of interdiffusion on a fine scale.

SOME SPECIAL METALLIC SYSTEMS FOR STRUCTURAL PURPOSES

Ductile Ordered Alloys

Long-range ordered phases and intermetallic compounds have long been a familiar subject in physical metallurgy, particularly from the standpoints of crystal structure, thermodynamic equilibrium, kinetics of formation, and second-phase strengthening dispersions. Both long- and short-range ordering have been studied in detail. But more recently there has been a new wave of interest in such alloy systems because of the ductility-related mechanical behavior of aluminides and similar phases, especially those having cubic Ni_3Al-type ($L1_2$) structures. It is a nice coincidence that intermetallic compounds have also come into prominence because of unusual ferromagnetic properties; this is discussed later in the section on magnetic alloys.

Excellent reviews of structure-property relationships in ductile ordered alloys have appeared within the past few years.[48–53] One reason for this focus has been the surprising degree of ductility and fabricability exhibited by these materials—a kind of mechanical behavior not commonly associated with intermetallic phases. It turns out that many $L1_2$ compounds are ductile at ambient temperatures both in the monocrystalline and polycrystalline states, but a well-studied exception is polycrystalline Ni_3Al, which suffers from intergranular weakness. It has been found, however, that small amounts of boron will segregate to the grain boundaries, strengthen these interfaces, and thus restore a level of ductility commensurate with that of the crystalline state. The effect of boron on the ductility and strength of polycrystalline Ni_3Al (24 atomic percent aluminum) is shown in Figure 29.[54] There is increasing evidence that the beneficial influence of boron is not one of simply displacing a harmful impurity (such as sulfur) from the grain boundaries but rather is a matter of enhancing the electronic bonding across the interface. For this reason the role of boron seems to be quite specific: it works superbly only on the nickel-rich side of Ni_3Al stoichiometry, but not on the aluminum-rich side, and it is not necessary for grain boundary strengthening in numerous other $L1_2$ alloys. In fact, the interfacial strength and hence intergranular ductility have been shown to increase with the valence difference between the two constituent atoms in a wide variety of $L1_2$-type A_3B phases.[55] This idea has been further substantiated by corresponding studies of ternary additions to Ni_3Al alloys.[56]

Many $L1_2$ intermetallic phases exhibit anomalous strengthening with increasing test temperature, often up to nearly the disordering temperature; Figure 30 shows several examples.[57] This strange mechanical behavior raises lively questions regarding both its origin and its potential use for high-temperature service. It should be emphasized, however, that the anomalous temperature dependence may be displayed to only a minor degree, or even not at all, by some $L1_2$ intermetallic phases. Nevertheless, we can expect that diffusion-dependent creep will be significantly retarded because of the relatively low atomic mobility typical of ordered lattices, as discussed below.

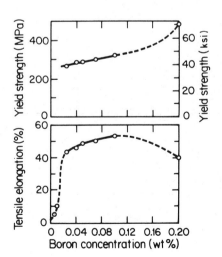

FIGURE 29 Effect of boron on the room-temperature ductility and strength of polycrystalline Ni_3Al (24 atomic percent aluminum). From Liu, White, and Horton.[54] Reprinted with permission.

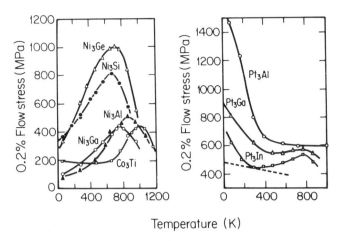

Temperature (K)

FIGURE 30   Temperature dependence of compressive flow stress of Ll_2 intermetallic compounds. Similar trends are found for the tensile flow stress. From Wee et al.[57] Reprinted with permission.

An important aspect of this increase in strength with temperature is associated with an unusually pronounced effect of temperature on strain hardening. It is evident from Figure 31 that the peak in high-temperature flow stress is primarily due to the operative strain hardening, which sets in at rather small plastic strains.[58] A feasible explanation of this extraordinary behavior is the cross-slip mechanism shown in Figure 32 and described in the caption.[59] Clearly, these conditions are special and therefore lead to unique phenomena that expand the range and possible usefulness of alloy properties.

FIGURE 31   Temperature dependence of tensile flow stress of Ni_3Al at various plastic offset strains larger than 10^{-5}. From Thornton, Davies, and Johnston.[58] Reprinted with permission.

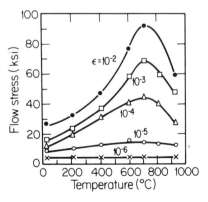

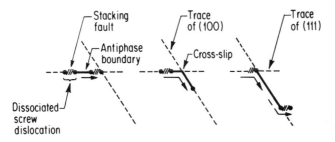

FIGURE 32 Cross-slip mechanism proposed to account for anomalous mechanical behavior of $L1_2$-ordered compounds. Superlattice dislocations are mobile on (111) planes, but the antiphase boundary (APB) happens to be more stable on (100) planes. Thermal activation at high test temperatures permits the dissociated partial dislocations to cross-slip onto (100) planes, thus producing sessile segments that resist further gliding on the primary slip plane by redissociating on other (111) planes.[59] Reprinted, with permission, from *Transactions of the Metallurgical Society,* Vol. 224, p. 382 (1962), a publication of The Metallurgical Society, Warrendale, Pa.

Many opportunities unfold for further insights and property improvements through off-stoichiometric variations (Figure 33)[60] and multicomponent alloying (Figure 34).[56] Generalizations concerning the effects of composition are not yet sufficiently well established, although the field is progressing rapidly. Alloying additions, such as niobium and tantalum, which tend to destabilize the cubic $L1_2$ phase (relative to other types of close-packed stacking), are effective strengtheners, but usually at the expense of decreased ductility. A related factor is the influence of composition on the difference

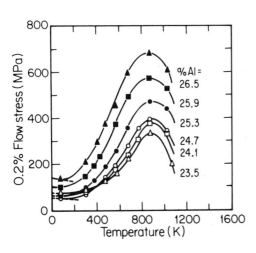

FIGURE 33 Effect of deviations from stoichiometry on the anomalous temperature dependence of flow stress of Ni_3Al alloys. From Noguchi, Oya, and Suzuki.[60] Reprinted with permission.

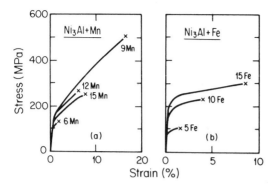

FIGURE 34 Tensile stress-strain curves (at room temperature) of Ni_3Al alloyed with manganese and iron. From Takasugi, Izumi, and Masahashi.[56] Reprinted with permission.

in antiphase-boundary energy between the {111} and {100} planes, which governs the driving force for the aforementioned thermally activated cross-slip mechanism.[57] Such subtle compositional effects may well account for a continuous range of behaviors from the anomalous temperature dependence of flow stress to the normal dependence observed with the more familiar alloys.[49]

Research on ordered $(Fe,Co,Ni)_3V$ alloys, paralleling the aluminides, has added considerable breadth and attraction to the subject of $L1_2$ phases and their properties.[50] Here it is found that lowering the electron-to-atom concentration (e/a), say, by substituting iron for cobalt and nickel, stabilizes the cubic close-packed stacking characteristic of $L1_2$ phases. This, in turn, promotes ductility, often exceeding 30 to 35 percent in tensile elongation. Such high ductility is maintained at elevated temperatures over most of the range

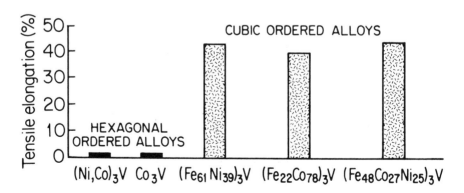

FIGURE 35 Room-temperature ductility of ordered $(Fe,Co,Ni)_3V$ alloys, comparing the hexagonal and cubic structures. From Liu.[50] Reprinted with permission.

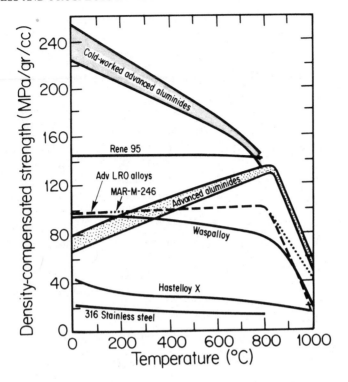

FIGURE 36 Comparison of density-compensated yield strength of ductile ordered alloys and some available high-temperature alloys. Advanced aluminides are Ni_3Al alloyed with hafnium, zirconium, and boron; cold-worked aluminides are plastically deformed 20 percent. Advanced long-range ordered (LRO) alloys are based on $(Fe,Co,Ni)_3(V,Al)$; MAR-M-246 is a modern gas-turbine superalloy. From National Materials Advisory Board publication NMAB-419.[48]

where the anomalous temperature-dependent strengthening is observed.[50] On the other hand, when e/a is increased, there is a progressive shift of the stacking sequence in the direction of hexagonal structures, thus decreasing the ductility, as illustrated in Figure 35.[50] There is also some indication that the atom-radius ratio (r_A/r_B) in the A_3B compounds may play a supplementary role in determining the stacking sequences, with smaller ratios tending to convert the atomic layering from cubic to hexagonal.[61]

An overall view of the engineering potential of ductile ordered alloys is highlighted by the density-compensated high-temperature strength curves in Figure 36.[48] The relatively low density of the aluminides contributes to specific-strength levels that are comparable with some of the strongest high-temperature alloys currently available. At the same time, the creep resistance of the ordered alloys looks attractive at temperatures below the respective disordering temperatures—e.g., 865°C for $(Fe_{33.3}Co_{66.7})_3V$, 895°C for $(Fe_{30}Co_{70})_3V$, and 950°C for $(Fe_{22}Co_{78})_3V$. Referred to these temperatures, the creep rates are some two orders of magnitude lower in the ordered state than in the disordered state, reflecting the reduced atomic mobility and stronger binding forces attributable to the long-range order.

Although one cannot do justice here to the expanding literature on ductile ordered alloys, it is certainly evident that a vast field of metallurgical research and development has opened up. The phases involved are capable of tremendous variations in fine structure: planar stacking sequences, fault densities, grain-size and ordered-domain refinements, degrees of disorder, lattice defects quenched in by thermomechanical treatments, and precipitation of second-phase dispersions. The groundwork has also been laid for careful attention to processing methods (including rapid solidification, surface modification, and heat treatment) for compositional, microstructural, and quality control to advance both the underlying fundamentals and the engineering applications of this provocative class of intermetallic alloys. Moreover, the phenomena at play that thus far have been studied largely in the ordered aluminides and vanadides should now be investigated in the analogous silicides and titanides.

Metal-Matrix Composites

The general concept of composite materials has great appeal. It offers the prospect of microstructurally combining various classes of materials, by design, to realize superior sets of properties not obtainable from any of the constituent materials serving alone. Actually, this is an old idea (witness straw in bricks, horsehair in plaster, and reinforcing bars in concrete), but modern engineering requirements have become much more demanding, particularly with regard to specific strength and stiffness for aerospace, military, and similar critical applications. The corresponding R&D effort is enormous; it includes polymer-matrix and ceramic-matrix as well as metal-matrix composites (MMCs), but in the present context we shall deal only with the last of these. It has been reported that, from 1978 through 1986, governmental funding for the MMC program in the United States amounted to almost $300 million.[62]

Common structural materials (metals, glasses, wood products) have about the same density-compensated stiffness, whereas nonmetallics such as carbon, boron, silicon carbide, and aluminum oxide enjoy much higher values by factors of 5 to 10. The latter materials are also intrinsically strong, but they tend to be brittle in bulk form. However, if these materials are produced as fibers and aligned, they can contribute both stiffness and strength when suitably embedded in a metallic matrix. In the resulting composite micro-

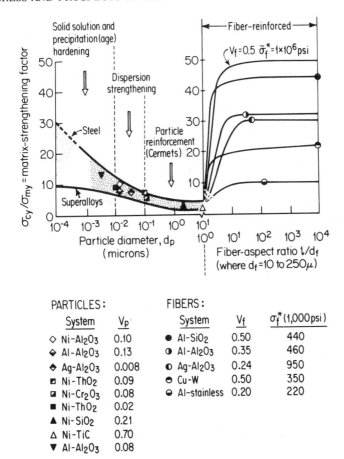

PARTICLES:

System	V_p
◇ Ni-Al$_2$O$_3$	0.10
◆ Al-Al$_2$O$_3$	0.13
◆ Ag-Al$_2$O$_3$	0.008
◪ Ni-ThO$_2$	0.09
◩ Ni-Cr$_2$O$_3$	0.08
■ Ni-ThO$_2$	0.02
▲ Ni-SiO$_2$	0.21
△ Ni-TiC	0.70
▼ Al-Al$_2$O$_3$	0.08

FIBERS:

System	V_f	σ_f^* (1,000 psi)
● Al-SiO$_2$	0.50	440
◓ Al-Al$_2$O$_3$	0.35	460
◑ Ag-Al$_2$O$_3$	0.24	950
◕ Cu-W	0.50	350
◒ Al-stainless	0.20	220

FIGURE 37 Effect of nonmetallic particles and fibers on the composite strengthening of metallic matrices, expressed as the ratio of yield strength of the composite to that of the matrix. Indicated points are experimental values. Curves for fiber-reinforced strengthening are based on calculations. Load is applied parallel to the fiber orientation. From Sutton and Chorne.[63] Reprinted with permission.

structure, the fibers act as reinforcing elements and are intended to take up most of the axial load being transmitted through the ductile matrix. The matrix is also supposed to accommodate plastically to breaks that may occur in the fibers. Figure 37 shows the fiber strengthening in a number of MMC systems having different fiber-aspect ratios and volume fractions.[63] A comparison is likewise given for the strengthening contributed by similar nonmetallic phases in the form of precipitates (up to 0.01 μm in diameter), dispersoids (0.01 to 0.1 μm), and particle reinforcements (0.1 to 10 μm).

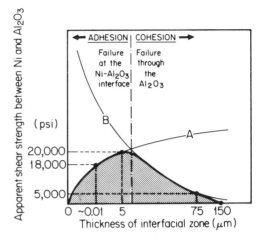

FIGURE 38 Effect of shear strength versus interaction-zone thickness between Ni and Al_2O_3 resulting from the competing effects of (A) bonding enhancement and (B) Al_2O_3 degradation. From Sutton and Feingold.[64] Reprinted with permission.

Much of the research on MMCs has been directed to the micromechanics and fracture of the relevant two-phase configurations and to experimental ways of incorporating fiber reinforcements in metal matrices. The efforts on both fronts have been extensive and singularly ingenious, yet serious difficulties remain to be resolved before MMCs can reach anything like their envisioned potential. The essential issue lies in proper bonding between the matrix and reinforcing fibers; it is basically an interfacial problem. Surprising as it may seem, this facet of MMCs has not received the broad attention that it deserves.

Polymer-matrix composites (PMCs) have been remarkably successful in fiber reinforcement because, among other things, most materials can be reliably glued with polymers (resins) at modest temperatures, whereas MMCs require elevated temperatures for liquid-metal infiltration or solid-state consolidation. These temperatures may be high enough to start detrimental interfacial reactions between the fibers and the matrix, inasmuch as they are invariably far from thermodynamic equilibrium with each other. Moreover, residual stresses are then introduced because of differential contractions during cooling to room temperature. These difficulties are intensifed by the fact that MMCs are often justified over PMCs because they can withstand use at higher temperatures, but such service tends to add further to the fiber-matrix interactions.

In principle, interfacial reactions may result in a precarious balance between the enhancement of fiber-matrix bonding on the one hand and fiber degradation on the other. These competing effects are represented in Figure 38 for the shear strength between nickel and aluminum oxide as a function of the interaction-zone thickness.[64] The right-hand trend is typical of prolonged or cyclic high-temperature exposure; it is also accompanied by a marked deterioration in transverse strength because of the interfacial weakening.

Interestingly enough, when there is near-equilibrium at the fiber-matrix interface, as in the case of directionally solidified eutectics having aligned microstructures, the interfacial bond strength is excellent. The two phases in MMCs of this *in situ* type are often crystallographically related, which may be a key factor in the observed interfacial stability. Unfortunately, the eutectic route to MMCs imposes severe compositional and phase-ratio restrictions on the alloy systems to be studied and thus detracts from the flexibility that is otherwise characteristic of MMC fiber-matrix combinations.

The importance of interfacial bonding, interdiffusion phenomena, and reaction-product formation in MMCs calls for detailed long-range study by sophisticated microanalytical techniques on carefully prepared and systematically varied fiber-matrix or layered specimens. In this connection there may be useful guidelines in the diffusion studies of fine-scale layered structures discussed earlier in the section on modulated structures. Analogous interfacial problems arise in the thin-film metallurgy of integrated circuits, as described in the following section, where the investigation of diffusion barriers is well advanced. Indeed, there is a thought-provoking case in point that suggests an interplay between the mechanical and electronic properties of MMC interfaces. In the Al/Al_2O_3/graphite junction shown in Figure 39,[65,66] the Al_2O_3, which is normally in a low-conductive state, can be voltage-switched to a high-conductive state. On peeling the aluminum away from the graphite substrate, it is found that the fracture path runs through the oxide when in the low-conductive state but follows the oxide-graphite interface when in the high-conductive state. Qualitatively speaking, the interface is stronger than the oxide in the low-conductive state and vice versa in the high-conductive state. One possible explanation is that a charge transfer takes place from the aluminum metal to the Al_2O_3 insulator in the former case, and the resulting space charge accumulation at the interface contributes an

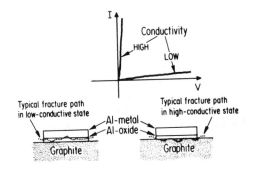

FIGURE 39 Change of fracture path in an Al/Al_2O_3/graphite composite system according to the conductive state of the Al_2O_3. From Tsai[65] and Mendez et al.[66] Reprinted with permission.

electrostatic adhesive force to strengthen the interface.[67] This space charge would then be neutralized when the oxide is in its high-conductive state. However, it is also conceivable that the strength of the oxide itself is affected by its electronic state, thus influencing the fracture path without significantly changing the interfacial strength per se.[67] This is an open question, but it casts a new light on the bonding between conductors and insulators. Once again, it calls attention to the lure and importance of interfacial research on MMCs.

METALS AS NONSTRUCTURAL MATERIALS

Metallic Films and Metallization of Integrated Circuits

Even though it is often useful to classify materials into metallic, ceramic, polymeric, and electronic categories, all these groupings have characteristic electronic (or electrical) properties. The electronic materials are typically designated as such because of their unique semiconducting properties and, consequently, their central role in microelectronic devices, but other classes of materials also contribute in essential ways. Indeed, integrated circuit performance may be determined not so much by the switching speed of the contacts as by the time delay for a signal to propagate through the metallic interconnections.[68] Moreover, the importance of such metallization in very-large-scale integrated (VLSI) circuits is destined to become increasingly critical in view of the urgent trends toward device densification and related complexities.

The term "metallization" in this context falls within the general realm of *thin-film metallurgy* and embraces contacts, gates, and diffusion barriers as well as interconnects; examples of these functions are shown schematically in Figure 40 for a metal-oxide-semiconductor transistor.[69] The opportunities for metallurgical research in these processing, structure, property, and performance relationships are enormous. It is a field that deserves strong attention by the metallurgical community, not only because of its technological vitality but also because many of the operative phenomena have been investigated in other aspects of metallurgy, such as vapor deposition, microstructures and defect structures, grain boundary diffusion versus lattice diffusion, electromigration, and interfacial reactions.

To take a case in point, the lifetime of integrated circuits is often governed by failure of the aluminum interconnects because of electromigration (current-enhanced atom transport) at high current densities. This is a circuit breakage problem that will become more acute, and perhaps even the ultimate limitation, in the continuing miniaturization of devices to submicron-scale dimensions.[68] A common type of interconnect failure stems from the fact that the diffusion flux induced by the electromigration is carried almost entirely

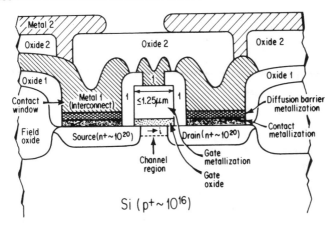

FIGURE 40 Schematic diagram of a multilevel metal-oxide-semiconductor transistor, showing metallization in its various functions. Dopant concentrations in the silicon regions are expressed in atoms/cm^3. From Green and Levy.[69] Reprinted with permission.

by grain boundaries.[70] Accordingly, two directions of metallurgical research suggest themselves: (1) to eliminate grain boundaries by increasing the grain size and (2) to reduce the grain boundary diffusivity.

The former approach invites detailed study of secondary grain growth (discontinuous coarsening) in thin films.[71] As expected, *normal* grain growth in thin films is driven by the reduction of grain boundary energy and leads to a maximum grain size on the order of the film thickness. However, if the film *surface* energy is sensitive to crystallographic orientation, discontinuous coarsening can ensue by the preferential growth of grains whose orientations correspond to the minimum energy, as shown in Figure 41.[71] A line of investigation that might then be considered lies in the subtle addition of trace elements, possibly by ion implantation, which will augment the anisotropy of surface energy and thus promote secondary growth to relatively large grains having mutually similar orientations. The latter circumstance has added benefits in that a textured microstructure, particularly with the {111} orientation, is found to improve the electromigration lifetime.[72] Moreover, the remaining grain boundaries will then be aligned normal to the film surfaces, a geometry that further tends to minimize void formation arising from electromigration.

By the same token, ion implantation can also be used for selective alloying to decrease grain boundary diffusivity. This effect explains why alloying the aluminum interconnects with a small percent of copper significantly retards the electromigration damage.[73] On the other hand, it should be feasible to inject less soluble atoms (e.g., refractory metals), which would segregate

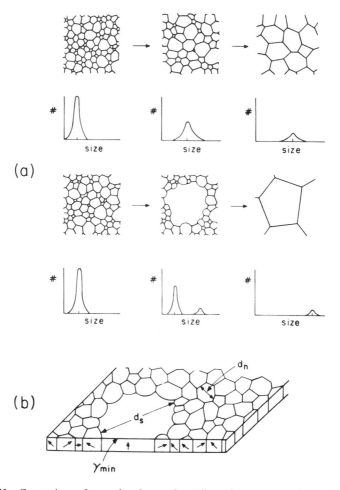

FIGURE 41   Comparison of normal and secondary (discontinuous coarsening) grain growth in a thin film: (a) stages of grain size distribution in the two cases; (b) secondary grain growth of orientations with minimum surface energy. From Thompson.[71] Reprinted with permission.

preferentially to grain boundaries without appreciable adverse effect on the electrical conductivity of the interconnect. There is independent evidence that solute enrichment at grain boundaries increases markedly as a function decreasing solid solubility.[74] A striking reduction in grain boundary diffusivity by solute segregation was described in an earlier section relative to the marked improvement in oxidation resistance of a cobalt-chromium alloy by yttrium ion implantation.

Another metallurgical phenomenon that is critical to VLSI circuit performance and lifetime involves the interdiffusion between thin-film multilayers; this was pointed up previously in a different context in the section on modulated structures. Of particular note is the undesirable interdiffusion that occurs at aluminum-silicon contacts, such bimetallic systems being rarely at equilibrium. Silicon can dissolve appreciably in solid aluminum at the processing or operating temperatures, causing aluminum to cross the interface into the silicon (often called "spiking") and thereby degrade or short-circuit the semiconductor junction.[73] Although the kinetics of this process can be slowed by prealloying the aluminum with silicon, much effort has been concentrated on the interposition of diffusion-barrier layers.[75] Various barriers have been explored, some with considerable promise, but an orderly rationale has not yet emerged. Barriers under investigation are the silicides of Co, Ni, Pd, and Pt; TiC and TiN; and refractory metal combinations, sometimes with noble or near-noble metals. In cases where undue interaction may take place between the barrier and the aluminum or silicon on either side, multiple barriers are of interest. Here again, an underlying hypothesis is that the detrimental interpenetration is dominated by grain boundary diffusion at the low temperatures involved and that this process can be alleviated by a large grain size or by "blocking" the grain boundaries with relatively insoluble solute or impurity atoms.

The point to be stressed for present purposes is that diffusion barriers in VLSI circuits as well as metallization more generally are rich frontiers for metallurgical research. One can sense that this kind of thin-film metallurgy will soon overlap the previously discussed field of nanoscale multilayered structures in which a high degree of coherency and orientation-alignment (approaching the monocrystalline state) is maintained between the metal layers—setting the stage for unexpected atomic-bonding, mechanical, and electrical properties. It can also be anticipated that other phenomena such as phase transformations and interface-related processes in thin-film and layered alloys will be profoundly different from what is now well known about the bulk systems.

Magnetic Alloys

Although ferromagnetism is normally regarded as an integral part of solid-state physics, many of the technologically important magnetic materials are metallic alloys and therefore fall within the general scope of metallurgy. Magnetic materials play a crucial role in modern electronic and electrical devices and enjoy a market of about $2 billion per year (growing at the rate of some 12 percent per year) in components that are 10 to 20 times greater in added value.[76] For present purposes we shall call particular attention to

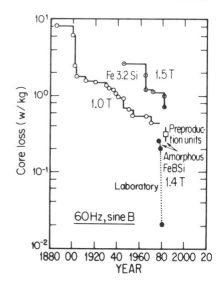

FIGURE 42   Progress in the reduction of core losses in silicon-steel and amorphous-alloy transformer materials. From Luborsky.[77] Reprinted with permission.

three advances in magnetic alloys that not only constitute important scientific achievements but also are likely to have significant societal impact.

Reference was made to metallic glasses in the earlier section on rapid solidification processing. These amorphous materials, especially those based on iron-boron-silicon and iron-boron-silicon-carbon compositions in the metalloid content range of 15 to 25 atomic percent, display remarkably low magnetic hysteresis and eddy-current losses, mainly as a result of their high electrical resistivity and freedom from magnetocrystalline anisotropy as well as from grain boundaries and other microstructural defects. These materials in ribbon thicknesses have 60-Hz core losses that are less than a third of the best grain-oriented silicon steels, the latter embracing significant improvements in grain-growth and texture control over a period of 50 years. Still more recent research on metallic glasses has shown further reductions in core losses to approximately 1/20 that of the silicon steels. These advances are summarized in Figure 42.[77]

The implications of these metallurgical developments are great. It is estimated that core losses in distribution transformers alone amount to about $0.74 billion annually in the United States, and that a third of this waste could be saved if amorphous alloy cores were used instead of the present materials.[77] A program is now under way to design and build one thousand 25-kVA distribution transformers for testing in service. Twenty-five of these transformers have already been constructed and are operating in various distribution systems. The test results thus far are in accordance with predictions, and the decision has been made to go ahead with production.

Corresponding opportunities for power transformers (500 to 1,500 kVA) and electric motors beckon further into the future. Meanwhile, numerous other magnetic applications for amorphous alloys are at hand: phonograph cartridges, audio and computer tape heads, dynamic microphones, magnetic shielding, and antitheft devices. A useful characteristic of these metallic glasses is that their magnetostriction can be controlled by alloying from zero, which is desirable in many devices, to sufficiently large values for force and displacement gauges. Considering the diverse applications of all these amorphous magnetic alloys, we have another textbook example in which a novel method of materials processing (RSP in this case) has led to the commercial development of previously unavailable materials and, in turn, to sharp improvements, or at least new potentials, in very different materials-dependent technologies.

RSP has also played a direct role in the discovery of the intermetallic compound $Nd_2Fe_{14}B$ as a high-performance permanent magnet[78]—eventually superior even to the previously developed samarium–transition metal types. Figure 43 shows how the magnetic energy product $(BH)_{max}$ of this ternary phase varies with the melt-spinning velocity.[78] The peak value of 14 megagauss-oersteds (MGOe) corresponds to a solidification rate that yields a rather uniform grain size of about 50 nm, which is presumably appropriate for single-domain particles. Slower rates permit the formation of coarser grains, whereas faster rates tend to inhibit crystallization altogether and an amorphous structure is then retained. Accordingly, the function of rapid solidification in this instance is not to produce a metastable phase but to achieve the proper grain size of a stable phase. In fact, this grain size can also be generated by careful devitrification of the amorphous structure. The magnetic measurements are made on powdered and subsequently compacted specimens.

This discovery has set the stage for more detailed fine-scale microscopy, systematic compositional variations, and powder-metallurgy processing to

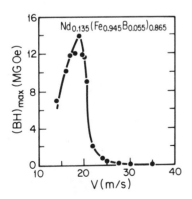

FIGURE 43 Room-temperature energy product $(BH)_{max}$ of a neodymium-iron-boron alloy as a function of melt-spinning velocity. From Croat et al.[78] Reprinted with permission.

obtain magnetically aligned, fully dense bulk materials.[79,80] With such efforts, the energy product has now been raised to the 40- to 45-MGOe level, shown in Figure 44 for the evolution of permanent-magnet alloys;[81] there is no reason to believe that a limit has yet been reached. Other rare-earth/transition-metal/metalloid intermetallic compounds now become attractive candidates for investigations along these lines. Additional research is also needed to attain higher Curie temperatures and better magnetic properties at elevated temperatures. But already the indications are that the high energy densities characteristic of these advanced magnetic intermetallic phases will spur new electronic-device designs toward greater efficiency and miniaturization— e.g., for electric motors, generators, actuators, and electroacoustical pick-ups.[81] Strong permanent magnets have even been proposed in place of electromagnets for use in accelerators and in electron storage rings for synchrotron radiation.[82] All these possibilities constitute another exciting prospect for front-line metallurgical research, development, and application.

Still another research and development sector for magnetic alloys lies in the magneto-optical recording of information.[83] Vacuum-deposited amorphous films of rare-earth/transition-metal alloys, such as GdCo, TbFe, GdTbFe,

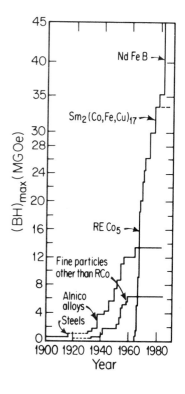

FIGURE 44   Evolution of permanent-magnet alloys during the 20th century, according to the energy product $(BH)_{max}$ as a figure of merit. From National Materials Advisory Board publication NMAB-426.[81]

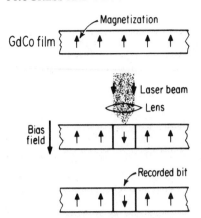

FIGURE 45 Schematic illustration of the magneto-optical recording process in an amorphous thin film of a rare-earth/transition-metal alloy. From Togami.[84] Reprinted with permission. Copyright © 1982 IEEE.

and GdTbCo, have the property of switching the direction of magnetization on a very fine scale, under the influence of a weak external field, when heated locally to 100° to 200°C by a pulsed laser-beam signal. After the beam is removed, the reversed domains persist because of hysteresis, as in Figure 45,[84] and so the recorded bits are "stored" for subsequent reading by magneto-optical (Kerr polarization rotation) effects. This application is expected to be in wide commercial service soon; it has the advantage of high bit density, noncontact recording and reading, and selective erasability by laser-beam heating in an oppositely biased external field.

The opportunities for creative metallurgical research on these thin-film amorphous alloy systems are immense—e.g., deposition techniques, compositional control, microstructural uniformity, amorphous-state stability and aging effects, corrosion mechanisms and protection, and new alloy chemistries. And once again, we note the emerging impact of thin-film metallurgy.

PHASE TRANSFORMATIONS

Although phase transformations pervade virtually all parts of metallurgy, we concentrate in this section on solid-state transformations. Such structural changes are an integral part of physical metallurgy and have been studied with high degrees of sophistication, both theoretically and experimentally. Phase transformations in the solid state are not only intriguing manifestations of nature's processes, but they are also useful to society for harnessing relationships among structure, property, and performance. Many branches of knowledge and instrumentation are brought to bear on this facet of metallurgy. Four examples are discussed here to illustrate some recent advances and critical issues.

Homogeneous and Heterogeneous Nucleation

Although solid-state transformations are frequently sensitive to lattice defects in the parent phase and thus tend to nucleate heterogeneously, evidence of homogeneous nucleation has been convincingly demonstrated in the past two years in selected alloy systems.[85,86] Copper-cobalt alloys are particularly appropriate for this objective in that both the copper-rich parent phase and the cobalt-rich precipitate phase have the same face-centered cubic crystal structure and are mutually coherent, thereby exhibiting low interfacial energy and simplifying its calculation. The corresponding nucleation rates for precipitation in a copper–1 atomic percent cobalt alloy are plotted in Figure 46, as determined experimentally by electron microscopy and as calculated from classical homogeneous nucleation theory involving thermal fluctuations surmounting an interface-related free-energy barrier.[85] The indicated agreement, assuming diffusivities based on vacancy concentrations characteristic of the solutionizing temperature, provides good support for the validity of homogeneous nucleation theory. Similar findings have been obtained for more dilute copper-cobalt alloys.[85] This signifies that, even though the smallest precipitated particles detected by electron microscopy (approximately 50 angstroms) were considerably larger than the critical nucleus size, the increasing particle-number density versus time was small enough (yet measurable) to permit unimpeded growth of the individual particles to detectable sizes before encountering overlapping diffusion fields between nearest-neighbor precipitates.

On the other hand, with higher supersaturations (e.g., copper–2.7 atomic

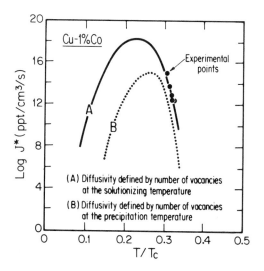

FIGURE 46   Calculated and experimental nucleation rates from homogeneous precipitation in a copper–1 atomic percent cobalt alloy as a function of temperature, normalized to the solvus temperature (T_c), after solutionizing at 870°C. From LeGoues and Aaronson.[85] Reprinted with permission.

percent cobalt), and in other face-centered cubic alloy systems (e.g., copper–1.9 atomic percent titanium and nickel–14 atomic percent aluminum), the nucleation rates may be orders of magnitude larger, and the corresponding number densities of precipitated particles increase into the range where the atom probe/field-ion microscope becomes an exceptionally powerful instrument for quantifying the early stages of precipitation.[87] In addition to number densities, this research technique is also capable of measuring small-particle compositions and particle-size distributions below 10 angstroms. However, in this high-particle-density regime, the nucleation stage is overlapped by solute depletion of the parent phase and by Ostwald ripening, both of which act to decrease the observed particle densities by re-solution of some of the previously precipitated particles. Nevertheless, the earliest detectable precipitates are found to have their equilibrium composition.

In a salient advance, these complications have been sorted out analytically, and calculated and experimental results for the critical nucleus size, mean particle size, and number density are compared in Figure 47 for a nickel–47 atomic percent aluminum alloy.[87,88] Calculated nucleation rates, based on homogeneous nucleation theory, are also shown in Figure 47. The interfacial energy (σ) and diffusivity (D) adopted for these computations can be derived directly from the longer aging times where only Ostwald ripening is operative. There is some uncertainty, however, as to whether the state of coherency characteristic of the nucleation stage is fully maintained throughout the coarsening period, but this does not interfere with the overall interpretation that follows.

It is evident from Figure 47 that the earliest measurements are already at a stage of decreasing particle-number density (N_v) despite the initially increasing transient nucleation rate (J). This means that Ostwald ripening sets in almost at the beginning of precipitation in this alloy and limits the fineness of the second-phase dispersion that might otherwise be available for maximum precipitation strengthening. This circumstance may also account for the rather constant mean particle size ($\overline{R}$) during the initial precipitation process, the growth of some nucleated particles being offset by the re-solution of others. In any event, the subsequent decrease in the calculated nucleation rate reflects the decreasing supersaturation of the parent solid solution as the transformation proceeds, and the critical nucleus size (R^*) increases accordingly.

Because of the complexities of the foregoing kinetic analysis, it has been applied so far only to homogeneous nucleation in face-centered cubic systems with coherent interphase interfaces. The next big step must cope to an increasing extent with dissimilar parent/product phases, semicoherent interfaces, and heterogeneous nucleation to establish a more general understanding and a more useful control of precipitation processes in a wider variety of alloy systems. It is a formidable long-range task, to be sure, but recent advances in theory, experimental techniques, and computer calculations are providing both direction and momentum.

It has long been recognized that defects in the parent phase, such as grain boundaries and dislocations, can offer preferred nucleation sites for solid-state diffusional transformations by reducing the interfacial and strain energies associated with the nucleation process.[89] However, the relevant mechanisms and kinetics are not well defined as yet. In contrast much progress in heterogeneous nucleation theory has been made in connection with martensitic (displacive and diffusionless) transformations. In view of the prominent shear-like deformation that accompanies this class of structural change, thermally activated homogeneous nucleation can be essentially ruled out; in fact, comparatively potent sites are necessary to start the transformation under the

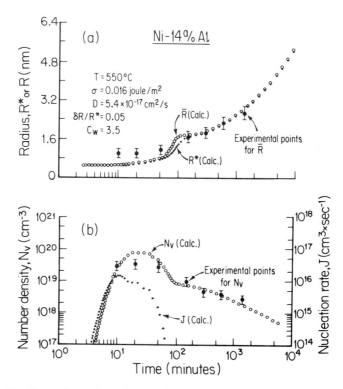

FIGURE 47 Comparison of calculated and experimental data for homogeneous precipitation in a nickel–14 atomic percent aluminum alloy as a function of time at 550°C: (a) critical nucleus size (R^*) and mean particle size ($\bar{R}$); (b) number density of particles (N_v) and nucleation rate (J). Incubation time (C_w) taken as 3.5 min for the first particles to become observable. From Kampmann and Wagner[87]; experimental points from Wendt and Haasen.[88]

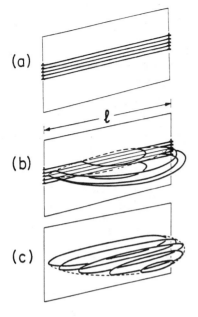

(a)

ℓ

(b)

(c)

FIGURE 48 Schematic representation of heterogeneous martensitic nucleation by dissociation of a stacked array of dislocations: (a) nucleation defect; (b) generation of interfacial dislocations in horizontal planes; (c) generation of interfacial dislocations in nearly vertical planes. From Olson and Cohen.[90] Reprinted with permission.

thermodynamic conditions where these phase changes are known to take place.

A likely type of preferred nucleation site for martensitic transformations consists of a stack or short wall of dislocations such as may exist in a grain boundary or subboundary of the parent phase, where the potency of the site is measured by the number of dislocations in the array. When the transformational driving force is sufficient, these dislocations can dissociate and produce a ribbon-shaped or plate-like particle, as shown schematically in Figure 48.[90] One consequence of this diffusionless mechanism is that it defines the dislocation structure of the interface and connects it directly to the crystallographic correspondence and relative displacements between the parent and product phases, the latter being generated simply by the motions of interfacial dislocations. An example of a semicoherent interface for a face-centered cubic to body-centered cubic martensitic transformation is described in Figure 49.[91]

There are far-reaching consequences of this concept of heterogeneous nucleation. First, martensitic transformations can now be couched in the language and phenomenology of dislocation theory, and thus many structural, kinetic, and mechanical aspects can be quantified accordingly. This new approach has been summarized recently in much detail.[92] It also points toward a more basic understanding of autocatalytic nucleation, which plays a major

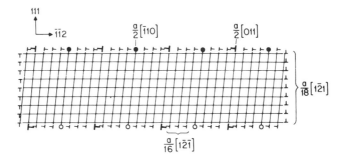

FIGURE 49 Semicoherent interface for face-centered cubic to body-centered cubic martensitic transformation. The $a/18$ [1$\bar{2}$1] and $a/16$ [1$\bar{2}\bar{1}$] dislocations (designated by light Ts) act to maintain coherency between the parent and product phases and accomplish the transformation during their motion by a lattice deformation, whereas the $a/2$ [011] and $a/2$ [$\bar{1}$10] dislocations (designated by heavy Ts and circles) are misfit dislocations that interrupt the coherency and accomplish a lattice-invariant deformation of the resulting semicoherent particle to relieve the long-range stress fields. All of the dislocations are in the form of loops around the particle. From Olson and Cohen.[91] Reprinted with permission.

role in the overall kinetics of martensitic transformations, particularly in the heat treatment of steel. In other words, although preexisting nucleation sites are essential for the start-up and early progress of martensitic transformations in ferrous alloys, their density is insufficient without the ongoing generation of new sites to achieve the technological hardening of steel.

The description of martensitic interfaces in the form of dislocation arrays makes it possible to deal with the growth problem in terms of dislocation mobilities under the operating driving-force and obstacle conditions. The nature of such calculations is presented in the next section; and in a later section on displacive diffusional transformations, it is shown how these ideas can be carried over to other phase transformations, including precipitation processes, in which lattice deformation and diffusion participate simultaneously. This establishes a spectrum among phase transformations that have previously been regarded as different in kind.

Martensitic Growth

For convenience of discussion, the propagation of martensitic interfaces can be divided into two categories: thermoelastic transformations, wherein the shape deformation attending the phase change is accommodated elastically by the alloy system; and nonthermoelastic transformations, wherein the shape deformation is accommodated plastically. In the former, a thermoelastic force balance prevails between the driving and retarding forces, and the interface can be made to move progressively and measurably under well-controlled experimental conditions. The interfacial mobility of thermoelastic copper-aluminum-nickel martensites has been investigated comprehensively in this way.[93] It is found that the effects of temperature and applied stress on the interfacial velocity are consistent with the concept of thermally activated interfacial motion, as suggested by the kinetic interrelationships in Figure 50.[93] Just as in the case of mechanically driven slip dislocations, the driving force for interfacial motion has both athermal (τ_μ) and thermal ($\tau_f - \tau_\mu$) components; similarly, activation energies and activation volumes are derivable from the experimental data, and specified models of interfacial structure can be tested against various modes of lattice friction and obstacles to growth.[93]

Nonthermoelastic martensites tend to propagate rapidly, in some instances even approaching the velocity of a shear wave in the parent phase. These transformations are difficult to nucleate and hence are effectively "overdriven" when the martensitic growth process sets in. Dissipation of the latent heat of transformation then becomes a complicating factor and must be taken into account. This has been done for the calculated interfacial-velocity versus particle-size curves plotted in Figure 51.[94] During the acceleration stage, the interfacial motion is assumed to be thermally activated at the lower velocities

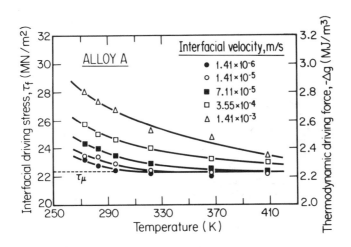

FIGURE 50 Interrelationships among interfacial driving stress, thermodynamic driving force, temperature, and interfacial velocity for martensitic growth in a copper–13.9 wt % aluminum–3.9 wt % nickel alloy. The operative driving force is calculated from the resolved mechanical stress (τ_f) which drives the moving interface; τ_μ is the athermal component of the driving stress. From Grujicic, Olson, and Owen.[93] Reprinted with permission.

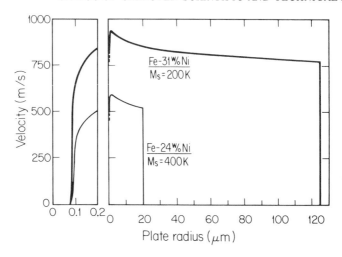

FIGURE 51   Calculated radial-growth velocities of disk-shaped martensitic particles in two Fe-Ni alloys at their respective martensite-start temperatures; thermal changes due to heat-transfer effects are taken into account. From Haezebrouck.[94]

and phonon-drag controlled at the higher velocities. The marked differences in martensitic growth characteristics between the two iron-nickel alloys in Figure 51 originate from differences in the respective dynamic flow stresses and drag coefficients.[94]

However, not yet incorporated into these calculations is the quantitative effect of local plastic accommodation, including the associated defect formation and strain hardening, on the resistance to interfacial motion. This is a crucial issue, not only because of the combination of dynamic phenomena at play here but because it may be forcing a general study of the no-man's-land between continuum and discrete-lattice solid-state science. It is somewhat reminiscent of the crack-tip/plastic-zone problem in fracture mechanics. Furthermore, the plastic accommodation process may hold the key to a deeper understanding of the autocatalytic nucleation that enters so significantly into the overall kinetics of nonthermoelastic martensitic transformations.

Transformation Plasticity and Toughening

The shear-like displacive nature of martensitic transformations allows these phase changes to operate as a deformation mechanism in parallel with ordinary slip processes.[95] Applied stress can promote the formation of martensite by contributing to the transformational driving force and by introducing new nucleation sites through accompanying plastic flow. At the same time, the acting stress will favor the formation of those martensitic crystallographic orientations that have optimal displacive components for "yielding" to the stress. The resulting transformation-induced plasticity (TRIP) reflects a novel interplay between the kinetics of a structural change and macroscopic stress-strain behavior. Indeed, there are now cases in which constitutive relations involving transformation plasticity have been derived to predict flow stress as a function of strain, strain rate, temperature, and stress state.[95] In austenitic steels having appropriate deformation-induced transformation characteristics, the uniform ductility in a tensile test has been increased about fivefold beyond that of the untransformed parent phase.[96]

Transformation plasticity offers an attractive mechanism for enhancing fracture toughness at high-strength levels by coming into play in the vicinity of an advancing crack, particularly in alloys that undergo shear instability before rupture. In such instances rather small amounts of mechanically induced transformation occurring in the plastic zone of a crack tip can delay the impending strain localization and thereby increase the fracture toughness substantially. Two examples are shown in Figure 52 for high-strength austenitic steels as a function of normalized test temperature.[96] The maximum toughness values correspond to about $K_{Ic} = 250$ MPa m$^{1/2}$ at $-70°$C, which is very tough for these 1300-MPa yield-strength steels. The beneficial effect on sharp-crack toughness arises not only from the transformation plasticity as such but also from a reduction of the triaxial stress state because of the volume expansion that attends the phase change.

The decrease in fracture toughness at lower test temperatures in Figure 52 is caused by the formation of too much martensite, which in itself is less tough than the parent phase. Hence, the eventual use of transformation toughening will require compositional modifications to decrease the temperature sensitivity of the transformation—e.g., by decreasing the entropy change of the transformation in order to reduce the temperature dependence of the thermodynamic driving force. Manganese is known to affect the transformational thermodynamics in that manner.

It is conceivable that the greatest potential for transformation toughening lies in its applicability to the retained austenite in martensitic steels. This is an unexplored field that warrants intense study, inasmuch as the technological use of ultrahigh-strength steels could be materially advanced even by modest increases in toughness.

Displacive-Diffusional Transformations

One can imagine a potential martensitic transformation under conditions where the driving force is not large enough for nucleation or interfacial motion to ensue. But if some compositional partitioning is permitted at the temperature in question, the driving force may then be sufficient for the phase change to proceed. The velocity of the interface, whether coherent or semi-coherent, will depend on diffusion as well as on the resistance to interfacial motion, and this interplay can result in some degree of solute trapping which, in turn, will determine the extent of partitioning and diffusion taking place. It is also possible that a steady-state balance in the functioning of these phenomena may be attained such that there is just enough diffusion to supply the necessary force for overcoming the resistance to interfacial motion. This type of phase transformation is, strictly speaking, neither displacement-controlled nor diffusion-controlled; rather, it represents a *coupled* displacive-diffusive mechanism of interfacial motion in which both lattice deformation and diffusion participate jointly and interactively.

The above transformational characteristics begin to take on some of the displacive-diffusional features of bainitic transformations, allowing for pre-cipitation processes in the product phase behind the advancing front.[97,98] This theory of bainite formation has not been definitively tested as yet, but it surely would be worth doing so, especially in view of the favorable me-

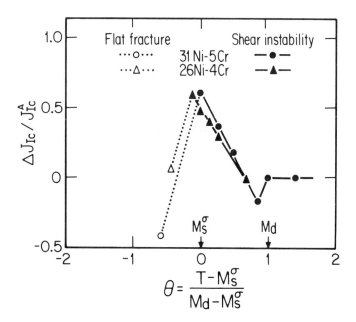

FIGURE 52   Fractional increase in J-integral fracture toughness as a function of temper-ature normalized according to martensitic transformation characteristics of two Fe-Ni-Cr alloys. During test, no transformation takes place at temperatures above M_d—i.e., fracture toughness is that of the parent austenitic phase (J_{Ic}^A); plastic-strain-induced transformation takes place between M_d and M_s^σ; and elastic-stress-assisted transformation takes place below M_s^σ. From Leal.[96]

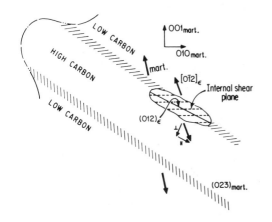

FIGURE 53 Schematic illustration of ϵ-carbide precipitation via an invariant-plane strain in compositionally modulated martensite in an iron–15 wt % nickel–1 wt % carbon alloy. Arrows indicate displacement directions in the martensite and in the carbide. The designated internal shear plane in the carbide is parallel to the carbide basal plane. From Taylor.[100]

chanical properties of bainitic microstructures being reported for high-strength, low-alloy steels.[99]

However, there appears to be an even broader significance to the concept of displacive-diffusional transformations in that some typical precipitation reactions display both shape and compositional changes. It has now been demonstrated that the well-known precipitation of ϵ-carbide from ferrous martensites falls in this category, as shown schematically in Figure 53.[100] These martensites first develop a compositionally modulated structure of coherent high- and low-carbon bands on aging near room temperature, as discussed earlier in the section on modulated structures, and then the ϵ-carbide precipitates with an invariant-plane strain, plate-like morphology composed of both homogeneous lattice and inhomogeneous internal deformations, comparable to a martensitic transformation except that carbon diffusion is also required to form the ϵ-carbide. The precipitation is heterogeneous, tends to nucleate along the modulated-band interfaces, and adopts a (012) habit that is close to the (023) habit of the modulated bands. In view of the lattice correspondence between the precipitated phase and its surroundings, the carbide interface is undoubtedly semicoherent. A similar type of displacive-diffusional interpretation has been applied to the precipitation of hydrides in vanadium and zirconium solid solutions.[101]

It may be turning out that precipitation processes in general, to the extent that coherent or semicoherent interfaces are involved, combine both lattice-distortive and diffusion-related phenomena (although not necessarily coupled and not necessarily shear-like) with different degrees of kinetic control. In this sense, precipitation reactions are likely to comprise a spectrum of phase transformations in which martensitic transformations constitute only a very special (diffusionless) case. This possibility offers new incentives and guidelines for future research on phase transformations.

CONCLUSION

There are many innovative areas of metallurgical research not treated in this review that should be recognized as significant opportunities for important advances in metallurgy. Among these are the electromagnetic handling of liquid metals, sensors and techniques for on-line process control, *in situ* observations of fast events, hydrogen embrittlement, atomic-bonding calculations, and computer modeling of processes and phenomena.

In this chapter we have attempted to integrate various viewpoints and suggestions, received mainly from the metallurgical community, into a valid perspective on some notable accomplishments of modern metallurgical research and on the sustained intellectual excitement that is inspiring further research on this vital class of materials. Metals not only represent a large majority of the elements in the periodic table and therefore constitute a pervasive part of the natural world, but they are generally useful to mankind and therefore invaluable to society. This confluence gives rise to a persistent driving force for probing metals ever more deeply and for using them ever more wisely. It is both a lofty challenge and a proud responsibility for metallurgical science and engineering.

ACKNOWLEDGMENTS

I am extremely grateful for the outpouring of ideas and opinions, both oral and written, that came to me in response to my informal requests for advice on many metallurgical fronts. The resulting communications grapevine operated with amiable efficiency and goodwill. In instances where the submissions could not be included, I am no less appreciative of the cooperation and involvement.

I am also deeply indebted to Marguerite Meyer, Miriam Rich, and John Mara at MIT, who helped so much in the preparation of the manuscript, and to NAE Fellow Dr. Peter Psaras, who waited so patiently to receive it.

NOTES

1. Committee on the Survey of Materials Science and Engineering, *Materials and Man's Needs,* Summary Report of the Committee on the Survey of Materials Science and Engineering (National Academy of Sciences, Washington, D.C., 1974).
2. H. C. Sorby, Report of the 34th Meeting, British Association for the Advancement of Science (Bath, 1864), Part II, p. 189.
3. J. H. Payer, D. G. Dippold, W. K. Boyd, W. E. Berry, E. W. Brooman, A. R. Buhr, and W. H. Fisher, *The Economic Effect of Corrosion in the United States* (Battelle Columbus Laboratories, 1977); J. J. Duga, W. H. Fisher, R. W. Buxbaum, A. R. Rosenfield, A. R. Buhr, E. J. Honton, and S. C. McMillan, *The Economic Effects of Fracture in the United States* (Battelle Columbus Laboratories, 1983).

4. M. F. Ashby, in *Retrospective/Prospective Reviews of Scientific Achievements,* NATO Science Committee 20th Anniversary Commemoration Conference, Paper No. 3, The Science of Engineering Materials (1978).

5. J. Billingham, Met. Mater. **1** (8), 472 (1985).

6. J. F. Watton, Ph.D. thesis in progress, Massachusetts Institute of Technology, 1985–1986.

7. J. D. Baird and R. R. Preston, in *Processing and Properties of Low Carbon Steel,* edited by J. M. Gray (American Institute of Mining, Metallurgical and Petroleum Engineers, New York, 1973), p. 1.

8. S. S. Hansen, unpublished data from Bethlehem Steel Corporation.

9. *Structural Materials in the United States and Long-Term Prospects for International Competition* (Materials Modeling Associates, Cambridge, Mass., 1985).

10. R. B. Pond, U.S. Patent No. 2 825 108 (1958).

11. W. Klement, Jr., R. H. Willens, and P. E. Duwez, Nature (London) **187,** 869 (1960).

12. D. Schechtman, I. Blech, D. Gratias, and J. W. Cahn, Phys. Rev. Lett. **53,** 1951 (1984).

13. M. Cohen, B. H. Kear, and R. Mehrabian, in *Rapid Solidification Processing—Principles and Technologies,* edited by R. Mehrabian, B. H. Kear, and M. Cohen (Claitor's Publishing Div., Baton Rouge, 1980), Vol. II, p. 1.

14. M. C. Flemings, S. Z. Uram, and H. F. Taylor, Trans. Am. Found. Soc. **68,** 670 (1960).

15. T. F. Kelly and J. B. Vander Sande, in *Rapid Solidification Processing—Principles and Technologies,* edited by R. Mehrabian, B. H. Kear, and M. Cohen (Claitor's Publishing Div., Baton Rouge, 1980), Vol. II, p. 100.

16. A. E. Vidoz, D. D. Crooks, R. E. Lewis, I. G. Palmer, and J. Wadsworth, in *Rapidly Solidified Powder Aluminum Alloys,* edited by M. E. Fine and E. A. Starke, ASTM STP 890 (1986, in press).

17. C. M. Adam and R. E. Lewis, in *Rapidly Solidified Crystalline Alloys,* edited by S. K. Das, B. H. Kear, and C. M. Adam (The Metallurgical Society, Warrendale, Pa., 1986), p. 157.

18. S. K. Das and C. F. Chang, in *Rapidly Solidified Crystalline Alloys,* edited by S. K. Das, B. H. Kear, and C. M. Adam (The Metallurgical Society, Warrendale, Pa., 1986), p. 137.

19. G. J. Yurek, D. Eisen, and A. Garratt-Reed, Metall. Trans. A **13A,** 473 (1982).

20. A. R. Cox, Pratt and Whitney Division, United Technologies Corp. (private communication).

21. W. J. Boettinger, S. R. Coriell, and R. F. Sekerka, Mater. Sci. Eng. **65,** 27 (1984).

22. J. S. Williams and J. M. Poate, in *Ion Implantation and Beam Processing,* edited by J. S. Williams and J. M. Poate (Academic Press, New York, 1984), p. 1.

23. E. McCafferty, P. G. Moore, J. D. Ayers, and G. K. Hubler, in *Corrosion of Metals Processed by Directed Energy Beams,* edited by C. R. Clayton and C. M. Preece (The Metallurgical Society, Warrendale, Pa., 1982), p. 1.

24. B. R. Appleton, in *Ion Implantation and Beam Processing,* edited by J. S. Williams and J. M. Poate (Academic Press, New York, 1984), p. 189.

25. G. Dearnaley, in *Ion Implantation Metallurgy,* edited by C. M. Preece and J. K. Hirvonen (The Metallurgical Society, Warrendale, Pa., 1980), p. 1.

26. K. Przybylski, in *Proceedings of the 10th International Symposium on Reactivity of Solids,* edited by P. Barret and L. C. Dafour, Mater. Sci. Monographs **28** (Elsevier, The Netherlands, 1985), p. 241.

27. K. Przybylski, A. Garratt-Reed, and G. J. Yurek, paper submitted to J. Electrochem. Soc.

28. S. M. Myers, in *Ion Implantation Metallurgy,* edited by C. M. Preece and J. K. Hirvonen (The Metallurgical Society, Warrendale, Pa., 1980), p. 21.

29. F. L. Versnyder and M. E. Shank, Mater. Sci. Eng. **6**, 231 (1970).
30. M. Gell, D. N. Duhl, and A. F. Giamei, in *Superalloys 1980*, 4th International Symposium on Superalloys, edited by J. K. Tien, S. T. Wlodek, H. Morrow III, M. Gell, and G. E. Mauer (American Society for Metals, Metals Park, Ohio, 1980), p. 205.
31. M. Gell and D. N. Duhl, in *N. J. Grant Symposium on Processing and Properties of Advanced High-Temperature Alloys*, edited by S. M. Allen, R. M. N. Pelloux, and R. Widmer (American Society for Metals, Metals Park, Ohio, 1986), p. 49.
32. J. P. Hirth, "Microstructure and mechanical properties of metals," this volume.
33. The research program described is directed to "Innovations in High-Strength Steel Technology" and is sponsored at the Massachusetts Institute of Technology by the National Science Foundation.
34. W. A. Backofen, *Deformation Processing* (Addison-Wesley, Reading, Mass., 1972), p. 218.
35. N. E. Paton, in *N. J. Grant Symposium on Processing and Properties of Advanced High-Temperature Alloys*, edited by S. M. Allen, R. M. N. Pelloux, and R. Widmer (American Society for Metals, Metals Park, Ohio, 1986).
36. M. F. Ashby, G. H. Edward, J. Davenport, and R. A. Verrall, Acta. Metall. **26**, 1179 (1978).
37. H. Gleiter and P. Marquardt, Z. Metallkd. **75**, 263 (1984); R. Birringer, U. Herr, and H. Gleiter, paper submitted for publication in Trans. Jpn. Inst. Metals (1986).
38. H. Gleiter (private communication).
39. Solid State Sciences Committee, *Report on Artificially Structured Materials*, National Research Council (National Academy Press, Washington, D.C., 1985).
40. T. Tsakalakos and J. E. Hilliard, J. Appl. Phys. **54**, 734 (1983).
41. T. Tsakalakos and A. F. Jankowski, in *Modulated Structure Materials*, edited by T. Tsakalakos (Martinus Nyhoff, Boston, 1984), p. 387.
42. P. C. Clapp, in *Modulated Structure Materials*, edited by T. Tsakalakos (Martinus Nyhoff, Boston, 1984), p. 455.
43. D. Baral, J. B. Ketterson, and J. E. Hilliard, J. Appl. Phys. **57**, 1076 (1985).
44. K. A. Taylor and G. D. W. Smith (unpublished research at Massachusetts Institute of Technology and Oxford University); see also L. Chang et al., J. Phys. (Paris), Colloque C9, suppl. 12, **45**, C9-409 (1984).
45. T. Tsakalakos and J. E. Hilliard, J. Appl. Phys. **55**, 2885 (1984).
46. R. Schwarz and W. L. Johnson, Phys. Rev. Lett. **51**, 415 (1983); W. L. Johnson, X. L. Yeh, and M. Atzmon, Acta Metall., in press.
47. J. H. Perepezko (private communication).
48. Committee on Application Potential for Ductile Ordered Alloys, National Materials Advisory Board, *Structural Uses for Ductile Ordered Alloys*, Pub. No. NMAB-419 (National Academy Press, Washington, D.C., 1984).
49. D. P. Pope and S. S. Ezz, Int. Metals Rev. **29** (3), 136 (1984).
50. C. T. Liu, Int. Metals Rev. **29** (3), 168 (1984).
51. N. S. Stoloff, in *High-Temperature Ordered Intermetallic Alloys*, edited by C. C. Koch, C. T. Liu, and N. S. Stoloff, Materials Research Society Symposium Proceedings **39**, 3 (1985).
52. Y. Mishima, Y. Oya, and T. Suzuki, in *High-Temperature Ordered Intermetallic Alloys*, edited by C. C. Koch, C. T. Liu, and N. S. Stoloff, Materials Research Society Symposium Proceedings **39**, 264 (1985).
53. H. A. Lipsitt, in *High-Temperature Ordered Intermetallic Alloys*, edited by C. C. Koch, C. T. Liu, and N. S. Stoloff, Materials Research Society Symposium Proceedings **39**, 351 (1985).
54. C. T. Liu, C. L. White, and J. A. Horton, Acta Metall. **33** (7), 213 (1985).

55. T. Takasugi and O. Izumi, Acta Metall. **33** (7), 1247 (1985).

56. T. Takasugi, O. Izumi, and M. Masahashi, Acta Metall. **33** (7), 1259 (1985).

57. D. M. Wee, O. Noguchi, Y. Oya, and T. Suzuki, Trans. Jpn. Inst. Metals **21**, 237 (1980).

58. P. H. Thornton, R. G. Davies, and T. L. Johnston, Metall. Trans. **1**, 207 (1970).

59. B. H. Kear and H. G. F. Wilsdorf, Trans. Metall. Soc. AIME **224**, 382 (1962).

60. O. Noguchi, Y. Oya, and T. Suzuki, Metall. Trans. A **12A**, 1647 (1981).

61. J. H. N. Van Vucht, J. Less-Common Met. **11**, 308 (1966).

62. J. Persh, keynote address, Sixth Metal-Matrix Composites Conference, in *Current Highlights*, MMC Information Analysis Center, Washington, D.C., **5** (2), 1 (1985).

63. W. H. Sutton and J. Chorne, in *Fiber Composite Materials,* Chap. 9 (American Society for Metals, Metals Park, Ohio, 1965).

64. W. H. Sutton and E. Feingold, in *Materials Science Research,* edited by W. W. Kriegel and H. Palmour III (Plenum, New York, 1966), p. 577.

65. S. D. Tsai, Ph.D. thesis, University of Texas, Austin (1980).

66. H. H. Mendez, D. Finello, R. Walser, and H. L. Marcus, Scripta Metall. **16**, 855 (1982).

67. L. D. Brown and H. L. Marcus, Annual Report to ONR, Contract N00014-84-K-0687, University of Texas, Austin (1985).

68. P. S. Ho, Semiconductor Int., 128 (1985).

69. M. L. Green and R. A. Levy, J. Metals **37** (6), 63 (1985).

70. K. N. Tu, in *Treatise on Materials Science and Technology,* edited by K. N. Tu and R. Rosenberg (Academic Press, New York, 1982), p. 237.

71. C. V. Thompson, J. Appl. Phys. **58**, 763 (1985); and in *Energy Beam-Solid Interactions and Transient Thermal Processing,* edited by D. K. Biegelsen, G. Rozgonyi, and C. Shank, Materials Research Society Symposium Proceedings **35**, 711 (1985).

72. S. Vaidya and A. K. Sinha, Thin Solid Films **75**, 253 (1981).

73. T. J. Garosshen, T. A. Stephenson, and T. P. Slavin, J. Metals **37** (5), 55 (1985).

74. D. Gupta, Metall. Trans. A **8A**, 1437 (1977).

75. M. A. Nicolet, Thin Solid Films **52**, 415 (1978); M. Wittmer, J. Vac. Sci. Technol. A **2** (2), 273 (1984); S. P. Muraka, J. Vac. Sci. Technol. B **2** (4), 693 (1984).

76. G. Y. Chin, in *Frontiers in Materials Technologies,* edited by M. A. Meyers and O. T. Inal (Elsevier, The Netherlands, 1985), p. 415.

77. F. E. Luborsky, in *Proceedings of the NATO Conference on Glasses—Current Issues,* edited by A. F. Wright and J. Dupuy (Martinus Nijhoff, The Hague, 1985), p. 139.

78. J. J. Croat, J. F. Herbst, R. W. Lee, and F. E. Pinkerton, J. Appl. Phys. **55**, 2078 (1984).

79. M. Sagawa, S. Fujimura, N. Togawa, H. Yamamoto, and Y. Matsuma, J. Appl. Phys. **55**, 2083 (1984).

80. R. W. Lee, Appl. Phys. Lett. **46** (8), 790 (1985).

81. Committee on Magnetic Materials, National Materials Advisory Board, *Magnetic Materials,* NMAB-426 (National Academy Press, Washington, D.C., 1985).

82. K. Halbach, J. Appl. Phys. **57**, 3605 (1985).

83. M. H. Kryder, J. Appl. Phys. **57**, 3913 (1985).

84. Y. Togami, IEEE Trans. Magn. **MAG-18**, 1233 (1982).

85. F. K. LeGoues and H. I. Aaronson, Acta Metall. **32** (10), 1855 (1984).

86. H. Wendt and P. Haasen, Scripta Metall. **19** (9), 1053 (1985).

87. R. Kampmann and R. Wagner, in *Decomposition of Alloys: The Early Stages,* edited by P. Haasen, V. Gerold, R. Wagner, and M. F. Ashby, 2nd Acta-Scripta Metallurgica Conference (Pergamon, Oxford, 1984), p. 91.

88. H. Wendt and P. Haasen, Acta Metall. **31** (10), 1649 (1983).

89. K. C. Russell, Adv. Colloid Interf. Sci. **13**, 205 (1980).

90. G. B. Olson and M. Cohen, in *Proceedings of the International Conference on Solid-Solid Phase Transformations*, edited by H. I. Aaronson, D. E. Laughlin, R. F. Sekerka, and C. M. Wayman (The Metallurgical Society, Warrendale, Pa., 1983), p. 1145.

91. G. B. Olson and M. Cohen, Annu. Rev. Mater. Sci. **11**, 1 (1981).

92. G. B. Olson and M. Cohen, in *Dislocations in Solids*, edited by F. R. N. Nabarro (North-Holland, Amsterdam, 1986), in press.

93. M. Grujicic, G. B. Olson, and W. S. Owen, Metall. Trans. A **16A** (10), 1713, 1723, 1735 (1985).

94. D. M. Haezebrouck, Ph.D. thesis, Massachusetts Institute of Technology, research in progress.

95. G. B. Olson and M. Cohen, in *E. R. Parker Symposium on Structure/Property Relationships*, edited by S. D. Antolovich, W. E. Gerberich, and R. O. Ritchie (The Metallurgical Society, Warrendale, Pa., 1986), p. 367.

96. R. H. Leal, Ph.D. thesis, Massachusetts Institute of Technology, 1984.

97. H. K. D. H. Bhadeshia, Acta Metall. **29**, 1117 (1981); H. K. D. H. Bhadeshia and A. R. Waugh, Acta Metall. **30**, 775 (1982).

98. J. W. Christian and D. V. Edmonds, in *Phase Transformations in Ferrous Alloys*, edited by A. R. Marder and J. I. Goldstein (The Metallurgical Society, Warrendale, Pa., 1984), p. 293.

99. F. B. Pickering, in *HSLA Steels—Technology and Applications*, edited by M. Korchynsky, American Society for Metals Conference Proceedings (1984), p. 1.

100. K. A. Taylor, Sc.D. thesis, Massachusetts Institute of Technology, 1985.

101. M. P. Cassidy, B. C. Muddle, T. C. Scott, C. M. Wayman, and J. S. Bowles, Acta Metall. **25**, 829 (1977); M. P. Cassidy and C. M. Wayman, in *Proceedings of the International Conference on Martensitic Transformations* (Massachusetts Institute of Technology, Cambridge, Mass., 1979), p. 202.

Microstructure and Mechanical Properties of Metals

JOHN P. HIRTH

By 1960 many of our present alloy systems had been developed as a result of the research effort during World War II. Thus, many alloy and stainless steels, nickel-base superalloys, brasses and bronzes, precipitation-hardened aluminum alloys, and titanium alloys were then available. The optical characterization of microstructures and of the phase transformations leading to them was extensive. Moreover, with the advent of transmission electron microscopy in 1956,[1] more detailed microstructural characterization at the atomic level was under way.

Fundamental advances in the relationship between mechanical properties and microstructural defects had been made, and the properties of straight, single dislocations were developed.[2,3] Irwin[4] showed that the strain-energy release rate in crack propagation could be related to local crack tip stress-intensity measures, extending the treatment of a brittle crack.[5] Moreover, Eshelby's energy momentum tensor, the basis for the modern theory for crack extension, was available.[6] Work had begun on more complex dislocation arrays, such as pileups,[7] and simple models for work hardening had been proposed.[8] Lastly, Orowan[9] had already suggested the key equation relating flow stress to the inverse spacing of dislocation obstacles such as second-phase particles. Yet, there was little translation of these ideas into concepts that could provide guidelines for alloy design.

This chapter presents a discussion of advances and remaining problems in four areas pertinent to property-microstructure interrelationships, including dislocation theory, fracture theory, properties of complex alloys, and environmental effects. To illustrate the advances and the interplay between fundamental work and macroscopic properties, the discussion is restricted to low-temperature flow and fracture under monotonic tensile loading. Parallel

111

advances have been made in the areas of fatigue, creep, friction, and wear, but this broader range of topics is outside the scope of this discussion.

DISLOCATIONS

Elastic Theory

In 1939 Burgers[10] developed a vector field theory for dislocations, including an expression for the displacement field of a dislocation loop in terms of line integrals over its length and an area integral over its enclosed area. In addition, Peach and Koehler[11] presented an expression for the virtual thermodynamic force on a dislocation segment. Yet, in 1960 these concepts had been developed extensively only for straight dislocations. The theory of curved dislocations appeared during the past 25 years.

Mura[12] transformed Burgers's equation into a line integral for displacement gradients in terms of an integrand containing the elastic Green function tensor. This led to the Brown formula[13–15] for the stress field at an arbitrary point, produced by a line segment of dislocation, in terms of elastic energy coefficients for an infinite straight dislocation pair passing through the point in question and the ends of the segment. The result applies for isotropic or anisotropic elasticity. Blin[16] also presented an expression, based on Burgers's equation, for the interaction energy of two dislocation loops. Manipulations of this expression and the Peach-Koehler result led to isotropic elastic expressions for the self- and interaction energies of dislocation segments,[17,18] the interaction force between segments,[19] and the displacement field of a segment.[20] By approximating an arbitrary curved dislocation as a connected set of straight segments, one can use this set of relations to determine the elastic fields of complex dislocation arrays. Examples include stacking-fault tetrahedra, loops, double kinks, and double jogs.[21]

The elastic interaction of an arbitrarily inclined dislocation and a free surface was expressed by Lothe[22] as an image interaction analogous to that in electrostatics. This interaction was also extended to the case of dislocation segments, with numerous subsequent applications.[23,24]

As an alternative to the eigenvalue sextic solution of Eshelby and co-workers,[25] Stroh developed an explicit solution for the anisotropic elastic field of a straight dislocation.[26] Another alternative formulation using Fourier analysis was presented by Willis.[27] The Stroh theory was elaborated as an integral theory, facilitating numerical calculations, by Barnett and Lothe.[28] Advanced anisotropic elastic calculations for complex dislocation configurations have now been initiated.[29]

Lattice Theory

With the advent of computers, atomic calculations have been used to estimate the Peierls stress and energy, the variation of energy with position

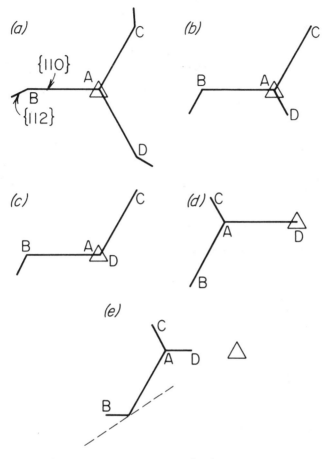

FIGURE 1 View of a screw dislocation along a ⟨110⟩ direction in a bcc crystal showing nascent dissociation into fractional dislocations on {110} and {112} planes.

of a dislocation caused by the periodicity of the lattice. A review of such work is given by Puls.[30] An important finding was that a dislocation is a center of dilatation producing an increase of about one atomic volume per plane cut by the dislocation, with about 40 percent residing in the highly nonlinear core region.[31] The other major success of such calculations was in explaining the large Peierls stress of body-centered cubic (bcc) metals on the basis of atomic-scale dissociations of screw dislocations into fractional dislocations[32,33] (see Figure 1). The threefold dissociated structure must be constricted, requiring stress-assisted thermal activation, for dislocation motion to occur. The dissociation also breaks the crystal symmetry, giving rise to new local defects called flips on the dislocation line where the rotation shown in Figure 1 changes sense. Lattice calculations of the energies of kinks, jogs, and flips have provided information on typical concentrations of these defects.[34]

Of interest in a broader context, the theory developed for dislocation motion by double-kink nucleation and growth[35] corresponds exactly to the theory for creation and motion of a soliton pair;[36] indeed, kinks can be regarded as solitons.

Grain Boundaries, Interfaces, and Partial Dislocations

The concept of grain boundary dislocations (GBD), with Burgers vector lengths unequal to those of lattice dislocations, and their geometrical description were presented by Bollmann[37] and represent a topic of great current interest.[38] Similar concepts have been applied to interphase interfaces.[39] Observations of these defects[38,40] suggest that they have important roles in phase transformations, creep, recrystallization, work hardening, and recovery, through their interaction with lattice dislocations and vacancies. In particular, non-uniform spacings of GBDs imply some degree of interface control in vacancy diffusion processes. Figure 2 shows an example of a GBD array.

Much of our knowledge of dislocation interactions has been gained from electron microscopy. In recent years, the weak-beam technique[41] and direct lattice resolution[42] have provided information at the near-atomic size scale. For face-centered cubic (fcc) metals, Figure 3 shows seven extended dislocation arrays, many of which provide important barriers to dislocation motion under ambient conditions. In alumina, for example, dislocations dissociated by climb into multiple partial dislocations illustrate a strong impediment to glide in ceramic crystals.[43]

Problem Areas

● Computer simulations are most efficiently used when pair potentials are used to describe atom interactions, whereas fundamental interactions are not of a pair nature, other than in the sense of an empirical fit. An improved first-principles method is needed to treat atom interactions more accurately near highly strained dislocation cores. Cluster calculations can be used for this purpose, but at present are limited to a few tens of atoms, insufficient to model bulk dislocations. Thus, an accurate representation of core structure, crucial to many mechanical and physical properties influenced by dislocations, remains to be done.

● Exact elastic field calculations for large numbers of dislocations have been performed only for special arrays such as pileups or grain boundaries. Multiple-dislocation calculations can only be approximated by smearing the dislocations into a continuous array of infinitesimal dislocations. Although

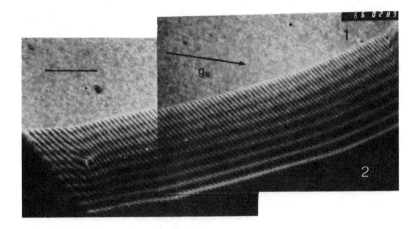

a

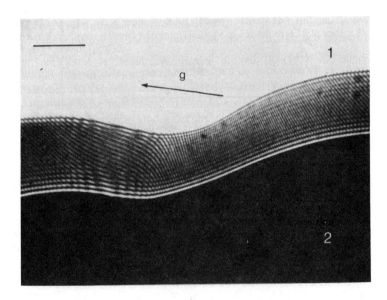

b

FIGURE 2 Dark-field micrograph ($g = [111]_1$) of dislocations in a $\Sigma = 31$ (17.90°/$[111]_{1/2}$) related grain boundary in type 304 stainless steel. $b = 9/31[9,8,14]_1 : 9/31[8,9,14]_2$, and the scale marker is 2,500 nm. From W.A.T. Clark.

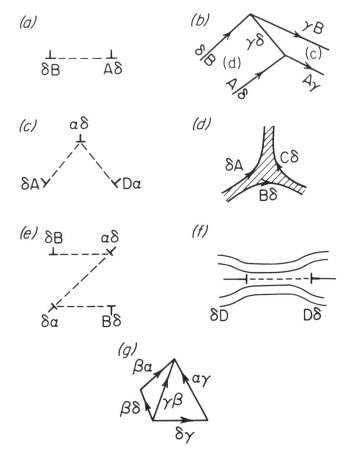

FIGURE 3 Dislocations extended on {111} planes into partial dislocations bounding stacking faults in fcc crystals. (a) single dislocation, (b) bend, (c) Lomer-Cottrell barrier, (d) extended node, (e) Z-dipole, (f) Frank loop, and (g) stacking-fault tetrahedron.

many properties, such as lattice curvature, are provided by such a model, as well as a connection with continuum plasticity theory, many details are lost in averaging. Perhaps the greatest need in extending dislocation theory to describe macroscopic flow behavior is that of developing a statistical procedure to describe the interaction among many dislocation segments and thereby to predict constitutive behavior.

• Nonlinear elastic theory has been applied to dislocations using only perturbation theory and small departures from linearity. Further work is needed to extend the theory to the nonlinear core region.

• Dislocations, and jogs, kinks, and flips that are present on them, interact with both ionic and electronic defects in ionic, covalent, insulating, and semiconducting crystals. The role of dislocations is becoming better understood, but many problems remain, for example, in associating band-gap levels with dislocation defects.

CRACKS

J Integral

Independent of Eshelby,[6] Rice[44] derived a path-independent integral *J*. For a perfectly brittle crack, *J* exactly equals the strain-energy release rate derived by Irwin.[4] Moreover, for small-scale yielding or deformation at the crack, the integral still represents the energy released by the external loading device and the system per unit of crack advance and, hence, represents the resistance of a material to crack propagation. The parameter is now measured extensively, and for ductile materials the critical value J_c replaces the critical stress intensity K_c for brittle crack initiation. For plastic (as opposed to nonlinear elastic) materials, *J* is significant only as a measure of the strength of the crack tip singularity in the continuum field before crack growth.

Attention in recent years has focused on crack configurations and crack-defect interactions at the atomic scale. A lattice-trapping barrier analogous to the Peierls barrier for dislocations exists for perfectly brittle cleavage cracking,[45] and cracks can propagate by stress-assisted thermal activation of double kinks (solitons).[46] The competition between brittle cleavage and crack blunting can be understood in terms of the probability of emission of a dislocation from a sharp crack, a problem solved in a circular dislocation loop approximation by Rice and Thomson.[47]

Screening

The screening of a crack tip by surrounding dislocations—that is, the cancellation of part of the externally applied field at the crack tip—has been extensively treated in two-dimensional calculations.[48] Screened configurations of pileups emitted from cracks have been observed.[49] Crack-defect interaction fields are available in both the isotropic[47,50] and anisotropic elastic[51,52] cases. Motion of other defects near the crack tip can also contribute to the energy release rate and hence to the apparent macroscopic value of *J*.[53] Screening can also be provided by other types of defects, such as those that occur in the transformation toughening of ceramics by dispersed zirconia particles. The particles undergo a phase transformation under the influence of the crack-tip strain field, and the strain fields of the transformed particles in the wake of the crack screen the crack tip.[54,55]

Problem Areas

• The *J* formalism works well for any single mode among the opening mode I, the in-plane shear mode II, and the antiplane shear mode III, but even then, not when extensive crack growth precedes instability. However, except for the perfectly brittle crack, there is no detailed theoretical model for mixed-mode cracking, which is an important element in failure by shear instability. Continuum mechanical, elastic-plastic solutions are difficult to obtain for moving cracks, but such asymptotic and numerical results as are now available[56] provide a promising framework for certain aspects of crack growth. Analogous results have been obtained for viscoplastic (for example, high-temperature creep) constitutive models.

• Nearly all crack defect calculations are performed in two-dimensional approximations. Three-dimensional theoretical calculations are needed for cracks with curved fronts, crack interactions with curved dislocations, and crack interactions with compact second-phase particles of various shapes. Meandering and branched cracks, known to enhance toughness, represent another challenging three-dimensional problem, and work has begun in this area.[57]

• Despite progress in treating the kinematics of rapid crack propagation,[58] there remain ambiguities in understanding the problems of acceleration and inertia.

PROPERTIES OF COMPLEX ALLOYS

Flow

Two key relations are successful in qualitatively describing the relation of properties to microstructure on the basis of dislocation concepts. The first of these is the Hall-Petch relation between strength and grain size:

$$\sigma = \sigma_0 + Kd^{-1/2}, \tag{1}$$

where σ is the flow stress, d is the grain diameter, and σ_0 and K are material constants. The expression dates from the 1950s, but extensive work has been performed recently to verify it.[59,60] The expression follows directly from dislocation pileup theory.[21] The flow stress in lamellar two-phase structures such as pearlite in steel also follows Equation (1), in which case d then represents the thickness of the metal lamellae.

The second relation is the Orowan-Friedel expression for breakaway of a dislocation from pinning particles (see Figure 4).

$$\sigma = \frac{E}{b\lambda} \cos \frac{\phi}{2}, \tag{2}$$

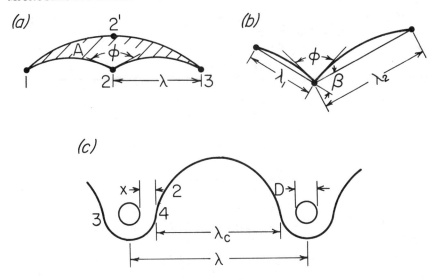

FIGURE 4 Glide plane and bow-out of dislocation from (a), (b) pinning points or (c) around particles. Area swept, A, critical angles ϕ and β, bow-out segment lengths λ, particle diameter D, and standoff distance x are depicted.

where E is the energy per unit length of dislocation, b is the length of the Burgers vector, λ is the obstacle spacing, and cos $\phi/2$ is a factor representing the obstacle strength; the dislocation breaks away from the obstacle at a critical angle ϕ.

The factor E has been calculated in a number of approximations, including the dislocation-segment, anisotropic elastic case.[61] Statistical averaging effects have been sampled by computer simulations of dislocation motion through point obstacles of varying pinning strengths randomly distributed in the glide plane.[62] The results agree with the form of Equation (2). Many experimental results for coherent or semicoherent precipitates or dispersed, equiaxed particles also agree with Equation (2).[62] Solutes that interact strongly with dislocations, such as interstitial carbon in bcc metals, also follow Equation (2), with λ now the solute-solute spacing proportional to $c^{1/2}$, where c is the solute concentration. Concentrated solid solutions interact primarily in the core region and give a strengthening increment linear in c. In other cases the situation is complicated in that simultaneous breakaway from multiple pinning points can occur. One theoretical estimate predicts a strengthening proportional to $c^{2/3}$ for this case.[63] In many solute cases the well-defined solution hardening is independent of temperature (except for the weak temperature dependence of the elastic constants) and gives rise to the so-called plateau stress over a limited temperature range.[63]

For strong dispersoids ϕ approaches zero and dislocations can completely bow out and bypass particles, leaving behind loops of dislocation that encircle the particles. The loops can assume various configurations, readily understandable on the basis of Ashby's concept of geometrically necessary dislocations.[64] These dislocations give rise to rapid work hardening in dispersion-strengthened alloys, of great benefit in inhibiting plastic instability and in giving rise to long-range back stresses.[65]

Ductile Fracture

In recent years ductile tensile fracture has been classified in three types.[66] The first is necking to a point or chisel point, as might occur for a pure fcc metal. The second is deformation or necking terminated by a shear instability leading to a mixed-mode crack following the shear trace, as might occur for a nominally pure bcc metal. The third involves necking or deformation leading to void formation at inclusions or second-phase particles and crack propagation by void linking through either local necking of ligaments or shear localization. The latter process is most pertinent to complex engineering alloys. Figure 5 shows the crack propagation process. Particles crack or decohere under the influence of the crack strain field and thereby nucleate a void. The void grows and limits the plastic flow to a region whose extent is of the order of the void spacing.[67] Thus, the smaller the void spacing, the less the plastic flow, the lower the energy release rate, the lower J_c, and the less the toughness. Smaller void spacings are associated with weak interfacial cohesion, brittle particles, large particles, and small spacing of particles. The particle size enters because the nucleation of a crack or a decohesion becomes less probable as the particle size decreases. A rough estimate for spherical particles indicates that the critical local stress for decohesion is proportional to the inverse square root of the particle size and that decohesion should not occur below a critical size of about 20 nm. For very fine particles, of approximately 1 nm, the particles become ineffective as obstacles. These numbers would change somewhat for other particle shapes, particularly those with sharp salient features. Hence, a "window" of sizes exists for optimum dispersion strengthening and toughening.

Theoretical calculations, with some experimental support, also indicate that voids, once formed, increase the susceptibility of a material to failure by macroscopic shear instability.[68] The susceptibility to shear instability is much greater under plane-strain conditions and when work hardening is low.[69,70] Surface instability in the form of surface rumpling is also a precursor to bulk shear instability and is amenable to experimental study.[70]

The presence of a metastable phase that transforms in the presence of a local stress or strain concentration provides another means of improving toughness. In transformation-induced plasticity, when a material necks or

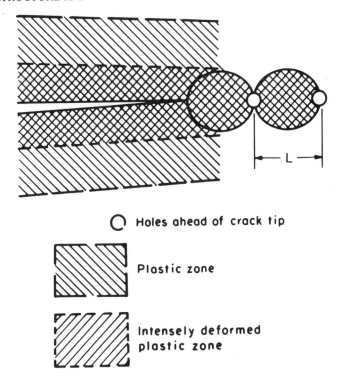

○ Holes ahead of crack tip

Plastic zone

Intensely deformed plastic zone

FIGURE 5 A crack tip and the intensely deformed plastic region of a size approximating the spacing *L* of holes formed at second-phase particles.

undergoes an incipient shear instability, the larger local strain rate and stress can induce martensite transformation, selectively hardening the region and inhibiting continued strain localization.[71] If the degree of metastability is properly adjusted so that these effects take place in the intensified stress region ahead of a crack, the toughness of the material can be improved.[72]

Contained ductile rupture can occur at low toughness values, as indicated by K_c or J_c.[73] A thin continuous ductile layer between two harder regions can fail by a ductile mechanism with very little volume of plastic flow. This phenomenon occurs in precipitate-free zones near grain boundaries in improperly heat-treated, precipitation-hardened alloys.

Brittle Fracture

Brittle crack propagation occurs with little energy release below a ductile-to-brittle transition temperature (DBTT). Yet, experimental estimates of *J* give values for metals[74] and ceramics,[75] respectively, of at least 10 and 3 times the surface energy; thus, a dissipation process other than the creation of surface is still active. Progress has been made in understanding the DBTT for the critical mode I stress intensity K_{Ic}(MPa m$^{1/2}$) that represents the resistance of a material to crack propagation. The intensified strain field of a crack causes a crack nucleation event that could be related to grain size at a critical distance ahead of the crack.[74] The event could correspond to the cracking or decohering of a second-phase particle such that the crack then propagates in an unstable manner into the matrix. The problem then becomes statistical and involves the spacing, position, and crack nucleation probability of particles and the position-dependent stress field of the crack;[75] some fractographic support exists for such a model.[76] Near the DBTT, particle cracking may not be the critical event. Instead the crack may propagate across a single grain and then be arrested. Nonpropagating microcracks spanning grains have been observed in heat-treated steel, with a maximum density at the DBTT.[77] The critical event would then be statistical as before but now involves unstable propagation of a favorably situated and oriented microcrack.

Dislocation pileups at the crystal plasticity level of description of plastic deformation, or shear instabilities at a more macroscopic level, could be important in providing stress concentrations to enhance crack nucleation. Even when a crack tip is stressed at the Griffith level, theoretical calculations show that there is usually enough of a stress concentration at the tip to move several dislocations, a tendency that is more likely the lower the strength of the material.

In ceramic materials where the matrix is normally completely resistant to dislocation motion, toughening can still be achieved by screening of the crack tip in a manner analogous to dislocation screening. In this case, the screening is provided by metastable dispersed particles (e.g., ZrO_2 in Al_2O_3) that undergo a phase transformation in the stress field of the crack tip and produce transformation stresses that screen the tip in the sense of decreasing the local stress that would tend to extend the crack.[78-80] Analogous toughening effects can be achieved if nonpropagating microcracks form in the region of the crack tip.[80,81]

Alloy Design

The concepts of flow and fracture in alloys are sufficiently sound and tested to provide at least qualitative guidelines for alloy design, a situation that did not exist in 1960. An ideal alloy should be strengthened primarily by hard dispersed second-phase particles, because these give large work hardening, resistance to failure by plastic instability, and thus some damage tolerance. The particles should be as fine as possible, but greater than the bypass size of about 1 nm, to minimize crack nucleation or decohesion. The volume fraction should be as large as possible (to minimize λ) without exceeding the percolation limit (approximately 18 volume percent) at which particle-particle contact becomes highly probable. Precipitation hardening, solid solution hardening, grain size minimization, and deformation each may promote secondary hardening. The cohesive strength of the particle interface should be high. Impurities and large inclusions should be avoided.

Many of these guidelines have been demonstrated in rapid solidification technology alloys.[82] In such alloys, segregation is minimized and overaging of particles formed during solidification and cooling is suppressed. Thus, the fine dispersoids desirable for strength can be formed.

Problem Areas

- The constant σ_0 in Equation (1) is not well understood theoretically.
- Pileup–pileup interactions can modify Equation (1).[82] Therefore, three-dimensional calculations are needed.
- Refinements needed in the interpretation of Equation (2) include consideration of screening effects caused by different elastic properties of obstacles; statistical averaging or computer simulation for finite-size obstacles and those with long-range strain fields; and further work on the weak, dilute solute case.
- Experimentally derived values of cohesive energies of particles, which would be valuable in providing a guideline for alloy design, are sparse.
- A detailed estimate of the decohesion probability for a dispersoid is required.
- Three-dimensional models of dislocations would be beneficial in understanding particle decohesion and crack-void interactions.
- More experiments are needed to test the statistical models for the DBTT.

IMPURITY AND ENVIRONMENTAL EFFECTS

Impurities

With the complications of multicomponent systems, adsorption, absorption, and diffusion, the roles of solute and environment cannot be discussed completely. However, several advances in the past 25 years are relevant to this discussion. Although there had been suggestions of such effects earlier, the role of impurities in enhancing embrittlement, specifically intergranular fracture, is now well established.[83] The key was the development of Auger electron microscopy. Such microscopy showed, for example, that elements in Groups V and VI of the periodic table adsorb to prior austenite grain boundaries to cause temper embrittlement of nickel-chromium steels. Coadsorption effects, with solute-solute interactions, are important in establishing the degree of embrittlement.

Hydrogen Embrittlement

Resolving an issue that had led to years of controversy, recent work has shown that hydrogen at moderate fugacity softens pure iron at room temperature and at low plastic strains.[84,85] The effects of flow and internal friction indicate that the mechanism is one of enhanced double-kink nucleation on screw dislocations.[86] Hydrogen also enhances the planarity of slip, on $\{110\}$ planes, in iron.[84]

In ductile fracture, hydrogen degrades steels by enhancing shear instability under plane-strain conditions, lowering the critical strain by about a factor of 2.[87] In uniaxial, smooth-bar, or notched-bar tension tests, hydrogen enhances void nucleation[88] and growth.[89] Hydrogen also enhances brittle fracture,[90] lowering K_{Ic} by a factor of 2 to 3, for example. The embrittlement tendency is greater with greater hydrogen fugacity or strength of the material. Hydrogen also promotes intergranular fracture, alone or in combination with Group V and VI elements. Work on Fe–3%Si single crystals[91] shows a monotonic decrease of crack opening angle with increased chemical potential of hydrogen, suggesting that hydrogen enhances "bond breaking" at the crack tip. However, the observation of enhanced dislocation motion by hydrogen[85] has led to the alternative postulation that hydrogen enhances flow near the crack tip[92] or near grain boundaries,[85] weakening them for a mixed-mode fracture akin to that mentioned in the foregoing discussion of ductile fracture.

Another category of hydrogen embrittlement involves preferential hydride formation in the highly stressed crack-tip region, cracking of the hydride, blunting of the crack when it reaches the matrix, and repetition. This category, verified by transmission electron microscopy, occurs for many transition metals.[93]

Stress Corrosion Cracking

Most investigators agree that a hydrogen embrittlement mechanism causes the stress corrosion cracking of ferritic steels and ferritic stainless steel in acids.[94] Hydrogen released within the crack in a local cathodic reaction diffuses to the crack tip and produces embrittlement analogous to that discussed above. Austenitic stainless steels crack in neutral and weak acids according to the film-rupture model:[95] slip breaks the passivating film and, with an intermediate repolarization rate, local attack occurs before a new film forms and the process repeats itself. Some investigators suggest that the latter steels also fail by hydrogen embrittlement.[96] Such embrittlement is possible because in the limited volume of the crack, depletion of hydroxyl ions and consequent acidification can occur. Similar controversy holds for other alloy systems, including aluminum and titanium alloys.[97]

Under stress corrosion conditions, the influence on toughness parallels the hydrogen case, with a lowering of K_c and a tendency for intergranular embrittlement. Moreover, the intergranular crack surfaces exhibit features resembling those for hydrogen embrittlement, so the same issue of the possibility of locally enhanced plastic flow is present.[92] Indeed, a similar situation prevails in the case of liquid-metal embrittlement.

Problem Areas

• Further research at the atomic scale is required to resolve the issue of a decohesion model versus a plastic-flow-weakening model for brittle intergranular cracking in hydrogen embrittlement, stress corrosion cracking, and liquid-metal embrittlement.

• Finite-element/finite-difference solutions are needed to predict local chemistries, pH values, and electric potentials within a crack in the presence of an electrolyte.

• All the problems that have been discussed for cracks in pure crystals, in particular those associated with interatomic potentials, apply for the present case as well and are exacerbated.

FUTURE PROSPECTS

Dislocations and Cracks

With an interdisciplinary approach involving crystal plasticity and continuum mechanics theory, observations at the atomic level, and improved abilities to make numerical calculations, the difficult problem of many-body dislocations should be solvable. Together with current results for simpler dislocation arrays, this would provide constitutive relations useful in both alloy design and structural design for metals and for ceramic materials at elevated temperatures.

Advances in the physical description of atomic interactions will improve our knowledge of the configuration and properties of dislocation cores and sharp crack tips. Together with three-dimensional elastic solutions for cracks, this would make possible a more detailed analysis of complex cracking problems, including many-body interactions. Such an advance would also be useful in analyzing fatigue crack propagation and eventually should be applicable in the more complex case of environmental interactions.

Structural Materials

The application of fundamental principles in alloy design has begun and is still an area of great potential. A crucial problem that should be resolvable is the determination of the particle-size "window" for optimum dispersion hardening and toughening. Another factor that should be incorporated in design concepts is that of controlled transformation toughening. Many of the concepts developed for dispersed phases are also applicable to composite fibers, specifically the concept of an optimum size. Some new concepts related to toughening—for example, a slipping but very viscous interface—are specific to fibers.[98] The critical problem of fiber-matrix interface properties can be solved to a large extent using current research techniques.

The discussion of dislocations and cracks is also applicable to crystalline polymers. For glassy polymers or amorphous metals, which may now become available in bulk form,[99] disclinations, dispirations, and other defects are also important. Although these defects have been studied extensively, they are less well characterized than dislocations. Further study should provide improvements for the amorphous structures analogous to those for metals and ceramics.

New Materials

Advances in electronics and the concomitant miniaturization of electronic devices have led to the development of new materials and new materials problems. Elimination of dislocations is critical to the operation of many semiconductor devices. Thus an understanding of the properties of defects will also have impact on solid-state electronics. The role of defects may be critical in determining whether strained superlattices (alternating thin layers, 10 nm or less, of different semiconductors or compound semiconductors) will have the stability to be useful in device applications.

The structural understanding of liquid crystals in terms of dislocations and disclinations should prove important. For the new quasicrystals[100] with five-fold symmetry (see Cahn and Gratias, in this volume), new types of defects may be discovered and may be necessary to describe mechanical and physical properties.

Finally, there are opportunities in what could be termed "micromaterials." In very-large-scale integrated circuitry, for example, there are problems regarding mechanical properties and microstructural control at the micrometer-size scale (along with special problems such as electrotransport). Macroscopic concepts are often inapplicable at this scale and new phenomenology will be developed. A further example is the extraordinary modulus enhancement for fine metallic-layer structures at thicknesses of approximately 2 nm, an effect that is yet to be either explained or exploited.[101]

SUMMARY

Many advances have been made during the period 1960–1985 in our understanding of the relations between microstructure and properties of materials. Theories of simple defect configurations have been developed, and new tools have emerged to view defects at the near-atomic scale. Qualitative guidelines for designing alloys apply to some of the new alloys produced by rapid solidification. Yet, our understanding is incomplete. Elastic fields, structures, and mechanisms in dislocation cores or crack tips represent unsolved problems. Statistical averaging methods are needed to make the connection between crystal plasticity and continuum plasticity.

ACKNOWLEDGMENTS

The support of this work by the National Science Foundation under grant DMR 8311620 is gratefully acknowledged. The author is pleased to acknowledge the helpful comments and discussions of A. S. Argon, M. Cohen, J. W. Hutchinson, W. D. Nix, and J. R. Rice.

NOTES

1. P. B. Hirsch, R. W. Horne, and M. J. Whelan, Philos. Mag. **1**, 677 (1956); W. Bollmann, Phys. Rev. **103**, 1588 (1956).
2. C. S. Smith, editor, *The Sorby Centennial Symposium on the History of Metallurgy* (Gordon and Breach, New York, 1965).
3. W. F. Flanagan, H. Margolin, and A. W. Thompson, editors, Symposium on 50th Anniversary of the Introduction of Dislocations, Metall. Trans. A **16A**, 2085–2231 (1985).
4. G. R. Irwin, J. Appl. Mech. **24**, 361 (1957).
5. A. A. Griffith, Philos. Trans. R. Soc. London, Ser. A **221**, 163 (1920).
6. J. D. Eshelby, Solid State Phys. **3**, 79 (1956).
7. J. D. Eshelby, F. C. Frank, and F. R. N. Nabarro, Philos. Mag. **42**, 351 (1951).
8. Reviewed in J. P. Hirth and J. Weertman, editors, *Work Hardening* (Gordon and Breach, New York, 1968).
9. E. Orowan, in *Symposium on Internal Stresses* (Institute of Metals, London, 1947), p. 451.
10. J. M. Burgers, Proc. Kon. Ned. Akad. Wetenschjap. **42**, 293, 378 (1939).
11. M. O. Peach and J. S. Koehler, Phys. Rev. **80**, 436 (1950).
12. T. Mura, Philos. Mag. **8**, 843 (1963).
13. J. Lothe, Philos. Mag. **15**, 353 (1967).
14. L. M. Brown, Philos. Mag. **15**, 363 (1967).
15. V. L. Indenbom and S. S. Orlov, Sov. Phys. Crystallogr. **12**, 849 (1968).
16. J. Blin, Acta Metall. **3**, 199 (1955).
17. T. Jossang, J. Lothe, and K. Skylstad, Acta Metall. **13**, 271 (1965).
18. J. D. Eshelby and T. Laub, Can. J. Phys. **45**, 887 (1967).
19. J. P. Hirth and J. Lothe, in *Physics of Strength and Plasticity*, edited by A. S. Argon (MIT Press, Cambridge, Mass., 1969), p. 39.
20. J. P. Hirth and J. Lothe, *Theory of Dislocations*, 2nd ed. (Wiley, New York, 1982), p. 146.

21. J. P. Hirth and J. Lothe, *Theory of Dislocations,* 2nd ed. (Wiley, New York, 1982), Chapter 10.
22. J. Lothe, in *Fundamental Aspects of Dislocation Theory,* edited by J. A. Simmons, R. deWitt, and R. Bullough, Spec. Pub. 317 (National Bureau of Standards, Washington, D.C., 1970), Vol. 1, p. 11.
23. Y. Maurissen and L. Capella, Philos. Mag. **30,** 679 (1974).
24. B. Pichaud and F. Minari, Scripta Metall. **14,** 1171 (1980).
25. J. D. Eshelby, W. T. Read, and W. Shockley, Acta Metall. **1,** 251 (1953).
26. A. N. Stroh, J. Math. Phys. **41,** 77 (1962).
27. J. R. Willis, Philos. Mag. **21,** 931 (1970).
28. D. M. Barnett and J. Lothe, Phys. Norvegica **7,** 13 (1973).
29. D. J. Bacon, D. M. Barnett, and R. O. Scattergood, Prog. Mater. Sci. **23,** 51 (1978).
30. M. P. Puls, in *Dislocation Modeling of Physical Systems,* edited by M. F. Ashby, R. Bullough, C. S. Hartley, and J. P. Hirth (Pergamon, Oxford, 1981), p. 249.
31. R. G. Hoagland, J. P. Hirth, and P. C. Gehlen, Philos. Mag. **34,** 413 (1976).
32. V. Vitek, R. C. Perrin, and D. K. Bowen, Philos. Mag. **21,** 1049 (1970).
33. Z. S. Basinski, M. S. Duesbery, and R. Taylor, Philos. Mag. **21,** 1201 (1970).
34. M. S. Duesbery, Acta Metall. **31,** 1747, 1759 (1983).
35. J. Lothe and J. P. Hirth, Phys. Rev. **115,** 543 (1959).
36. A. Seeger, Z. Metallkd. **72,** 369 (1981).
37. W. Bollmann, *Crystal Defects and Crystalline Interfaces* (Springer-Verlag, Berlin, 1970).
38. R. W. Balluffi, editor, *Grain Boundary Structure and Kinetics* (American Society for Metals, Metals Park, Ohio, 1980).
39. G. Garmong and C. G. Rhodes, Acta Metall. **22,** 1373 (1974).
40. R. W. Balluffi, Metall. Trans. A **13,** 2069 (1982).
41. D. J. H. Cockayne, I. L. F. Ray, and M. J. Whelan, Philos. Mag. **20,** 1265 (1969).
42. Reviewed by R. Sinclair, in *Introduction to Analytical Electron Microscopy,* edited by J. J. Hren, J. I. Goldstein, and D. C. Joy (Plenum, New York, 1979), p. 507.
43. T. E. Mitchell, L. W. Hobbs, A. H. Heuer, J. Castaing, J. Cadoz, and J. Philibert, Acta Metall. **27,** 1677 (1979).
44. J. R. Rice, J. Appl. Mech. **35,** 379 (1968).
45. C. Hsieh and R. Thomson, J. Appl. Phys. **44,** 2051 (1973).
46. J. E. Sinclair, Philos. Mag. **31,** 647 (1975).
47. J. R. Rice and R. Thomson, Philos. Mag. **29,** 73 (1974).
48. R. Thomson, *Solid State Physics,* in press.
49. S. M. Ohr and J. Narayan, Philos. Mag. **41,** 81 (1980).
50. J. P. Hirth and Robert H. Wagoner, Int. J. Solids Struct. **12,** 117 (1956).
51. C. Atkinson, Int. J. Fract. Mech. **2,** 567 (1966).
52. J. E. Sinclair and J. P. Hirth, J. Phys. F. **5,** 236 (1975).
53. J. P. Hirth, R. G. Hoagland, and C. H. Popelar, Acta Metall. **32,** 371 (1984).
54. R. M. McMeeking and A. G. Evans, J. Am. Ceram. Soc. **65,** 242 (1982).
55. B. Budiansky, J. W. Hutchinson, and J. C. Lambropoulos, Int. J. Solids Struct. **19,** 337 (1983).
56. W. J. Drugan, J. R. Rice, and T. L. Sham, J. Mech. Phys. Solids **30,** 447 (1982).
57. J. R. Rice, J. Appl. Mech. **52,** 571 (1985); Int. J. Solids Struct. **21,** 781 (1985).
58. L. B. Freund, in *The Mechanics of Fracture,* edited by F. Erdogan (American Society of Mechanical Engineers, 1976), Pub. No. ASME AMD-19, p. 105.
59. R. W. Armstrong, Adv. Mater. Res. **4,** 101 (1970).
60. A. W. Thompson, Metall. Trans. A **8,** 833 (1977).
61. R. O. Scattergood and D. J. Bacon, Philos. Mag. **31,** 179 (1975).
62. U. F. Kocks, A. S. Argon, and M. F. Ashby, Prog. Mater. Sci. **19,** 1 (1975).

63. P. Haasen, in *Dislocations in Solids,* edited by F. R. N. Nabarro (North-Holland, Amsterdam, 1979), Vol. 4, p. 155.
64. M. F. Ashby, in *Strengthening Methods in Crystals,* edited by A. Kelly and R. B. Nicholson (Elsevier, Amsterdam, 1971), p. 137.
65. K. Tanaka and T. Mori, Acta Metall. **18,** 931 (1970); O. B. Pederson and L. M. Brown, *ibid.* **25,** 1303 (1977).
66. J. F. Knott, in *Fracture 1977,* edited by D. M. R. Taplin (University of Waterloo Press, Waterloo, Canada, 1977), Vol. 1, p. 61.
67. J. R. Rice and M. A. Johnson, in *Inelastic Behavior of Solids,* edited by M. F. Kanninen et al. (McGraw-Hill, New York, 1970), p. 641.
68. V. Tvergaard, A. Needleman, and K. K. Lo, J. Mech. Phys. Solids **29,** 115 (1981).
69. J. W. Rudnicki and J. R. Rice, J. Mech. Phys. Solids **23,** 371 (1975).
70. J. W. Hutchinson and V. Tvergaard, Int. J. Mech. Sci. **22,** 339 (1980).
71. J. P. Bressanelli and A. Moskowitz, Trans. Am. Soc. Met. **59,** 223 (1966).
72. G. B. Olson and M. Cohen, Metall. Trans. A **13,** 1907 (1982).
73. F. A. McClintock, in *Ductility,* edited by H. W. Paxton (American Society for Metals, Metals Park, Ohio, 1968), p. 255.
74. R. O. Ritchie, J. F. Knott, and J. R. Rice, J. Mech. Phys. Solids **21,** 395 (1973).
75. A. G. Evans and A. H. Heuer, J. Am. Ceram. Soc. **63,** 241 (1980).
76. A. R. Rosenfield, D. K. Shetty, and A. J. Skidmore, Metall. Trans. A **14,** 1934 (1983).
77. M. Cohen and M. R. Vukcevich, in *Physics of Strength and Plasticity,* edited by A. S. Argon (MIT Press, Cambridge, Mass., 1969), p. 245.
78. D. L. Porter and A. H. Heuer, J. Am. Ceram. Soc. **62,** 298 (1979).
79. R. M. McMeeking and A. G. Evans, J. Am. Ceram. Soc. **65,** 242 (1982).
80. B. Budiansky, J. W. Hutchinson, and J. C. Lambropoulos, Int. J. Solids Struct. **19,** 337 (1983).
81. R. G. Hoagland, C. W. Marschall, A. R. Rosenfield, G. Hollenberg, and R. Ruh, Mater. Sci. Eng. **15,** 51 (1974).
82. R. Mehrabian, editor, *Rapid Solidification Processing, Principles and Technology III* (National Bureau of Standards, Washington, D.C., 1983).
83. Z. Qu and C. J. McMahon, Jr., Metall. Trans. A **14,** 1101 (1983).
84. H. Matsui, H. Kimura, and S. Moriya, Mater. Sci. Eng. **40,** 207 (1979).
85. T. Tabata and H. K. Kirnbaum, Scripta Metall. **17,** 947 (1983); **18,** 231 (1984).
86. J. P. Hirth, Metall. Trans. A **11,** 861 (1980); A. Seeger, Phys. Status Solidi A **55,** 547 (1979).
87. O. A. Onyewuenyi and J. P. Hirth, Metall. Trans. A **14,** 259 (1983).
88. H. Cialone and R. J. Asaro, Metall. Trans. A **10,** 367 (1979).
89. R. I. Garber, I. M. Bernstein, and A. W. Thompson, Metall. Trans. A **12,** 225 (1981).
90. H. H. Johnson, in *Hydrogen Embrittlement and Stress Corrosion Cracking,* edited by R. Gibala and R. F. Hehemann (American Society for Metals, Metals Park, Ohio, 1984), p. 3.
91. H. Vehoff and P. Neumann, Acta Metall. **28,** 265 (1980).
92. C. D. Beachem, Metall. Trans. **3,** 437 (1972); S. P. Lynch in *Fracture 1977,* edited by D. M. R. Taplin (University of Waterloo Press, Waterloo, Canada, 1977), Vol. 2, p. 859.
93. D. G. Westlake, Trans. Am. Soc. Met. **62,** 1,000 (1969); S. Gahr, M. L. Grossbeck, and H. K. Birnbaum, Acta Metall. **25,** 125 (1977).
94. R. M. Latanision, O. H. Gastine, and C. R. Compeau, in *Environment-Sensitive Fracture of Engineering Materials,* edited by Z. A. Foroulos (The Metallurgical Society, Warrendale, Pa., 1979), p. 18.
95. A. J. Bursle and E. N. Pugh, in *Environment-Sensitive Fracture of Engineering Materials,* edited by Z. A. Foroulos (The Metallurgical Society, Warrendale, Pa., 1979), p. 18.

96. A. R. Troiano and R. F. Hehemann, in *Hydrogen Embrittlement and Stress Corrosion Cracking*, edited by R. Gibala and R. F. Hehemann (American Society for Metals, Metals Park, Ohio, 1984), p. 231.

97. V. A. Marichev, Fiz. Khim. Mekh. Mat. **16**, 13 (1980).

98. A. G. Evans, B. Budiansky, and J. W. Hutchinson, *Report of the DARPA Materials Research Council* (University of Michigan, Ann Arbor, Mich., 1984).

99. M. Atzmon, J. D. Verhoeven, E. D. Gibson, W. L. Johnson, Appl. Phys. Lett. **45**, 1052 (1984).

100. D. Shechtman, I. Blech, D. Gratias, and J. W. Cahn, Phys. Rev. Lett. **53**, 1951 (1984).

101. T. Tsakalakos, *Modulated Structure Materials* (Nijhoff, Amsterdam, 1985).

Condensed-Matter Physics and Materials Research

BERTRAND I. HALPERIN

The discipline of physics is intimately connected with all aspects of materials science, including the synthesis of new materials, the characterization of their properties, and the development of new materials applications. In materials synthesis, for example, it is clear that complicated nonequilibrium growth processes or annealing processes are important in the formation of many new materials and that a physical understanding of these processes, at least at an empirical level, is essential for improving the production of such materials. It is equally clear that long-term progress in materials synthesis is, in turn, dependent on careful characterization of the materials that are being produced and that developments in experimental physics have greatly enlarged the scope and the accuracy of materials characterization.

Over the past quarter century, new and better materials have played, and will continue to play, an enormous role in expanding the horizons of physics itself. This emphasis reflects in part my need, as a physicist, to thus acknowledge my personal debt to the creators of new materials. However, I also believe that the needs of condensed-matter physicists for improved materials, the interest that physicists have shown in the work of materials developers, and the excitement that has accompanied the periodic discoveries of new physical phenomena in condensed-matter systems, have often been vital motivating forces in the development of new materials.

It is not possible here to discuss systematically even the highlights of recent developments in condensed-matter physics that owe their existence to materials science.[1] Rather, this chapter is limited to a few illustrative examples. It necessarily excludes several of the most exciting developments. For example, there has been enormous progress in our ability to calculate from first principles the electronic energies of solids, including the energies of defects and surfaces.[2] The importance of this work for the future of materials science should be obvious to readers of this volume. Other areas of research are excluded because they are discussed elsewhere in this volume. (See, for example, the discussion of icosahedral quasicrystals by Cahn and Gratias and the discussion of new techniques in surface science by Plummer et al.) The references cited in this chapter, and the experimental curves displayed in the text, are intended to be illustrative of their subjects. These are not necessarily the most important contributions in each case, and no attempt has been made to construct a balanced list of all the key references in the four subjects discussed. It is hoped that the references given will be sufficient to help the interested reader gain entry to the literature in these areas.

This chapter presents four particular examples where materials science and physics have combined to advance our understanding of nature. The fractional quantized Hall effect and the field of heavy-electron systems are two cases where experiments on newly developed materials or structures have yielded results so surprising as to change our understanding of the behavior of interacting electron systems in certain conditions. The two remaining examples, research on novel forms of structural order and on quantum interference effects in electron transport in ultrasmall structures and disordered systems, illustrate the larger symbiotic relationship that exists between physics and materials science. Here we shall find examples where theoretical predictions of unusual properties have led to the experimental investigation of novel materials and structures, and where experimentation has confounded previous expectations.

HEAVY-ELECTRON COMPOUNDS

One of the most fascinating subjects in condensed-matter physics is heavy-electron compounds.[3-9] The conduction electrons in these metallic compounds have effective masses of 100 to 1,000 times the free-electron mass as opposed to values of about 10 for transition metals. It has been said that the carriers in heavy-electron compounds behave more like protons or helium atoms than electrons! The huge effective mass is manifest directly in the large electronic specific heats, at low temperatures, and in the similarly large Pauli paramagnetic susceptibilities. The Fermi degeneracy temperature, which marks the onset of the low-temperature regime for the specific heat and various properties, is on the order of 100 K in many of these compounds as opposed to 10,000 K and higher in ordinary metals. These heavy-electron compounds show many other amazing properties as well.

The table on page 133 lists selected heavy-electron compounds, together with their low-temperature specific-heat coefficients, $\gamma \equiv C^{el}/T$. (The corresponding coefficient for free electrons would be about 1 mJ/mol-K^2.) To illustrate the variety of properties of the heavy-electron compounds, we note

Low-Temperature Specific-Heat Coefficients of Selected Heavy-Electron Compounds

Compound	Low-Temperature Specific-Heat Coefficient (mJ/mol-K^2)
$CeCu_2Si_2$	1,100
UBe_{13}	1,100
UPt_3	450
U_2Zn_{17}	530
UCd_{11}	840
$NpBe_{13}$	$\gtrsim 900$
$CeAl_3$	1,600
$CeCu_6$	1,600
$CePb_3$	$200 \leqslant \gamma \leqslant 1,400$

that the first three compounds are superconducting at low temperatures, the next three are magnetically ordered, the next two are neither superconducting nor magnetically ordered, whereas the last compound, $CePb_3$, is antiferromagnetic but becomes superconducting in the presence of a sufficiently large magnetic field![3,5,8,10]

The compounds UBe_{13} and UPt_3 differ significantly from ordinary superconductors. They are generally believed to exhibit "triplet superconductivity," or pairing in a state of odd parity, similar to that which occurs in liquid ^3He.[5,6,8,9] On the other hand, the superconductivity in $CeCu_2Si_2$ is thought to be of the conventional singlet (even-parity) type, as is found in all other known superconducting metals.[11]

The heavy-electron materials all contain elements such as cerium or uranium in which the outermost f-electron shell is partially filled. The properties of these compounds differ, however, from what was expected on the basis of our previous understanding of f-electron materials. The usual, naive picture is that the f-electrons are localized on individual atoms, so that they have infinite effective mass and only their spin degrees of freedom need be taken into account, and that there should exist, in addition, a band of itinerant electrons, constructed from atomic s and d orbitals, with an effective mass of order 10, as in ordinary transition metals. The primary effect of the weak interaction between the two types of electrons, in this picture, is to give a weak effective interaction between the spins, so that there will be magnetic ordering at low temperatures, generally in some kind of antiferromagnetic state. The spin degrees of freedom will give a large contribution to the specific heat, for temperatures in the vicinity of the magnetic-ordering temperature, but the spin contribution freezes out rapidly below this temperature, leaving only the much smaller contribution of the itinerant s and d electrons. Electrical conductivity by the s and d electrons would persist below the magnetic-ordering temperature and might be expected to increase as ordering reduces the scattering by the spins.

This description works well, in fact, for most known rare-earth metals and their conducting compounds. It does not apply, however, in the case of the heavy-electron compounds. Somehow, in these materials, the itinerant electrons acquire some of the characteristics of the massive *f*-electrons, and the localized spins do not exist as separate degrees of freedom, at sufficiently low temperatures.

The specific-heat curve for UBe_{13} shown in Figure 1 is evidence that there exists only one type of electron in heavy-electron compounds. The solid curve is the specific-heat anomaly of an ordinary Bardeen-Cooper-Schrieffer superconductor, rescaled by a factor of 1,000 to match the value of the linear specific-heat coefficient just above the transition temperature T_c. If the electrons responsible for superconductivity were relatively light *s* and *d* electrons, while the background specific heat was given by independent spin degrees of freedom, the discontinuity at T_c would be much smaller than the value observed.

Further indication of the subtlety of the heavy-electron materials is given by comparing the electrical resistances of the two superconductors UBe_{13} and UPt_3 in the normal state (see Figure 2). Whereas the resistance of UPt_3 decreases monotonically from room temperature down to the transition tem-

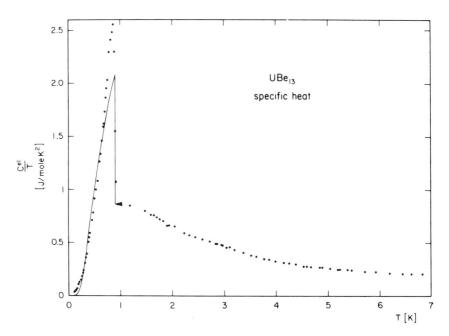

FIGURE 1 Electronic specific heat, divided by temperature, of the heavy-electron superconductor UBe_{13}. From Ott et al.[7] Reprinted with permission.

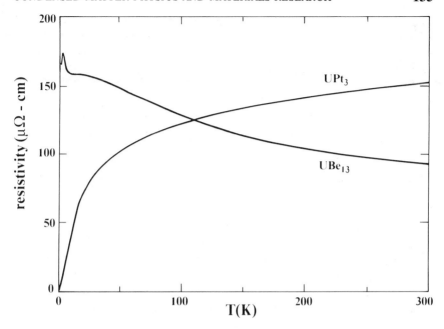

FIGURE 2   Temperature dependence of the electrical resistivities of UBe_{13} and UPt_3 between their superconducting transitions and 300 K. From Fisk et al.[5] Reprinted with permission.

perature, about 1 K, the resistance of UBe_{13} is observed to increase slowly down to a temperature of about 10 K, then rise more sharply to a maximum around 2.5 K before it decreases because of fluctuations associated with the superconducting transition at lower temperatures. The rising resistance in UBe_{13} is reminiscent of the Kondo effect produced by impurity spins in many dilute alloys, and it has led to the description of the uranium compound as a "Kondo lattice." Indeed, it seems likely that something related to the Kondo effect is occurring in all of the heavy-electron compounds.[8] However, a satisfactory theoretical understanding of these materials has not yet been achieved.

In all cases the heavy-electron materials are difficult to work with, and it is difficult to produce samples that are chemically pure and free of defects. Therefore, experimental measurements of these compounds have been strongly dependent on improvements in the production of these materials.

THE QUANTIZED HALL EFFECT

The discovery of the quantized Hall conductance by von Klitzing, Dorda, and Pepper in 1980 was certainly one of the most surprising developments in condensed-matter physics in recent years.[12] The discovery two years later of the fractional quantized Hall effect by Tsui, Stormer, and Gossard[13] was perhaps equally surprising to workers in the field and has caused, in some ways, an even greater revolution in our theoretical understanding.

The original, integral quantized Hall effect, as well as the fractional quantized Hall effect, occurs in two-dimensional electron systems at low temperatures in strong magnetic fields. The original experiments of von Klitzing and co-workers[12] were performed on high-quality silicon metal-oxide-semiconductor field effect transistors (MOSFETs). The fractional quantization is seen only in systems with unusually high mobility and was first observed in modulation-doped GaAs-GaAlAs heterojunctions, grown by molecular beam epitaxy techniques. The fractional effect has been subsequently reported in several other types of semiconductor heterojunctions and more recently has been observed in high-mobility silicon MOSFETs as well.[14] In any case, the discovery of this effect was made possible only by the remarkable state of the art in materials science in the design and fabrication of semiconductor inversion layers.

The experimental discovery of von Klitzing and co-workers was the existence of a series of plateaus in the Hall resistance R_H, which satisfy the following simple equation to a high degree of accuracy:

$$\frac{1}{R_H} = \frac{ne^2}{h} , \tag{1}$$

where h is Planck's constant, e is the electron charge, and n is an integer that varies from one plateau to another. Recent experiments have confirmed that the ratios of Hall conductances of various steps in silicon and GaAs inversion layers agree with the ratios of simple integers at a level of 1 part in 30 million,[15] and it is believed that Equation (1) is exact, in the limit of zero temperature. For the ranges of magnetic field and carrier concentration where the Hall plateaus are observed, the voltage drop parallel to the current vanishes, in the limit of zero temperature, so that the current flows without any dissipation. We may recall that the Hall resistance is defined as the ratio V_y/I_x, where I_x is the electrical current flowing in the sample, and V_y is the voltage difference in the perpendicular direction, measured between two contacts on opposite edges of the sample. Under the conditions of the quantized Hall effect, the Hall resistance is independent of the precise shape or size of the sample.

For the fractional quantized Hall effect, one sees in addition to the integer steps, plateaus in the Hall resistance where the integer n in Equation (1) is replaced by a simple rational fraction, denoted by ν. Well-established plateaus have been observed at values equal to 1/3, 2/3, 4/3, 5/3, 2/5, and 3/5. There is indirect evidence of Hall plateaus at various other fractions with odd denominators, including 7/3, 8/3, 3/7, 4/7, 4/9, and 5/9. There is no convincing evidence of a plateau at any fraction with an even denominator, although there have been reports of resistance anomalies that could be associated with such plateaus.[14]

The explanation for the integral quantized Hall effect, though subtle, can be formulated in a single electron picture, where the charge carriers move independently in the potential of random impurities, and electron-electron interactions have only the effect of a weak perturbation.[16] The fractional quantized Hall effect, however, is entirely a manifestation of the interaction between the electrons in the layer. The explanation given by Laughlin in 1983, together with subsequent extensions, suggests that the carriers in the fractional quantized Hall effect have essentially entered a new state of highly correlated electron matter.[17-21] The ground state of the electrons is an incompressible liquid, the density of which is locked to the density of magnetic flux in the system. The elementary charged excitations from this state are quasiparticles whose electric charge is a fractional multiple of the electron charge[17] and whose collective states resemble those that would be expected for particles obeying "fractional statistics," intermediate between bosons and fermions.[21,22]

Although the basic details of the integral and fractional quantized Hall effect appear to be understood, there remain many quantitative questions as well as qualitative observations that are poorly understood.[14]

NOVEL FORMS OF STRUCTURAL ORDER

One of the major areas of interest to condensed-matter physicists in recent years has been the study of novel forms of structural order. A few examples are given here.

There has been much experimental and theoretical work in the area of incommensurate crystalline structures. Electronic charge-density wave structures, incommensurate with the atomic lattice but related to the dimensions of the Fermi surface in reciprocal space, have been studied extensively in layered transition-metal chalcogenides and also in quasi one-dimensional materials, including organic conducting salts and $NbSe_3$.[23,24] The latter material has been particularly fascinating because the charge-density wave is apparently unpinned from the crystal lattice on application of a relatively weak electric field, resulting in interesting nonlinear effects in the electrical transport. The theory of the transport process and the associated finite-frequency noise remains controversial.[24]

Incommensurate structures commonly occur when a physisorbed layer solidifies on a crystalline substrate, and similar incommensurate structures are found in intercalated materials.[25,26] Incommensurate distortions also occur in certain conventional insulating materials. The most dramatic and surprising incommensurate structure, however, is surely the newly discovered icosahedral quasicrystal, observed in rapidly quenched aluminum-manganese alloys and in several other systems[27] (see Cahn and Gratias, in this volume). The subject of partially ordered systems is a particularly fascinating area of the study of structural order. It embraces the various liquid-crystal phases, superionic conductors, and so-called plastic crystals, all of which are intermediate between a liquid and a conventional solid.[28-30] All these materials have some type of long-range structural order or broken symmetry, in contrast to the disorder of liquids, but the structural order is not enough to specify a unique equilibrium position for each of the constituent atoms.

One partially ordered system that illustrates the richness of this field is the hexatic phase of smectic liquid crystals. The existence of this phase was proposed by Birgeneau and Litster[31] in 1978 on the basis of theoretical work that Nelson and I did on two-dimensional systems.[32] In 1981, Pindak, and co-workers[33] found the hexatic phase experimentally through x-ray studies of a material known as n-hexyl-4'-n-pentyloxybiphenyl-4-carboxylate (650BC). The molecules in the hexatic phase are arranged in layers, but in the plane of the layers there is no long-range translational order of the positions of the molecules. Nevertheless, there is long-range order in the orientation of the bonds between neighboring molecules in the layers so that the material possesses sixfold anisotropy in the plane. In other words the hexatic phase has the anisotropy characteristic of a hexagonal crystal but lacks the translational order in the plane of the layers. These properties are manifest in the x-ray diffraction pattern by the appearance of six diffuse spots in the x-y plane, where an ordinary hexagonal crystal would have infinitely sharp Bragg peaks.

Many interesting forms of order occur in phases that exist at surfaces or in very thin films, including suspended smectic films, adsorbates on crystal surfaces, and reconstructions of clean crystal surfaces.[25,33] There are also forms of "induced order" that may be found at the surface of a bulk liquid or liquid crystal.[34] These subjects interest condensed-matter physicists because of the problems posed by the greater importance of fluctuations in some two-dimensional systems than in the analogous three-dimensional systems. And, improvements in experimental techniques and in materials preparation have made many of these systems accessible for the first time. For example, the development of glancing-incidence x-ray diffraction, together with synchrotron x-ray sources, has given us a sensitive and powerful method to study order just inside the surface of a bulk material.[34]

Many types of nonequilibrium structures can also be properly characterized as novel forms of structural order, in particular, various macroscopic structures, such as dendrites and other complex forms of crystal growth, loose aggregate structures, and structures formed by spinodal decomposition.[35-37] On the atomic level, the structure of glasses continues to be of great interest to condensed-matter physicists.[38]

However, the various novel forms of structural order pose problems in finding the correct description of different types of order and in understanding the phase transitions between them. Microscopic causes of the different types of order need to be understood to anticipate when particular types of order will occur. And, there are interesting problems concerning the classification of defects in various structures and the description of hydrodynamic modes and of other forms of time-dependent behavior.

ELECTRICAL CONDUCTION IN ULTRASMALL STRUCTURES AND QUANTUM INTERFERENCE EFFECTS IN DISORDERED ELECTRON SYSTEMS

The interest of ultrasmall structures for materials science and for condensed-matter physics is obvious. At a certain point, a small particle, a narrow wire, or a thin film can no longer be considered just a "small piece" of the constituent material but begins to acquire new properties because of the small size. Similarly, the properties of a composite material containing fine particles, wires, or layers may differ from those of the constituent substances. In the area of electrical conduction, there are particularly interesting finite-size effects, arising from the quantum-mechanical wave nature of the electrons in the material. These finite-size effects are also closely related to subtle quantum interference effects that occur even in bulk disordered electron systems and are related, in turn, to problems of metal-insulator transitions in disordered systems. The problems become even more subtle when there is a superconducting transition in the system under study. A few examples give some indication of the range of these effects.

Figure 3 shows the electrical resistance per unit length of a small MOSFET channel plotted as a function of the gate voltage, which is a measure of the carrier concentration in the sample.[39] The channel is 200 nm long by 50 nm wide, which is several times the wavelength of the conduction electrons in the inversion layer. There are several runs at each of the indicated temperatures, and although there is a certain amount of variation from run to run, it is clear that the dominant feature of the curves is the existence of an apparently random structure, which is intrinsic to the sample in question and reproducible from run to run. If different samples are examined, however, different structures are observed. This structure may be described as arising from a series of resonances, or more accurately, from the interference of different electron waves, that undergo multiple scattering and multiple reflections along different paths in the sample.[40,41]

Figure 4 shows the magnetoresistance of an evaporated aluminum film 20 nm thick. The curve labeled "1-D" was obtained from a narrow sample 0.5 μm wide and 500 μm long, and the curve labeled "2-D" was obtained from a sample that was macroscopic in width as well as length, deposited at the

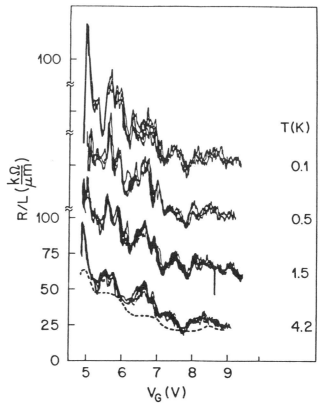

FIGURE 3   Electrical resistance per unit length of a small MOSFET channel (200 nm long, 50 nm wide). Gate voltage V_G controls carrier density sample. From Skocpol et al.[39] Reprinted with permission.

same time as the 1-D sample.[42,43] Both samples are too large, relative to the wavelength of the electrons in the metal, to show a large, random dependence on the magnetic field strength, analogous to the structure in the MOSFET sample in Figure 3. The samples show a systematic dependence on the magnetic field strength, however, which can again be explained as a subtle interference effect between electron waves traveling along the various multiple-scattering paths in the sample. (This interference effect is frequently referred to as weak localization.[44]) The theoretical interpretation of these data, which is indicated by the solid-line fit to the data points, requires separate consideration of the rates of elastic scattering, inelastic scattering, and spin-orbit scattering, all of which play essential but differing roles in the phenomenon. The contribution of incipient superconducting fluctuations

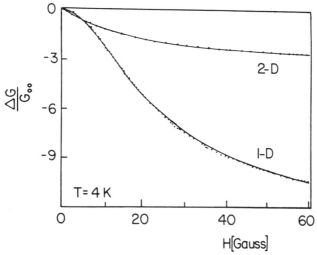

FIGURE 4　Magnetoresistance of an evaporated aluminum film 20 nm thick, measured at temperature $T = 4$ K. From Gordon.[43]

is negligible in these data but must be taken into account to understand the magnetoresistance at lower temperatures.[42,43]

Figure 5 shows the magnetoresistance of a drawn platinum wire 150 nm in diameter and 2.5 mm long at three temperatures in the range from 1.5 K to 4 K.[45] These data again can be explained by the weak localization type of quantum interference effect. Despite the fact that the wire here is narrower than the 1-D sample in Figure 4, the interpretation in this case involves a three-dimensional (bulk) theory, which is a reflection of the difference in materials parameters between the platinum and aluminum samples.

It is interesting to note that platinum wires as thin as 8 nm have been made by the same technique as the sample in Figure 5.[46] In this procedure, the wire is drawn while it is encased in a silver supporting matrix, which is subsequently etched away. As yet, however, there have been no successful attempts to attach leads to these ultrathin specimens, so the electrical properties have not yet been measured.

A quantum interference effect related to the weak localization effects discussed above was first observed in 1981 by Sharvin and Sharvin[47] using a thin magnesium film deposited on a fine quartz fiber as shown in Figure 6. The electrical resistance of this sample was found to depend periodically on the magnetic flux through the hole in the magnesium cylinder in a fashion that is reminiscent of the classic Aharanov-Bohm effect. In this case, however, the observed period is equal to $h/2e$, which is half the normal flux quantum.[48] More recently, measurements on small one-dimensional rings

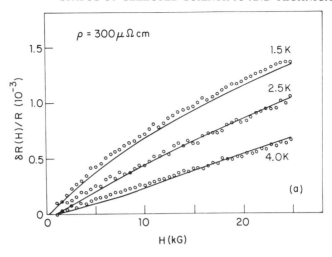

FIGURE 5   Relative change in resistance of a drawn platinum wire, 150 nm in diameter, in parts per thousand, due to magnetic field H at the three indicated temperatures. From Sacharoff, Westervelt, and Bevk.[45] Reprinted with permission.

have shown a dependence on the flux through the hole in the ring with a period h/e, in addition to the period $h/2e$, as is illustrated in Figure 7.[49,50]

Figure 8 shows the current versus voltage characteristic of a superconducting amorphous tungsten-rhenium line 25 nm wide, 10 nm thick, and 1,000 nm long, which was fabricated using electron-beam lithography and the "contamination resist" technique.[51,52] The three steps in the voltage are believed to arise from the entry of individual phase-slip centers into the

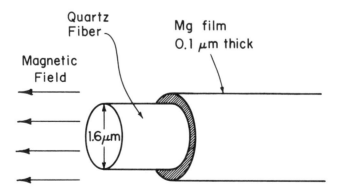

FIGURE 6   Experimental configuration used by Sharvin and Sharvin[47] to study quantum interference effects due to magnetic flux through hole in a wire.

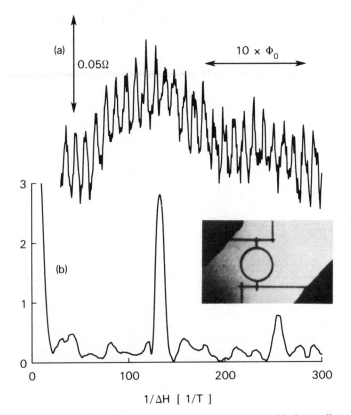

FIGURE 7 (a) Magnetoresistance of a one-dimensional ring, with inner diameter 784 nm, made from a wire strip 41 nm wide, measured at temperature $T = 0.01$ K. (b) Fourier power spectrum of (a). Peaks are at inverse periods e/h and $2e/h$ for the flux through the ring. Insert shows electron-micrograph of ring. From Webb et al.[49] Reprinted with permission.

destruction of superflow in the sample. Thus, one sees here direct evidence for still another kind of small-sample effect.

Small-sample effects can appear in superconductivity experiments in cases where the relevant dimensions are almost macroscopic. Figure 9 shows the resistance transition of a two-dimensional array of superconducting-normal-superconducting (SNS) junctions, constructed with islands of lead on a normal copper film.[53,54] The separation between the edges of adjacent islands is approximately 6 μm, and the distance between centers is 25 μm. Although the islands become superconducting below a temperature T_{cs} of approximately 7 K, the array as a whole can carry a supercurrent only below a temperature T_c of approximately 2.4 K. Throughout the intermediate temperature region

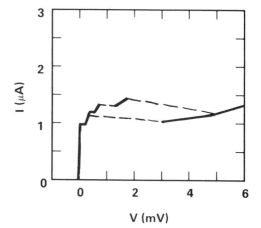

FIGURE 8   Current versus voltage for a superconducting amorphous tungsten-rhenium line 25 nm wide, 10 nm thick, and 1,000 nm long. From Chaudhari et al.[51] Reprinted with permission.

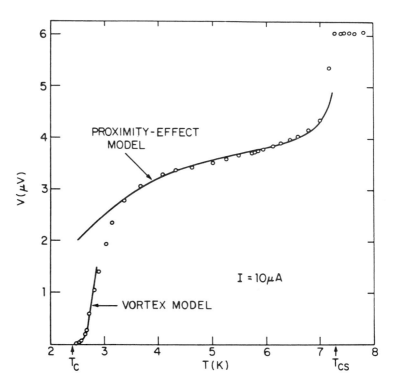

FIGURE 9   Resistance transition of a two-dimensional array of superconducting Pb islands on a normal-metal Cu film. Data points show voltage drop, for a fixed current of 10 μA, in the temperature range from the transition temperature T_{cs} of the islands, down to the transition temperature T_c for the cooperative superconductivity of the array. From Abraham.[54]

$\vdash$————$\dashv$
25μm

FIGURE 10   Portion of an array of superconducting junctions similar to that used for data in Figure 9. From Abraham.[54]

shown in Figure 9, the Josephson coupling energy between the neighboring islands of lead is comparable to, or smaller than, the thermal energy unit kT. The solid curve labeled "proximity-effect model" is the fit to a theory in which there is no phase coherence of the superconducting order-parameter between adjacent islands, because the Josephson coupling is very small compared to kT in this region. The curve labeled "vortex model" is a fit to a theory of the phase transition of a superconducting array, based on the theory of Kosterlitz and Thouless, for a two-dimensional superfluid or X-Y spin model.[55] In this temperature range, near T_c, the Josephson coupling is comparable to kT, and there is a considerable amount of correlation between the phases of neighboring islands. However, the long-range coherence is still destroyed by the presence of a number of thermally excited vortex defects.

It should be noted that when superconducting particles become sufficiently small, much smaller than the islands in the sample in Figure 9, quantum mechanical fluctuations may be large enough to destroy the superconductivity of a coupled array even at zero temperature. This situation has been much discussed theoretically, and effects of such quantum fluctuations have been observed recently in experiments.[56]

A micrograph of a portion of a square array of SNS junctions, similar to the sample used in Figure 9, is shown in Figure 10. Figures 11 and 12 show, respectively, electron micrographs of the MOSFET device used to obtain the curves shown in Figure 3 and of a drawn platinum wire 8 nm in diameter.

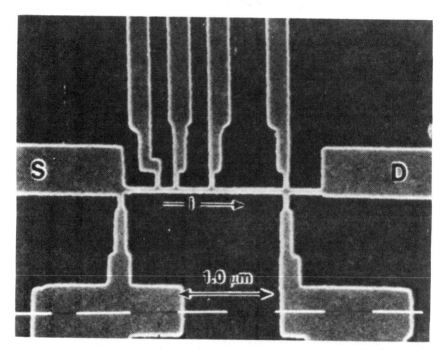

FIGURE 11   Narrow MOSFET channel of type used to obtain data in Figure 3. S and D denote source and drain contacts; other contacts are voltage probes, which divide channel into samples of various lengths. From Skocpol et al.[39] Reprinted with permission.

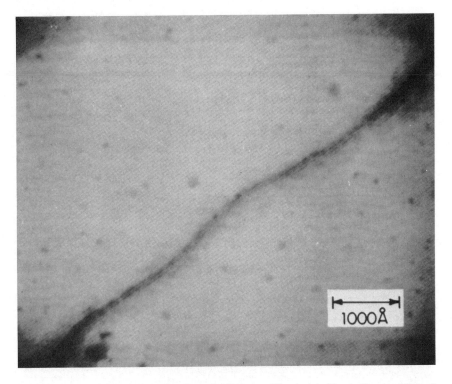

FIGURE 12   Drawn platinum wire, 8 nm in diameter. The data in Figure 5 were obtained from a sample made by the same technique but 20 times larger in diameter. From Sacharoff, Westervelt, and Bevk.[46] Reprinted with permission.

ACKNOWLEDGMENTS

In the preparation of this chapter, I have received extensive help from R. Westervelt, Z. Tesanovic, and C. Lobb. I have also benefited greatly from suggestions by H. Ehrenreich, W. Skocpol, R. Laibowitz, T. Geballe, J. D. Weeks, M. Kardar, D. R. Nelson, and P. C. Hohenberg. This work was supported in part by the Harvard Materials Research Laboratory and by National Science Foundation grant DMR 85-14638.

NOTES

1. For an overall view of current problems in condensed-matter physics, see *Physics Through the 1990s: Condensed-Matter Physics* (National Academy Press, Washington, D.C., 1986).
2. See, for example, M. Schluter and L. J. Sham, Phys. Today **35**, 36 (1982); M. L. Cohen, Phys. Scripta **T1**, 5 (1982); J. Callaway and N. H. March, in *Solid State Physics,* edited

by H. Ehrenreich and D. Turnbull (Academic Press, New York, 1984), Vol. 38, p. 135; K. C. Hass and H. Ehrenreich, Ann. Phys. (NY) **164**, 77 (1985).

3. G. R. Stewart, Rev. Mod. Phys. **56**, 755 (1984).
4. F. Steglich, J. Aarts, C. Bredl, W. Lieke, D. Meshede, W. Franz, and H. Schafer, Phys. Rev. Lett. **43**, 1892 (1979).
5. Z. Fisk, J. L. Smith, H. R. Ott, and B. Batlogg, J. Magn. Magn. Mat. (in press) (Proceedings of 5th Crystalline Field Conference, Sendai, 1985).
6. C. M. Varma, Comments Solid State Phys. **11**, 221 (1985).
7. H. R. Ott, H. Rudigier, Z. Fisk, and J. L. Smith, Physica B (European Physical Society Meeting, den Haag, 1984).
8. P. A. Lee, T. M. Rice, J. W. Serene, L. J. Sham, and J. W. Wilkins, Comments Solid State Phys. (in press).
9. B. Batlogg, D. Bishop, B. Golding, C. M. Varma, Z. Fisk, J. L. Smith, and H. R. Ott, Phys. Rev. Lett. **55**, 1319 (1985).
10. C. L. Lin, J. Teter, J. E. Crow, T. Mihalisin, J. Brooks, A. I. Abou-Aly, and G. R. Stewart, Phys. Rev. Lett. **54**, 2541 (1985).
11. F. Steglich, U. Rauchschwalbe, U. Gottwick, H. M. Mayer, G. Sparn, N. Grewe, U. Poppe, and J. J. M. Franse, J. Magn. Magn. Mat. (in press) (Proceedings of the Conference on Magnetism and Magnetic Materials, San Diego, 1985).
12. K. von Klitzing, G. Dorda, and M. Pepper, Phys. Rev. Lett. **45**, 494 (1980).
13. D. C. Tsui, H. L. Stormer, and A. C. Gossard, Phys. Rev. Lett. **48**, 1559 (1982).
14. A collection of recent papers on the quantized Hall effect may be found in the Proceedings of the Sixth Conference on Electronic Properties of Two-Dimensional Electron Systems, Kyoto, 1985, to appear in Surface Science.
15. L. Bliek et al., Metrologia **19**, 83 (1983).
16. T. Ando, Y. Matsumoto, and Y. Uemura, J. Phys. Soc. Jpn. **39**, 279 (1975); R. B. Laughlin, Phys. Rev. B **23**, 5632 (1981); D. J. Thouless, J. Phys. C **14**, 3475 (1981).
17. R. B. Laughlin, Phys. Rev. Lett. **50**, 1395 (1983).
18. B. I. Halperin, Helv. Phys. Acta **56**, 75 (1983).
19. F. D. M. Haldane, Phys. Rev. Lett. **51**, 605 (1983).
20. R. B. Laughlin, Surf. Sci. **142**, 163 (1984).
21. B. I. Halperin, Phys. Rev. Lett. **52**, 1583, 2390(E) (1984).
22. D. Arovas, J. R. Schrieffer, and F. Wilczek, Phys. Rev. Lett. **53**, 722 (1985).
23. See, for example, P. Bak, Rep. Prog. Phys. **45**, 587 (1982); L. Pfeiffer, T. Kovacs, and F. J. Di Salvo, Phys. Rev. Lett. **52**, 687 (1984).
24. L. Sneddon, Phys. Rev. B **29**, 719 (1984); A. Zettl and G. Gruner, *ibid.* 755 (1984); J. H. Miller, Jr., J. Richard, R. E. Thorne, W. G. Lyons, J. R. Tucker, and J. Bardeen, *ibid.* 2328 (1984); L. F. Schneemeyer, F. J. Di Salvo, S. E. Spengler, and J. V. Waszczak, *ibid.* **30**, 4297 (1984).
25. S. K. Sinha, editor, *Ordering in Two Dimensions* (North-Holland, New York, 1980).
26. R. Clarke and C. Uher, Adv. Phys. **33**, 469 (1984); R. Clarke, J. N. Gray, H. Nomma, and M. J. Winokur, Phys. Rev. Lett. **47**, 1407 (1984); S. Minamura and N. Wada, Bull. Am. Phys. Soc. **29**, 381 (1984).
27. D. S. Schectman, I. Blech, D. Gratias, and J. W. Cahn, Phys. Rev. Lett. **53**, 1951 (1984).
28. P. G. de Gennes, *The Physics of Liquid Crystals* (Clarendon, Oxford, 1974); S. Chandrasekhar, *Liquid Crystals* (Cambridge University Press, London, 1977).
29. M. B. Salamon, editor, *Physics of Superionic Conductors* (Springer-Verlag, Berlin, 1979).
30. G. Gray and P. Windsor, editors, *Liquid Crystals and Plastic Crystals* (Ellis, Horwood, 1974).
31. R. J. Birgeneau and J. D. Litster, J. Phys. (Paris) Lett. **39**, 399 (1978).

32. B. I. Halperin and D. R. Nelson, Phys. Rev. Lett. **41**, 121 (1978).

33. R. Pindak, D. E. Moncton, S. C. Davey, and J. W. Goodby, Phys. Rev. Lett. **46**, 1135 (1985).

34. P. Pershan and J. Als-Nielsen, Phys. Rev. Lett. **52**, 759 (1984).

35. A. R. Bishop, L. J. Campbell, P. J. Channel, editors, *Proceedings of the Third International Conference of the Center for Nonlinear Studies* (Los Alamos, 1983), published as Physica 12D (1984).

36. F. Family and D. Landau, editors, *Kinetics of Aggregation and Gelation* (North-Holland, Amsterdam, 1984).

37. J. S. Langer, Rev. Mod. Phys. **52**, 1 (1980).

38. D. Adler and J. Bicerano, editors, *Proceedings of the International Conference of the Structures of Non-Crystalline Solids* (Bloomfield Hills, Mich., July 1985), in Non-Cryst. Solids **75**, 1–516, (1985).

39. W. J. Skocpol, L. D. Jackel, R. E. Howard, P. M. Mankiewich, D. M. Tennant, A. E. White, and R. C. Dynes, in Proceedings of Sixth Conference on Electronic Properties of Two-Dimensional Electron Systems, Kyoto, 1985, to appear in Surface Science.

40. P. A. Lee and A. D. Stone, Phys. Rev. Lett. **55**, 1622 (1985); B. L. Al'tshuler, JETP Lett. **41**, 648 (1985).

41. See also M. Ya. Azbel, A. Hartstein, and D. P. DiVincenzo, Phys. Rev. Lett. **52**, 1641 (1984); I. M. Lifshitz and V. Ya. Kirpichenkov, Sov. Phys. JETP **50**, 499 (1979).

42. J. M. Gordon, C. J. Lobb, and M. Tinkham, Phys. Rev. B **28**, 4046 (1983); *ibid*. **29**, 5232 (1984).

43. J. M. Gordon, Ph.D. thesis, Harvard University, 1984.

44. For a recent collection of papers in this area, see *Localization, Interaction and Transport Phenomena*, edited by B. Kramer, G. Bergmann, and Y. Bruynseraede (Springer-Verlag, Berlin, 1985). See also P. A. Lee and T. V. Ramakhrishnan, Rev. Mod. Phys. **57**, 287 (1985).

45. A. C. Sacharoff, R. M. Westervelt, and J. Bevk, Phys. Rev. B **29**, 1647 (1984).

46. A. C. Sacharoff, R. M. Westervelt, and J. Bevk, Rev. Sci. Instrum. **56**, 1344 (1985).

47. D. Yu. Sharvin and Yu. V. Sharvin, Pis'ma Zh. Eksp. Teor. Fiz. **34**, 285 (1981) [JETP Lett. **34**, 272 (1981)].

48. B. L. Al'tshuler, A. G. Aronov, and B. Z. Spivak, Pis'ma Zh. Eksp. Teor. Fiz. **33**, 101 (1981) [JETP Lett. **33**, 94 (1981)].

49. R. A. Webb, S. Washburn, C. P. Umbach, and R. B. Laibowitz, Phys. Rev. Lett. **54**, 2696 (1985).

50. M. Buttiker, Y. Imry, R. Landauer and S. Pinhas, Phys. Rev. B **31**, 6207 (1985).

51. P. Chaudhari, A. N. Broers, C. C. Chi, R. Laibowitz, E. Spiller, and J. Viggiano, Phys. Rev. Lett. **45**, 930 (1980).

52. R. B. Laibowitz and A. N. Broers, in *Treatise on Materials Science and Technology*, edited by K. N. Tu and R. Rosenberg (Academic Press, New York, 1982), Vol. 24, p. 285.

53. D. W. Abraham, C. J. Lobb, M. Tinkham, and T. M. Klapwyjk, Phys. Rev. B **26**, 5268 (1982).

54. D. W. Abraham, Ph.D. thesis, Harvard University, 1983.

55. J. M. Kosterlitz and D. J. Thouless, in *Progress in Low Temperature Physics*, Vol. VII-B, edited by D. R. Brewer (North-Holland, Amsterdam, 1978); B. I. Halperin and D. R. Nelson, J. Low Temp. Phys. **36**, 599 (1979).

56. Y. Imry and M. Strongin, Phys. Rev. B **24**, 6353 (1981); S. Doniach, *ibid*. 5063 (1981); O. Entin-Wohlman, A. Kapitulnik, and Y. Shapira, *ibid*. 6464 (1981); M. Ma and P. A. Lee, *ibid*. **32**, 5658 (1985); H. Fukuyama (preprint); A. Kapitulnik and G. Kottliar, Phys. Rev. Lett. **54**, 473 (1985).

Quasi-Periodic Crystals:
A Revolution in Crystallography

JOHN W. CAHN and DENIS GRATIAS

Science evolves with the search for laws of nature, their testing, and ultimately their confident application. Occasionally an established law is contradicted by experiment and the period of ensuing ferment is one of the most rewarding times to be a scientist. This chapter describes such a time, specifically, the period of research that has resulted from the discovery by Daniel S. Shechtman in 1983 of a metallic solid, the discrete electron diffraction pattern (Figure 1) of which exhibited icosahedral point symmetry.[1,2] This is a symmetry that could not occur in crystals according to the laws of crystallography, yet in many ways this solid behaves like a crystal.

The laws of nature are both a boon and a bane to scientists, who are taught to work within them because they cannot be changed. All of the marvelously rich phenomena of the physical world conform to these laws, and knowledge of the laws is an important guide to invention, by allowing scientists to know which things are possible and which are impossible. Sometimes scientists do not heed the laws and expend great effort in an obviously useless search to do something that would violate, for example, a law of thermodynamics. Nevertheless, some versions of these laws are imprecise, and the exceptions point to their limitations and the need for reformulation. The law that Shechtman's discovery violated was based not on a fundamental, immutable law of nature but on an axiom of crystallography, namely, that all crystals are periodic.

Materials science is a composite science, containing elements of many other disciplines—including mathematics, physics, chemistry, electronics, mechanics, and crystallography. The continuing search for new materials with different properties makes use of many laws from these disciplines. The laws are often applied in complex and unusual combinations requiring

151

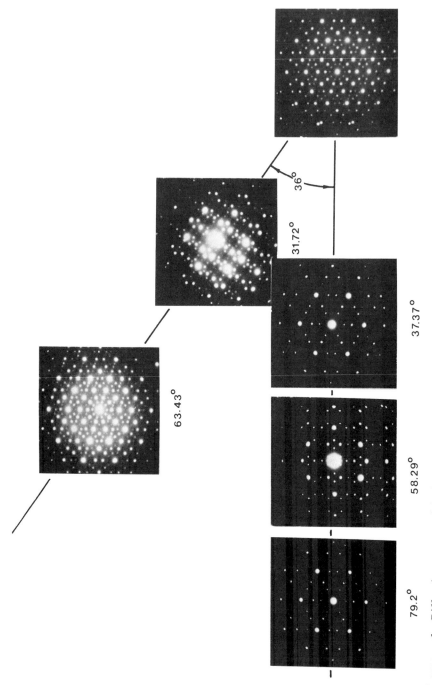

FIGURE 1 Diffraction patterns of the icosahedral Al-Mn crystals aligned along various axes.

new formulations or theorems that are more directly applicable. The search for new materials also provides opportunities for formulating and testing new laws, which then move into the other disciplines. Thus, Shechtman's discovery in materials science is having repercussions in mathematical and chemical crystallography and in solid-state physics. It challenged a law that was mature, well tested, and confining in a way that could have been foreseen but was not.

CLASSICAL CRYSTALLOGRAPHY

As is so often the case in science, crystallography began by focusing on what was then observable—the external form of crystals. These forms obeyed certain rules, and the apparently limitless shapes were in fact found to be combinations of only a few forms: the form of any given crystal was a combination of forms conforming to 1 of 32 point groups. Only 51 different forms were found, and all were shown to be predictable from an axiom that the internal structure of crystals was composed of repeating units arranged with three-dimensional translational periodicity. Translational periodicity permits only 1-, 2-, 3-, 4-, and 6-fold rotational axes, and 32 crystallographic point groups are the only combinations allowed.

Throughout the nineteenth century, before x-ray diffraction in 1912 confirmed[3] the periodicity, this axiom allowed rapid development of crystallography. Many aspects of crystal physics were established. For instance, J. W. Gibbs and G. Wulff calculated the equilibrium shape of a crystal in terms of orientation-dependent surface free energies. Gibbs also formulated thermodynamic barriers to crystal growth resulting from the difficulty of adding a new layer to an existing crystal. The axiom of periodicity worked with few exceptions, and these exceptions could be fitted into the laws by adding such concepts as composite crystals—for example, two or more crystals grown together (called twins or multiple twins) to give rise to objects with additional symmetries. The translational periodicity ceases where the boundary between crystals is crossed.

X-ray diffraction not only confirmed the internal periodicity but also produced methods for identifying the arrangement of atoms within the unit cells. External form lost its preeminence in crystallography, and today crystals are identified almost exclusively by their diffraction patterns, not by their form. The axiom of periodicity not only became a definition of what is a crystal, but it also took on the force of a law of nature.

Soon after x-ray diffraction came into use, deviations from periodicity were discovered.[4] Among the first of these were modulated structures in which modulations of distortion, composition, order, and magnetic or electric polarization were superimposed on an otherwise periodic structure. The wavelength of these modulations was soon suspected to be incommensurate with the lattice periodicity, opening up the possibility that these structures were not periodic. Because the modulations were small distortions and the underlying lattice otherwise conformed to the laws of crystallography, the lack of periodicity could be ignored.

Shechtman's icosahedral solid exhibited a forbidden rotational symmetry. It also exhibited discrete diffraction, indicating some kind of translational regularity.

FERMENT IN RELATED FIELDS

By the time of Shechtman's research, several important developments had occurred in related fields that had immediate bearing on his discovery.

Mathematicians realized early that aperiodic functions could have discrete Fourier spectra. Fourier analysis of periodic functions led to the exploration of a special kind of aperiodic function called almost-periodic functions and quasi-periodic functions.[5,6] Both of these functions have Fourier spectra with individual discrete peaks. In one variable,

$$f(x) = \sum_{n=0}^{\infty} (A_n \cos k_n x + B_n \sin k_n x).$$

If the function is periodic, the k_n are all multiples of a single wave number related to the wavelength λ:

$$k_n = 2\pi n/\lambda.$$

If the k_n are not of this form, then the function is quasi-periodic if there is a finite set of lengths $\lambda_1, \lambda_2, \ldots, \lambda_n$ such that each k_n can be expressed as a sum of integer multiples of $2\pi/\lambda_i$:

$$k_n = \sum_{i=1}^{N} 2\pi p_{in}/\lambda_i.$$

If N is infinite, the function is almost periodic.

The quasi-periodic functions are most interesting. In particular they can be considered a cut of a higher-dimensional periodic function. For instance the quasi-periodic function

$$f(x) = \sin x + \sin \sqrt{2}x$$

is a cut of the two-dimensional periodic function

$$f(x,y) = \sin x + \sin y$$

along the line $y = \sqrt{2}x$.

This property of quasi-periodic functions was exploited by crystallographers to analyze modulated structures.[7-9] The suggestion that a singly mod-

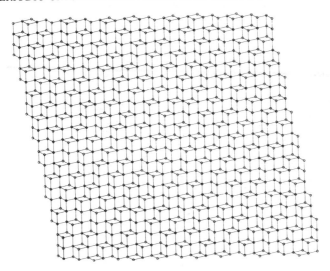

FIGURE 2   A quasi-periodic two-dimensional tiling generated by sectioning a three-dimensional cubic lattice along an irrational plane.

ulated three-dimensional crystal could be described as a three-dimensional cut of a four-dimensional crystal was actively pursued.

Since we live in a three-dimensional world, most people find this hard to visualize. On the other hand, two-dimensional quasi-periodic structures are readily exhibited by an irrational cut of a three-dimensional periodic crystal. Figure 2 is a drawing of an array of cubes intercepted by an irrational plane. The resultant structure is quasi-periodic and has a sharp diffraction pattern. Two-dimensional modulated structures are frequently seen in surface physics. But higher-dimensional periodic functions could have rotational symmetries not possible in three-dimensional periodic functions. In particular, 5-, 8-, 10-, and 12-fold axes can occur in four dimensions, and the combination of six 5-fold, ten 3-fold, and fifteen 2-fold axes that defines icosahedral symmetry can first occur with six-dimensional periodicity. Six dimensions also permit 7-, 9-, 14-, and 18-fold axes. Since no new rotational symmetries occur in going from two to three dimensions, the only analogue in our three-dimensional world is that of going from one dimension (2-fold possible) to two dimensions (3-, 4-, and 6-fold added). Figure 3 shows a set of two-dimensional tilings produced by sectioning higher-dimensional cubic lattices.

Icosahedral molecules and icosahedral packing units were observed in materials 30 years ago.[10] F. C. Frank pointed out that often the lowest energy arrangement of 13 atoms consisted of 12 atoms arranged on the corners of an icosahedron, surrounding a central atom. Of course, such arrangements could not be packed periodically without losing the 5-fold axes. Yet, this

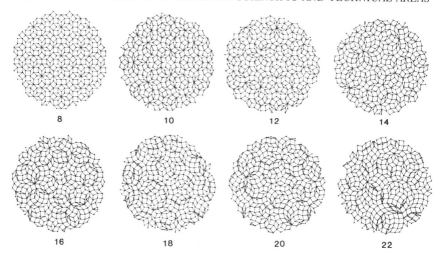

FIGURE 3   Quasi-periodic tilings with 8-, 10-, . . . , 22-fold diffraction rotation axes produced by sectioning, respectively, 4-, 5-, . . . , 11-dimensional cubic lattices.

arrangement began to become an important feature in descriptions of the structures of liquids and glasses. Distorted icosahedra were also frequently seen in crystals with large unit cells. The idea that liquids and glasses might be understood as simpler structures in a higher-dimensional curved space has been widely explored.[11] In a computer simulation of freezing of a liquid, a tendency for icosahedral bond orientational order was noted, but in such small model systems periodic boundary conditions were imposed, making strict icosahedral symmetry impossible.[12]

Along with crystallographers, mathematicians studying infinite tilings had made the assumption of periodicity. Aperiodic tilings suddenly appeared, the most famous of which were discovered by Richard A. F. Penrose and had 10-fold symmetry.[13] It was not immediately appreciated that these were quasi-periodic and could be generated by cuts of five-dimensional cubic structures.

More than five years before, an architect[14] found that geodesic domes having exact icosahedral symmetry could be infinitely extended. He noted that this phenomenon was an example of three-dimensional aperiodic tiling and attributed it to earlier work of J. Kepler and E. S. Federov. More than a decade later, Mackay[15] rediscovered this structure and recognized its implications for an aperiodic tiling of three-dimensional space. He coined the word *quasilattice* and demonstrated empirically that it might have a discrete diffraction pattern.

It has been possible to prove by theoretical counterexamples that the lowest energy packing of atoms and molecules, the ground state, is not always periodic.[16] For certain theoretical interaction models, the ground state has been shown to be quasi-periodic. In some of these models there are no equilibrium periodic states at any temperature. Many two-dimensional surface phase diagrams show widespread existence of quasi-periodic phases extending to low temperatures. There is no thermodynamic basis for requiring periodicity.

In 1977 an attempt to use Landau theory to predict crystallization of a liquid yielded the rather surprising conclusion that an icosahedral arrangement of density waves was a likely possibility, but since this was obviously inconsistent with translational periodicity, the result was an enigma.[17]

RAPID SOLIDIFICATION AND METASTABLE PHASES

Metastable phases abound in the natural world. Natural diamonds form as equilibrium crystals at high pressure, and they survive metastably at ambient pressure because the rate of conversion to the equilibrium state, graphite, is unmeasurably slow. More generally, metastable phases form and survive without ever being stable because the stabler phases form slowly. Materials scientists create nonequilibrium materials through processing cycles designed to capitalize on such kinetic differences, thereby vastly increasing the range of available materials. The heat-treatment cycles of steel discovered 3,000 years ago create carbide particles instead of the equilibrium graphite and thereby give steel its unusual properties. One of the more widely used processing techniques that create metastable materials is rapid solidification, developed by Pol Duwez in the late 1950s.[18] Crystals vary by many orders of magnitude in their crystallization rates. Such diverse elements as nickel and phosphorus can crystallize from their melts at rates of 10 m/s. Quartz crystallization from its melt can be 10 orders of magnitude less. A rate-limiting factor in the crystallization of liquid mixtures is diffusion. If no crystal can form with the same composition as the melt, crystal growth rate is limited to about 10 cm/s. Rapid solidification thus favors phases with wide solid solution ranges over intermetallic compounds with narrow composition ranges. When during rapid solidification a liquid is cooled below its melting point, it becomes metastable and can crystallize to metastable solids that are more stable than the liquid. The degree of metastability is small, approximately 0.01 eV/atom, but there are an amazingly large number of different metallic phases with almost the same energy that become accessible. The simplest are the solid, supersaturated solutions, which play an important role in twentieth-century metallurgy.

Solid solubilities change with temperature, and the excess solutes can be made to precipitate from the solid state to give desirable precipitation-hardened alloys. Precipitation hardening, discovered this century,[19,20] has been responsible for most modern structural alloys, and rapid solidification promised to increase the solute content available for precipitation.

This was indeed the purpose of the study that Shechtman joined at the National Bureau of Standards. He was spending his sabbatical there on a cooperative program with the Johns Hopkins University, funded by the Air Force. He began looking at rapidly solidified aluminum alloys with transition elements. His tool was the transmission electron microscope. He encountered the expected increase in the solubility of manganese in face-centered aluminum and was pushing to higher manganese content when he encountered a new phase unlike any that had ever been seen. He called it the Z-phase.

CRYSTALLOGRAPHY ON THE ELECTRON MICROSCOPE

The modern electron microscope is an extraordinarily versatile tool. It not only gives a magnified image with a 2-angstrom resolution but also permits a host of physical measurements to be made with monoenergetic focused and collimated electrons. Chemical analysis can be made by x-ray emission spectroscopy from volumes as small as 10^{-20} m^3. A wide variety of microelectron diffraction techniques can be made on columnar volumes as small as a few nanometers in diameter and as long as the specimen is thick—10 to 100 nm.

The sample Shechtman examined contained crystals that were microns in diameter. A flip of a switch revealed that the diffraction pattern of these crystals contained an apparent 10-fold symmetry. Rotating the specimen revealed quickly instead that the symmetry was one of six 5-fold inversions axes (Figure 1). The overall symmetry was icosahedral, forbidden for translational periodicity. The diffraction patterns revealed sharp, discrete spots, which we now know result from quasiperiodicity.

The initial reaction to this finding was that it must be multiple twinning of ordinary periodic crystals, but several transmission electron microscopy techniques rule this out unambiguously. Among them is dark-field microscopy, in which an image is formed from the electrons that have been diffracted into a single spot. Only that portion of the specimen that contributes to the diffraction lights up. The individual crystals of any multiple twin are easily revealed by this technique. Microtwinning is ruled out by convergent-beam micro-microdiffraction, which shows that all spots come from the smallest regions in the crystal.[1] The convergent-beam technique not only has confirmed the 5-fold symmetry but also has been used to determine which of the two point groups m$\overline{3}$5 and 235 belonging to the m$\overline{3}$5 Laue groups is the correct one for these alloys.[21] High-resolution transmission electron microscopy[22-27] and field-ion microscopy[28] further confirm the symmetry and that these are not periodic crystals, multiply twinned.

Without these tools, these crystals would not have been discovered until large, single crystals were made. Powder patterns do not reveal the rotational symmetry and can always be fitted to a model if a large enough unit cell is assumed.

Simultaneous with the paper[2] announcing this finding there appeared a theoretical paper showing that icosahedral quasicrystals could be understood in terms of cuts of 12-dimensional crystals.[29] Because of our residual doubts, the announcement paper received wide circulation before it was submitted for publication and this stimulated an immediate paper by Levine and Steinhardt,[30] followed shortly by three other papers[31-33] that all showed icosahedral symmetry to be consistent with quasiperiodicity and gave diffraction intensities from a quasilattice that were qualitatively in good agreement with the electron diffraction patterns. In the year since publication we have received more than 100 preprints on many aspects of these new materials. Two other point groups, 10/m (decagonal)[34] and 12 (dodecagonal)[35] have been reported. Icosahedral diffraction patterns have been reported from many different alloys, and the possibility that a stable icosahedral phase (Al_5Li_3Cu) exists and that large, single crystals can then be grown seems to have been confirmed.[36,37] Our research about the structure and properties of these crystals was hampered by the imperfections of rapidly grown crystals, but it can now proceed.

NOTES

1. D. Shechtman and I. Blech, Metall. Trans. **16A**, 1005 (1985).
2. D. Shechtman, I. Blech, D. Gratias, and J. W. Cahn, Phys. Rev. Lett. **53**, 1951 (1984).
3. W. Friedrich, P. Knipping, and M. Laue, Ann. Phys. **41**, 971 (1913).
4. C. H. Johansson and J. O. Linde, Ann. Phys. **25**, 1 (1936).
5. H. A. Bohr, *Almost Periodic Functions* (Chelsea, New York, 1947).
6. A. S. Besicovitch, *Almost Periodic Functions* (Cambridge University Press, New York, N.Y., 1932).
7. P. M. deWolf, in *Modulated Structures*, NATO ASI Series E 83, edited by Tsakalakos (Martinus Nijhoff, The Hague, 1984).
8. A. Janner and T. Janssen, Acta Crystallogr. Sect. A **36**, 399 (1980).
9. N. G. de Bruijn, Ned. Akad. Wetensch. A **84**, 39 (1981).
10. F. C. Frank, Proc. R. Soc. London **215**, 43 (1952).
11. D. Nelson and B. I. Halperin, Science **229**, 233 (1985).
12. P. J. Steinhardt, D. R. Nelson, and M. Ronchetti, Phys. Rev. B **28**, 784 (1983).
13. M. Gardner, Sci. Am. **236**, 110 (1977).
14. S. Baer, Zome Primer (Zomework Corp., Albuquerque, 1970).
15. A. L. Mackay, Physica A **114**, 609 (1982).
16. C. Radin, University of Texas (preprint).
17. S. Alexander and J. McTague, Phys. Rev. Lett. **41**, 702 (1978).
18. P. Duwez, R. H. Willens, and W. Klement, J. Appl. Phys. **31**, 1126 (1960).
19. A. Wilm, Metallurgie **8**, 225 (1911).
20. P. D. Merica, R. G. Waltenberg, and H. Scott, Scientific papers of the U.S. Bureau of Standards, No. 347 (Washington, D.C., 1919), Vol. 15, p. 271.
21. L. Bendersky and M. J. Kaufman, Philos. Mag. B **53**(3), L75 (1986).

22. D. Shechtman, D. Gratias, and J. W. Cahn, C. R. Acad. Sci. II **300**(18), 909 (1985).

23. K. Hiraga, M. Watanabe, A. Inoue, and T. Masumoto, Sci. R. Toh., **A-32**, 309 (1985).

24. L. Bursill and J. Lin, Nature **316**, 50 (1985).

25. R. Portier, D. Shechtman, D. Gratias, and J. W. Cahn, J. Micros. Spectros. Electron. **10**, 107 (1985).

26. K. M. Knowles, A. L. Greer, W. O. Saxton, and W. M. Stobbs, Philos. Mag. B **52**(1), L31 (1985).

27. R. Gronsky, K. M. Krishnan, and L. E. Tanner, in *Proceedings of the Electron Microscopy Society of America Annual Meeting* (Electron Microscopy Society of America, McLean, Va., 1985).

28. A. J. Melmed and R. Klein, Phys. Rev. Lett. **56**(14), 1478–1481 (1986).

29. P. Kramer and R. Neri, Acta Crystallogr. Sect. A **40**, 580 (1984).

30. D. Levine and P. J. Steinhardt, Phys. Rev. Lett. **53**, 2477 (1984).

31. M. Duneau and A. Katz, Phys. Rev. Lett. **54**, 2688 (1985); "Quasiperiodic patterns and icosahedral symmetry," Ecole Polytechnique, France (preprint).

32. P. A. Kalugin, A. Kitaev, and L. Levitov, JETP Lett. **41**, 119 (1985); J. Phys. Lett. **46**, L601 (1985).

33. C. L. Henley, J. Non-Cryst. Solids **75**, 91–96 (1985).

34. L. Bendersky, Phys. Rev. Lett. **55**, 1461 (1985).

35. H. U. Nissen, T. Ishimasa, and R. Schlogle, Helv. Phys. Acta **58**, 819 (1985).

36. M. S. Ball and D. J. Lloyd, Scripta Metall. **19**, 1065 (1985).

37. E. Ryba and C. Bartge, Pennsylvania State University (private communication).

New and Artificially Structured
Electronic and Magnetic Materials

FRANCIS J. DI SALVO

New materials research is the primary route to the discovery of new physical or chemical phenomena and to the understanding of how the atomic, electronic, and bulk structures of materials lead to their observed properties. This research leads not only to fundamental discoveries, but also, not infrequently, to technological applications. Such research is interdisciplinary; many of the successful programs involve scientists and ideas from the fields of chemistry, electrical engineering, materials science, and physics. Indeed, the Materials Research Laboratories (MRL) program was instituted not only to give researchers from these disciplines shared access to expensive equipment but also to help overcome the traditional segregation of scientists in university departments, thus facilitating more and broader collaboration.

This chapter focuses on new materials, including superconductors, metals, semiconductors, and ionic conductors that exhibit novel electrical or magnetic properties. It assesses the status of research on such new materials in the United States and, at least in part, the MRL program, and makes recommendations for meeting the challenges of tomorrow. The topics chosen and ideas expressed here are those of a small group of chemists, physicists, materials scientists, and electrical engineers from university, government, and industrial laboratories.[1] Although each of us has sought the opinions of our colleagues at work and at scientific meetings, we do not claim to represent the entire scientific community in new materials research. Our general consensus, similar to that reflected in previous reports,[2-7] is that the health of new materials research in the United States, specifically in the areas of conducting and magnetic materials, is only fair. Some areas are doing rather poorly, and others relatively well.

This conclusion is based on an examination of major discoveries of new phenomena in materials in the last 20 years. Although we may have missed some important discoveries, the trends discussed here are accurate. Having examined the key elements in a discovery and where and how it took place, we looked for recent changes in these patterns that may portend further change. The following summary is in two parts, the first of which deals with bulk materials, and the second with artificially structured materials.

BULK MATERIALS

The table on page 163 lists some materials in which new phenomena have been discovered or in which a particular property has been considerably enhanced in the last decade or two. Also included are some materials in thin-film form. These can also be prepared in bulk form, but their usefulness arises from the ability to make films or wires (e.g., NbN and Nb_3Sn). Since the compounds are stable in bulk form, they are included here. It is immediately evident from this table that the new compounds—that is, their composition and crystal structure—were often discovered by one group, usually not in the United States, and that the new phenomena were discovered by another group, most often in the United States. In a few cases the compounds were discovered as a result of seeking the particular property (e.g., $Fe_{14}Nd_2B$ or $RbAg_4I_5$). In some cases the structure type has been known for a long time, but the particular compound had never been examined in a way that revealed something new. In those cases the table shows the structure type rather than a reference to its discovery. The discovery of metal insulator transitions in 1946 did not trigger immediate worldwide interest; rather, that field blossomed in the mid-1950s and again in the late 1960s, and important advances are continuing today.

The organization of the table is somewhat misleading in the following ways. First, the understanding and the synthesis method to discover particular materials have most often been developed in programs that produced materials with rather ordinary properties.

Second, by focusing on properties, we ignore the most common motivations for the original synthesis, which are usually to develop a new chemistry, or to make materials with new or unusual structures, or to elucidate reaction mechanisms particularly when new preparative conditions or techniques are discovered. The purpose for such studies is usually to understand the relation between chemical bonding and crystal structure. Indeed, many of the compounds listed in the table were discovered by ''accident'' rather than by design, while researchers were examining the phases that result from new combinations of elements. These searches were often empirical, motivated by the expectation that new structures would result, the exact nature of which was not certain. Since there is as much art as science in the consistent discovery of new materials, the scientists who most frequently find new

Materials in Which New Phenomena Have Been Discovered in the Past Two Decades

Phenomenon	Prototype Compound	Structure Type or Where–When Compound Was Reported	Where–When Phenomenon Was Reported
Charge density waves	$2H\text{-}TaSe_2$	Holland–1964[8]	U.S.–1974[9] England–1974[10]
Sliding charge density waves	$NbSe_3$	France–1975[11]	U.S.–1976[12]
Polymeric conductors	$(CH)_x \cdot AsF_5$	Japan–1974[13]	U.S.–1977[14]
Organic charge transfer conductors	TTF·TCNQ	TCNQ–U.S.– 1963[15] TTF–U.S.– 1970[16]	U.S.–1973[17]
High-field superconductors	$PbMo_6S_8$	France–1971[18]	U.S.–1972[19]
Magnetic superconductors	$SmRh_4B_4$	USSR–1972[20]	U.S.–1977[21]
Mixed-valence compounds	SmB_6	Germany–1932[22] France–1932[23]	USSR–1965[25]
	SmS	Italy–1961[24]	U.S.–1970[26]
Heavy fermions	$CeCu_2Si_2$ UBe_{13}	$ThCr_2Si_2$ U.S.–1949[27]	Germany–1979[28] Switzerland/U.S.– 1983[29]
Semimagnetic semiconductors	$Cd_{1-x}Mn_xTe$ EuO	ZnS U.S.–1961[31,32]	Poland–1978[30] —
Large coercive force magnets	$Fe_{14}Nd_2B$	U.S.–1984[33] Japan–1984[34]	— —
Spin glasses	$Au_{1-x}Mn_x$	Au	U.S.–1972[35]
Metal insulator transitions	V_2O_2 Si:P	Al_2O_3 Si	France–1946[36] U.S.–1955[37]
Intercalation compounds	Li_xTiS_2 C_nK	Germany–1965[38] Germany–1926[39]	U.S.–1976[40] U.S.–1966[41]
Superionic conductors	$RbAg_4I_5$	U.S.–1967[42] England–1967[43]	—
Hydrogen storage interstitials	FeTi-H $LaNi_5$-H	CsCl $CaCu_5$	U.S.–1967[44] Holland–1973[45]
Technologically developed superconductors (films)	Nb_3Sn NbN	β-W NaCl	U.S.–1981[46,47] Japan–1985[48] Germany–1983[49]
High-dielectric-constant microwave resonators	$Ba_2Ti_9O_{20}$	Holland–1958[50]	U.S.–1974[51]

materials with novel structures characteristically have a broad background in synthesis.

Third, the table does not show the methodology of the "synthesis loop" that is often established after a new property is discovered or upon organizing a research program aimed at enhancing a particular property. In such a loop there is a close coupling between the synthesizers and the characterizers of materials. One measurement leads to ideas about new compounds of a similar structure, which leads to more and broader measurements, which leads to more synthesis, and so on. Although the synthesis practiced in this loop is often "derivative chemistry" (that is, not a search for completely new materials), it usually leads to a material in which the novel property is optimized for detailed research studies (for example, uncomplicated by other phenomena) or for some technological application. It is particularly in this synthesis loop that the interdisciplinary nature of materials research is apparent and necessary. The establishment and maintenance of such a loop are enhanced when the collaborators are at the same institution or in the same building and optimized when they are in the same group.

The trend in novel solid-state synthesis is toward ternary and quaternary compounds with complex crystal structures. Methods of synthesis other than brute force (for example, high temperatures) are needed and are beginning to be developed. Low-temperature methods should allow the preparation of many new compounds and structure types that are unstable at high temperatures. Indeed, materials prepared at or near room temperature may be metastable. Such materials are likely to assume greater technological importance. For example, materials with high superconducting transition temperatures, Tc, are difficult to prepare because their structures are often unstable at high temperatures. Low-temperature methods may be the most successful route to the preparation of superconductors with even higher Tc's. In part because of this emerging trend, a closer contact between the methods of solid-state synthesis and those of inorganic and organic chemistry will lead to many new discoveries. In some areas there is hope of developing a "rational synthesis" similar to the approach of organic chemistry. Such rational approaches are seen in the Zintl principle[52] or in cluster condensation ideas.[53] However, a rational synthesis for any solid-state phase is a challenge of considerable magnitude, since the bonding in solid-state compounds covers the spectrum of types—metallic, covalent, and ionic. New phenomena will be discovered both in these new complex phases and in known phases as they are examined under new or extreme conditions such as ultralow temperatures and high pressures.

That the new compounds listed in the table were with few exceptions synthesized originally in Europe is no surprise. Inorganic chemistry, especially solid-state chemistry, is strong in France and Germany. In the United States, synthesis of solid-state compounds has been considered out of date and a little dull, and few academic departments have even one professor involved in synthesis of new solid-state compounds. The MRL program addresses only part of the materials synthesis needs at universities. By and large, the synthesis done at MRLs is an important part of the synthesis loop, doing "derivative chemistry" on materials that are already of scientific or technological interest. This is an important job, and it should be continued. However, from the point of view of discovering new compounds with new physical or chemical properties, the MRL program is not enough. The MRLs could play a leading role in establishing interdisciplinary groups—for example, solid-state science rather than solid-state physics or solid-state chemistry—concerned with the preparation of novel phases and the examination of their properties. Industrial materials research in solid-state compounds also suffers from insufficient attention to the synthesis of novel materials.

In the past this mode of operation—European scientists discover the compound, U.S. scientists discover the phenomena—may have been considered enough justification for ignoring the search for totally new compounds. However, after years of watching scientists in the United States take advantage of discoveries made elsewhere, the European materials science community is reorganizing its mode of research and broadening its interests. The change is most advanced in France, where many of the synthesis groups have been expanded to include physical measurement. Those groups discover not only the material but the phenomena as well. Their first publication will no longer report just the synthesis and structure of the new material, but will report electrical, magnetic, thermal, and other measurements. If such a group cannot make a particular measurement, it will find a scientist in France to collaborate with. This change is now orchestrated by Centre Nationale de Recherche Scientifique (CNRS). In France it is not uncommon to find university groups headed by one professor and including both solid-state chemists and solid-state physicists, some of whom are permanent staff members paid through CNRS. Such mixed groups are a way to optimize the search-and-discovery process in new-materials research. The traditional structure of university departments in the United States is a liability in trying to produce such groups, but some way to establish, encourage, support, and expand such efforts is clearly needed. If this is not done, the discovery of new phenomena in new compounds by scientists in the United States will occur less and less frequently.

In Japan the situation is also beginning to change. Little novel synthesis was done in Japan in the past. Researchers often adopted topics already popular in the United States. Indeed, they often studied materials synthesized by collaborators in the United States. Now, however, they realize that they need an active new-materials synthesis program. For example, the Institute of Solid State Physics in Tokyo has as a top priority the establishment of a first-rate solid-state synthesis program. When such materials programs are in place, they will be formidable, since the Japanese already tend to work in collaborative interdisciplinary groups, especially in industry.

To build a leadership position in novel solid-state synthesis requires a more concerted effort by funding agencies to emphasize such research. Increased funding is necessary to train more students and to provide the equipment and tools necessary to compete with European research groups. This need for increased funding is largely due to years of neglect when little equipment for such solid-state studies was purchased by even the few researchers in the field. Standard tools of the trade include apparatus for handling air-sensitive materials, high-temperature and high-vacuum ovens, and x-ray diffraction facilities and associated computers. Also to be included are the myriad apparatus for characterizing these compounds: electrical and magnetic measurements, solid-state nuclear magnetic resonance, thermal analysis from perhaps as low as 0.1 K to as high as 1500 K, dielectric and optical measurements, electron paramagnetic resonance, and so on. Easy access to such equipment is needed, perhaps not directly in a solid-state synthesis group, but in a departmental or MRL facility or through close collaboration within the university. At most universities such a collection of accessible apparatus does not exist. Although more such facilities are needed, cost will prohibit a large number. Many researchers will have to collaborate with scientists and institutions that have such equipment. Such a buildup is also impeded by the paucity of scientists in the United States who are familiar with solid-state synthesis techniques. There are, however, glimmers of hope. In recent American Chemical Society meetings the solid-state synthesis sessions have been attracting scientists from other branches of chemistry as well as some physicists.[54] The preparation of compounds in film form, especially by "physical" methods such as sputtering or evaporation, to produce stable phases and (less frequently) metastable phases, is better established in university and industrial laboratories. Work on such techniques is getting a boost because of current technological needs and because of its connection with research in artificially structured materials.

In summary, if we wish to maintain our leadership in the discovery of new phenomena in solid-state compounds, our approach must change, perhaps drastically. The health of novel-state synthesis, with the exception of organic synthesis, is poor. Too few university professors are in the field; the number of U.S. groups is smaller than the number in Europe. Finally, some mechanism must be found to establish and support many more truly interdisciplinary groups in the university setting; that is, we must continue further down the path that MRLs have already initiated.

ARTIFICIALLY STRUCTURED MATERIALS

Artificially structured materials are a class of new materials with intentionally produced spatial variations in composition. Many of these materials are not in thermal equilibrium but are kinetically stable. For example, in thermal equilibrium the concentration of dopants in a semiconductor would be uniform, but at the temperature of preparation and especially at room temperature the bulk diffusion process is so slow that variations in concentration are essentially permanent.

The methods used to produce such materials are dominated by this consideration, so that the growth of the material takes place well below any melting point of the material(s) in question. The common techniques include evaporation onto a substrate (e.g., deposition of polycrystalline metals onto any substrate), molecular beam epitaxy, chemical reaction of a feed gas to deposit a solid on a substrate (e.g., chemical vapor deposition or metal organic chemical vapor deposition), and growth of a material from a saturated solvent (e.g., liquid-phase epitaxy). These techniques are usually employed to produce films microns thick rather than bulk material.

The overwhelming majority of research in this area concerns semiconductor materials, especially Group III–V materials such as gallium arsenide. The organization of and motivation for such research is considerably different than for bulk compounds. Whereas high-quality research in materials science and in semiconductor physics is an important outcome of the research, the research is primarily motivated by technological needs in high-speed devices and in lightwave communications (e.g., solid-state lasers, detectors, and integrated optical systems).

These materials are new in a different sense than bulk materials are, in that their crystal structure and bulk electrical properties have long been well known. What is new is that their composition can be controlled and varied on length scales as short as 5–10 angstroms to produce materials with new properties. (In the remainder of this section the word "structure" denotes compositional changes and not the crystal structure.)

The previously mentioned growth techniques, as well as related methods such as sputtering, can be used to deposit almost any kind of inorganic material on flat or variously shaped surfaces. Depending on the materials in question and on the deposition conditions, the films produced may be homogeneous or inhomogeneous (on length scales from tens of angstroms to microns). This presentation is limited to Group III–V semiconductors produced by molecular beam epitaxy (MBE), since the majority of research on films and epitaxial layers, as well as much of the scientific excitement, has been centered on these materials. Although this discussion is limited to the MBE technique, other techniques, such as chemical vapor deposition, or hybrid methods, such as gas-source MBE, may also produce materials that are very similar in structure and electronic properties.

Compound semiconductor MBE began with research at industrial[55] and government[56] laboratories in the United States in the late 1960s and early 1970s. It especially caught on after the discovery that high-purity epitaxial materials with atomically smooth interfaces could be produced by this method.[57]

At present, practically every research and development laboratory for high-technology industry in the United States and Japan, as well as some in Europe, is heavily involved in MBE (especially of Group III–V compounds) as well as a rapidly increasing number of government laboratories and of university groups in physics, electrical engineering, or materials science departments.

The wide variety of structures that can be produced by MBE fall into two main classes—*homo*epitaxial and *hetero*epitaxial. Homoepitaxy is essentially the trivial case where a single-crystal film is grown on a single-crystal substrate of the same composition. This can be useful in producing defect-free layers or sharp doping interfaces in the same material (e.g., abrupt p-n junctions).

Heteroepitaxy is the epitaxial growth of two or more different compositions in a single film. Heteroepitaxic growth is affected by the degree of lattice mismatch between the two materials that meet at an interface. The lattice mismatch is the percentage difference between atom spacings along a plane of the same crystallographic orientation as the interface plane in the respective bulk phases of the two materials. If the mismatch is small (less than a few tenths of a percent), an atomically coherent, defect-free interface can be prepared between two thick layers (typically microns) of different composition. If the mismatch is large, defects such as misfit dislocations are produced. Even in that case the crystal lattices of the two phases joined at the interface may have a definite relationship to each other, i.e., the interface can be coherent. Such defects usually degrade the electrical performance of such materials or of devices made in this way.

A recent experimental advance, strained-layer epitaxy, first proposed theoretically many years ago,[58] overcomes this lattice mismatch problem. When one or both of the material layers are made very thin (typically tens to hundreds of angstroms), the thin layer is strained (i.e., stretched or compressed) to the same interatomic spacing as the substrate and no defects are generated at the interface. This technique can be used to produce thick films if a superlattice of thin layers (i.e., multiple interleaved layers) is produced. Strained-layer superlattice epitaxy greatly expands the classes of semiconductors that can be considered for defect-free heteroepitaxial growth of materials with optimal electronic properties.

Many semiconductor structures have been produced by MBE, and their complexity is increasing. The correct choice of materials permits the spatial variation of the band gap (perpendicular to the film surface) and the doping type (n or p) to be arbitrarily tailored.[59] The band-edge discontinuities that occur between two different semiconductors can be modified, even removed, by properly grading the interface composition or by adding thin, heavily doped layers at the interface. By modifying the composition, the effective mass can also be independently controlled. The production of such artificially structured materials may be called "band-gap engineering."[60]

A particularly useful doping technique has also emerged from MBE—modulation doping.[61] If a semiconductor is sandwiched between layers of another with lower electron affinity, the carriers produced by doping will fall into the "well" produced by the material with the greater electron affinity. If the well is thin (a few hundred angstroms or less), the carrier will occupy the lower quantum levels of the well. Furthermore, it will be able to move parallel to the well—i.e., in the plane of the film—without scattering from the impurities (dopants) used to produce them, because the impurities are outside the well. Modulation-doped semiconductors of this variety have the highest-mobility carriers ever produced in the given semiconductor (e.g., greater than 10^6 cm^2/V-s at 1 K for electrons in GaAs).[62,63]

Besides the great array of structures and devices that have been and will be thought of, fundamentally new physical phenomena have been observed in some of the high-mobility materials. The quantized Hall effect, discovered first in silicon inversion layers[64] (for which Klaus von Klitzing won the 1985 Nobel Prize in physics) and subsequently in GaAs heterostructures,[65] is now fairly well understood.[66] In the highest-mobility materials, the fractional quantized Hall effect (FQHE) has also been observed.[67] It arises from interactions between carriers in two dimensions, which leads to a series of new ordered states,[68] and is a subject of intense theoretical research. The solution of this problem is likely to bring a much deeper understanding of the nature of interacting electron systems, an understanding that will likely have importance in fields far beyond semiconductor physics.

The future of semiconductor MBE research and development is bright. Band-gap engineering, superlattices and quantum wells with modulation doping, and strained-layer superlattices will produce rapid technological advances and possibly more fundamental discoveries like the FQHE. New materials advances likely in the future include *in situ* (ultrahigh-vacuum) processing of MBE wafers to produce devices without exposing the wafer to air. Whereas the dimensions of heterostructures can now be controlled only in the direction of growth, techniques such as *in situ* processing will eventually permit production of heterostructures whose dimensions are precisely controlled in the lateral direction as well. The kinds of structures and devices that would then be possible are perhaps limitless.

Future possibilities for MBE preparation are not limited to Group III–V semiconductor systems but include novel metal superlattices and systems that contain mixtures of metals, semiconductors, and insulators. MBE or related techniques may also be used to produce metastable crystal structures in thin-film form. That is, these techniques may also be exploited to produce new solid-state compounds, such as high-temperature superconductors. It is at this juncture that the fields of solid-state synthesis and artificially structured materials obviously overlap. In fact, single-crystal superlattices of magnetic and nonmagnetic metals with structural perfection approaching that attainable with semiconductor MBE have been reported.[69] Also, single-crystal layers of magnetic metals have been grown on semiconducting substrates.[70] It seems likely that new physical phenomena will emerge from such studies of novel materials prepared by MBE and related techniques.

OBSTACLES AND ROUTES TO FURTHER DEVELOPMENT

In view of the current possibilities and excitement in the field of artificially structured materials, can there also be problems? Although the field of MBE in the United States is stronger and attracts more research entrants than that of new bulk compounds, there are challenges. The first is being addressed by the electronics industry and is not directly influenced by the MRLs or even the broader engineering and scientific community, but it is important to the future of MBE and MBE research. The problem is that, although MBE and most device structures and concepts were developed in the United States,[71] the Japanese have moved the technique into large-scale production of devices more rapidly than has the United States or Europe. The Japanese have demonstrated 1-K high-speed random-access memory chips using modulation-doped GaAs[72] and are rapidly developing 4- and 16-K devices. Their heavy investment in MBE technology[73] further suggests that they will soon threaten U.S. dominance in the invention of devices as well. We must meet this competition or the Japanese will dominate the market and sharply reduce the incentive for U.S. industry to fund further research. This situation could very well lead to an eventual decrease in funding from the National Science Foundation and other agencies for university research in MBE.

The second problem is related to the first in an indirect way. MBE research is expensive. It requires ultrahigh-vacuum apparatus and techniques. A state-of-the-art machine, with the proper surface analytical tools, costs $500,000 to $1 million. The measurement of properties requires at least a well-equipped electronics laboratory and often access to ultralow-temperature and high-magnetic-field laboratories. Indeed, the high magnetic fields necessary for studying details of the FQHE are available only at the National Magnet Laboratory. Because of the expense of MBE research, not all university investigators who want to carry out MBE experiments or study MBE materials and devices can do so. There is a shortage of trained scientists to fill all the openings in MBE research and development.

Despite the need for increased funding of research in artificially structured materials, the problem is larger than can be addressed by MRLs or the National Science Foundation alone. To meet the needs will require support at universities from all government agencies, from industrial research and development groups, and from universities themselves. Special efforts are needed to pull these resources together. The technologies that will emerge have a high probability of forming the basis for the electronics industry of the next century and are vital to our technological and military strength.

At the university level, individual research groups are often too small to carry out MBE growth, structure and device design, and measurements of electronic properties. Intergroup collaboration, within and between institutions, will need to be supported by both government and industry. One approach could be to build specific ties between university groups and industrial or government laboratories. Such ties might include exchanges among institutions, mini-sabbaticals for faculty members and scientists, and arrangements whereby graduate students could perform their thesis research at industrial or government laboratories. This would allow university groups to be somewhat larger—thus producing more graduates with MBE backgrounds—and to have access to more and better equipment. It would also allow more industrial and government researchers to work in MBE (at low cost) and would help produce Ph.D. graduates who have the background needed to fill research and development positions. A more rapid diffusion of technical and scientific knowledge between these groups would also ensue, to the benefit of all.

Another possible approach to these difficulties is to create several MBE centers at universities. This could allow the buildup of a core of experts who would collaborate with each other and with other scientists in the region to produce structures or devices on a proposal basis. Industry should also be a part of this effort, perhaps by partially funding the centers or on a fee-for-use basis.

The size of the U.S. research effort in artificially structured materials is much larger than that in new solid-state synthesis. This difference in size is reasonable and necessary, since artificially structured materials are so closely related to electronics and telecommunications technologies. Indeed, research on artificially structured materials must continue to grow in the cooperative ways already outlined.

In contrast, the discovery of new solid-state compounds in the United States has been almost nil. This field needs considerable attention by funding agencies if the United States is to continue to lead the world in the discovery of new phenomena in solids. At the proper equilibrium, the ratio of scientists pursuing novel solid-state synthesis to those pursuing artificially structured materials (or synthesis of materials already known to be technologically interesting) would be larger than it is today although still considerably less than unity. The nation needs to establish and support more solid-state synthesis groups. This might traditionally be thought of as solid-state chemistry, but such groups could also flourish in materials science, physics, or applied physics departments.

In any case, some access to characterization of these new materials must be established. Indeed, the current success in artificially structured materials is due to the excellent interdisciplinary and collaborative nature of much of the work, especially in industrial laboratories. In some cases it would be reasonable to have physical measurements available in a solid-state synthesis group. In others, collaborators in other groups or fields and at industrial and government laboratories could suffice. However, individual egos, university organizational structure, tenure procedures, and funding usually work against such collaborative arrangements. Other creative possibilities for encouraging the growth of solid-state synthesis have been proposed by the Solid State Sciences Committee of the National Research Council and more are needed.

CONCLUSIONS

The synthesis of new solid-state compounds in the United States has been a neglected field for decades. Rather, this country has focused on discovering new or enhanced properties in materials previously discovered—primarily in Europe. The high quality of such research in Europe, coupled with new interdisciplinary group organization and the emerging emphasis on new materials in Japan, makes it unlikely that the United States will continue to be the first to discover new properties or uses of materials. To maintain our position, it is imperative that the United States build a first-rate scientific presence in novel solid-state synthesis.

The greatest scientific and technological impact of this effort will occur only with strong interaction between synthesizers and characterizers; that is, this should be an interdisciplinary research activity. The field of artificially structured materials, as typified by the MBE growth of semiconductors, is by comparison strong and robust. Challenges posed by the shortage of scientists trained in the field as well as a slow translation of research results into production can best be overcome by sharing and coordinating academic, industrial, and government resources in a national collaborative effort. Failure to do so could well result in Japanese companies dominating the technology that will most likely be the basis of advanced electronic devices in the twenty-first century, or probably even in the 1990s.

NOTES

1. A. Y. Cho and Arthur C. Gossard (molecular beam epitaxy), AT&T Bell Laboratories, Murray Hill, N.J.; John Corbett (solid-state chemistry), Department of Chemistry, Iowa State University of Science and Technology; Frank Y. Fradin (superconductivity, transport props), Materials Sciences and Technology Division, Argonne National Laboratory, Argonne, Ill.; M. Brian Maple (superconductivity, magnetism), Department of Physics, University of California, La Jolla; and Stephen von Molnar (physics of rare-earth compounds), Thomas J. Watson Research Center, IBM Corp., Yorktown Heights, N.Y.
2. J. L. Warren and T. H. Geballe, "Research opportunities in new energy-related materials,"

Report to Council on Materials Science, U.S. Department of Energy, in Mater. Sci. Eng., **50**, 149 (1981).

3. P. C. Hohenberg, "Trends and opportunities in materials research," Report to Materials Research Advisory Committee, NSF Pub. 84–17 (National Science Foundation, Washington, D.C., 1984).

4. National Research Council, Solid State Sciences Committee, *Synthesis and Characterization of Advanced Materials* (National Academy Press, Washington, D.C., 1984).

5. National Research Council, Physics Survey Committee, *Physics Through the 1990s*, especially the following two volumes in the series: *Condensed-Matter Physics,* and *Scientific Interfaces and Technological Applications* (National Academy Press, Washington, D.C., 1986); see also National Research Council, Solid State Sciences Committee, *Report on Artificially Structured Materials* (National Academy Press, Washington, D.C., 1985).

6. R. M. White, "Opportunities in magnetic materials," Science **229**, 11 (1985).

7. J. D. Corbett, "New materials from high-temperature synthesis," Pure Appl. Chem. **56**, 1527 (1984).

8. F. Kadyk, R. Heisman, and F. Jellinek, Rec. Trav. Chem. **83**, 768 (1964).

9. J. A. Wilson, F. J. Di Salvo, and S. Mahajan, Phys. Rev. Lett. **32**, 882 (1974).

10. P. M. Williams, G. S. Parry, and C. B. Scruby, Philos. Mag. **29**, 695 (1974).

11. A. Merschaut and J. Rouxel, J. Less-Common Met. **39**, 197 (1975).

12. P. Monceau, N. P. Ong, A. M. Portis, M. Merschaut, and J. Rouxel, Phys. Rev. Lett. **37**, 602 (1976).

13. T. Ito, H. Shirakowa, and S. Ikeda, J. Polym. Sci. **12**, 11 (1974).

14. H. Shirakowa, E. J. Louis, A. G. MacDiarmid, C-K. Chaing, and A. J. Heeger, J. Chem. Soc., Chem. Commun. 578 (1977).

15. L. R. Melby, R. J. Harder, W. R. Hertler, W. Mahler, R. E. Benson, and W. E. Mochel, J. Am. Chem. Soc. **84**, 3374 (1963).

16. F. Wudl, G. M. Smith, and E. J. Hirfnagel, Chem. Commun. 1453 (1970); D. L. Coffen, Tetrahedron Lett. 2633 (1970).

17. J. Ferraris, D. O. Cowan, V. Walatha, Jr., and J. H. Perlstein, J. Am. Chem. Soc. **95**, 948 (1973).

18. R. Chevrel, M. Sergent, and J. Prigent, J. Solid State Chem. **3**, 515 (1971).

19. B. T. Matthias, M. Marezio, E. Corenzwit, A. S. Cooper, and H. E. Barz, Science **175**, 1465 (1972); S. Foner, E. J. McNiff, and E. J. Alexander, Phys. Lett. **49A**, 269 (1974).

20. Yu. B. Kuz'ma and N. S. Bilonizhko, Sov. Phys. Crystallogr. **16**, 897 (1972).

21. B. T. Matthias, E. Corenzwit, J. M. Vandenberg, and H. E. Barz, Proc. Natl. Acad. Sci. **74**, 1334 (1977); H. Hamaker, L. D. Woolf, H. B. MacKay, Z. Fisk, and M. B. Maple, Solid State Commun. **32**, 289 (1979).

22. M. Von Stackelberg and F. Neumann, Z. Phys. Chem. **B19**, 314 (1932).

23. G. Allard, Bull. Soc. Chim. France **51**, 1213 (1932).

24. A. Iandelli, in *Rare Earth Research,* edited by E. V. Kleber (Macmillan, New York, 1961), pp. 135–141.

25. E. E. Vainshtein, S. M. Blokhin, and Yu. B. Paderno, Sov. Phys. Solid State **6**, 2318 (1965).

26. A. Jayaraman, V. Marayanamurti, E. Bucher, and R. G. Maines, Phys. Rev. Lett. **25**, 368, 1430 (1970).

27. N. C. Bänziger and R. E. Rundle, Acta Crystallogr. **2**, 258 (1949).

28. F. Sleglich, J. Aarb, C. D. Bredl, W. Lieke, D. Meschede, W. Franz, and H. Schäfer, Phys. Rev. Lett. **43**, 1892 (1979).

29. H. R. Ott, H. Rudugier, Z. Fisk, and F. L. Smith, Phys. Rev. Lett. **50**, 1595 (1983).

30. J. A. Gaj, R. R. Galazka, and M. Nawrocki, Solid State Commun. **15**, 193 (1978).

31. B. T. Matthias, R. M. Bozorth, and J. H. Van Vleck, Phys. Rev. Lett. **7**, 160 (1961).

32. F. Holtzberg, T. R. McGuire, S. Methfessel, and J. C. Suits, Phys. Rev. Lett. **13**, 181 (1964).
33. J. J. Croat, J. F. Herbst, R. Whee, and F. E. Pinkerton, J. Appl. Phys. **55**, 2078 (1984).
34. M. Sagawa, S. Fujimura, N. Togawa, H. Yamamoto, and Y. Matsuura, J. Appl. Phys. **55**, 2083 (1984).
35. V. Canella and J. A. Mydosh, Phys. Rev. B **6**, 4220 (1972).
36. M. Föex, C. R. Acad. Sci., **223**, 1126 (1946).
37. H. Fritzche, Phys. Rev. **99**, 406 (1955).
38. W. Rudorff, Chimia **19**, 489 (1965).
39. K. Fredenhagen and G. Cadenbach, Z. Anorg. Allg. Chem. **158**, 249 (1926).
40. M. A. Whittingham, J. Electrochem. Soc. **123**, 315 (1976).
41. N. B. Hannay, T. H. Geballe, B. T. Matthias, K. Andres, P. Schmidt and D. MacNair, Phys. Rev. Lett. **14**, 225 (1965).
42. B. B. Owens and R. G. Argue, Science **157**, 308 (1967).
43. J. N. Bradley and P. D. Greene, Trans. Faraday Soc. **63**, 424 (1967).
44. R. H. Wiswall and J. J. Reilly, Inorg. Chem. **6**, 2220 (1967); **11**, 1691 (1972).
45. F. A. Kuijpers, Philips Res. Rep. (suppl.) **2** (1973).
46. M. Suenaga, in *Proceedings of NATO Advanced Study Institute on Superconductor Materials Science: Metallurgy, Fabrication, and Applications,* Series B: Physics B68, S. Foner and B. Schwartz, editors (Plenum, New York, 1981), pp. 201–268.
47. M. S. DiOrio and M. R. Beasley, IEEE Trans. Magn. **21**, 532 (1985).
48. A. Shoji, M. Aoyagi, S. Kosaku, F. Shinoki, and H. Hayakawa, Appl. Phys. Lett. **46**, 1098 (1985).
49. M. Dietrich, C. H. Dustman, F. Schmaderer, and G. Wahl, IEEE Trans. Magn. **19**, 406 (1983).
50. G. H. Jonker and W. Kwestroo, J. Am. Ceram. Soc. **41**, 390 (1958).
51. H. M. O'Brien, Jr., J. Thomson, Jr., and J. K. Plourde, J. Am. Ceram. Soc. **57**, 450 (1974).
52. H. Schäfer and B. Eisenmann, Rev. Inorg. Chem. **3**, 29 (1981).
53. A. Simon, Angew. Chem. **20**, 1 (1981).
54. See, for example, the Sept. 30, 1985, issue of *Chemical and Engineering News* for its report on the American Chemical Society Meeting in Chicago in August 1985.
55. R. F. Steinberg and D. M. Scruggs, J. Appl. Phys. **37**, 4586 (1966).
56. J. E. Davey and T. Pankey, J. Appl. Phys. **39**, 1941 (1968).
57. A. Y. Cho, J. Appl. Phys. **41**, 2780 (1970); **42**, 2074 (1971); Appl. Phys. Lett. **19**, 467 (1971).
58. F. C. Frank and J. H. Van der Merwe, Proc. R. Soc. London, Sect. A **198**, 205 (1949).
59. R. J. Malik, J. R. Hayes, F. Capasso, K. Alavi, and A. Y. Cho, IEEE Trans. Electron Devices Lett. **EDL-4**, 383 (1983).
60. F. Capasso, Physica, **129B**, 92 (1985).
61. R. Dingle, H. L. Störmer, A. C. Gossard, and W. Wiegmann, Appl. Phys. Lett. **33**, 665 (1978).
62. J. C. M. Hwang, A. Kastalsky, H. L. Stormer, and V. G. Keramidas, Appl. Phys. Lett. **44**, 802 (1984).
63. N. Sano, H. Kato, and S. Chiko, Solid State Commun. **49**, 123 (1984).
64. K. von Klitzing, G. Dorda, and M. Pepper, Phys. Rev. Lett. **45**, 494 (1980).
65. D. C. Tsui and A. C. Gossard, Appl. Phys. Lett. **37**, 550 (1981).
66. R. B. Laughlin, Phys. Rev. B **23**, 5632 (1981).
67. D. C. Tsui, H. L. Störmer, and A. C. Gossard, Phys. Rev. Lett. **48**, 1559 (1982).
68. R. B. Laughlin, Phys. Rev. Lett. **50**, 1395 (1983).

69. J. R. Kwo, E. M. Gyorgy, D. B. McWhan, M. Hong, F. J. Di Salvo, C. Vettier, and J. E. Bower, Phys. Rev. Lett. **55**, 1402 (1985).
70. G. A. Prinz and J. J. Krebs, Appl. Phys. Lett. **39**, 397 (1981).
71. A. Y. Cho, "Introduction" in *The Technology and Physics of Molecular Beam Epitaxy,* edited by E. H. C. Parker (Plenum, New York, 1985), pp. 1–13.
72. T. Mimura, M. Abe, A. Shibatomi, and M. Kobayashi, in *Collected Papers of the Second International Conference on Modulated Semiconductor Structures* (Kyoto, Japan, Sept. 9–13, 1985).
73. T. E. Bell, "Japan reaches beyond silicon," IEEE Spectrum October 1985, p. 46.

Materials Research
in Catalysis

JOHN H. SINFELT

A catalyst is a substance that accelerates a chemical reaction without being consumed in the process. The association of catalysis with rates of chemical reactions was made by the German chemist Wilhelm Ostwald around the year 1900. Ostwald's insight provided a basis for scientific inquiry into catalysis and paved the way for the widespread investigation and application of catalytic phenomena. In the years since 1900 the science of catalysis has progressed steadily, accompanied by enormous technological advances that profoundly affect the lives of all of us.[1] Catalytic processes now provide the basic technology for the manufacture of a host of vitally important materials, ranging from fertilizers to synthetic fibers and petroleum products such as gasoline and heating oil. Catalysts are used in the manufacture of an estimated $750 billion worth of products annually in the United States alone.[2]

Catalytic processes are commonly divided into two categories: homogeneous and heterogeneous.[3] The former refer to processes in which the catalyst and the reactants are present in a single phase, as in a solution. In heterogeneous catalysis, by contrast, the reactants and the catalyst are present in separate phases—for example, reactants in a vapor phase in contact with a solid catalyst. The reaction is frequently conducted in a flow system in which the vapor is passed through a vessel containing a bed of catalyst granules or pellets.[4] The composition of the vapor changes as it is depleted of molecules of reactant and enriched in molecules of product in its passage through the catalyst bed. A catalytic process involves a sequence of steps in which the active catalytic entities participating in the steps are continually regenerated, so that the catalyst is used over and over in the formation of product molecules from reactants.[5] Such a sequence of steps is referred to as a closed sequence.[6] In the case of heterogeneous catalysis at the surface of a solid, the active catalytic entity is a site on the surface or a complex of the site with a reactant molecule. For example, a chemical reaction, $A + B \rightarrow C$, might proceed by the following sequence of steps:

$$A + S \rightarrow A\text{-}S$$
$$A\text{-}S + B \rightarrow C + S.$$

The molecule A is adsorbed on a site S to form a surface complex $A\text{-}S$, which then reacts with a molecule of reactant B to form the product molecule C and regenerate the site S. This simple sequence illustrates features common to all catalytic processes, namely, the generation of a reactive intermediate from the reactant, the transformation of the intermediate to a product, and the regeneration of the active catalyst site.

An intriguing aspect of catalysis is the specificity observed. For example, silver catalysts are unique in their ability to catalyze the partial oxidation of ethylene to ethylene oxide:[7]

$$2C_2H_4 + O_2 \rightarrow 2C_2H_4O.$$

On other solid catalysts, the ethylene undergoes predominantly complete oxidation to carbon dioxide and water. In this example a change in the catalyst actually leads to a pronounced change in the distribution of reaction products, because the different catalysts have markedly different effects on alternative reaction paths. In some cases the observed reaction product is the same for a number of catalysts, but the specific activity (reaction rate per unit surface area or per surface site) varies widely. A good example is the catalytic hydrogenolysis of ethane to methane, $C_2H_6 + H_2 \rightarrow 2CH_4$, on metals,[8,9] where the specific activity of osmium is almost 8 orders of magnitude higher than that of platinum (Figure 1). These examples demonstrate clearly that the chemical nature of the surface is highly important in heterogeneous catalysis.

Heterogeneous catalysis involves the participation of species chemisorbed on the surface. Maximum catalytic activity is achieved when chemisorption of the reactant is fast but not very strong.[6,10] If the adsorption bond is too strong, the catalyst will tend to be highly covered by reactant species that are not readily transformed or by product species that do not desorb readily from the surface. At the other extreme, if the adsorption bond is very weak, the catalytic activity may be severely limited by a low rate of chemisorption, since the activation energy for chemisorption commonly increases as the heat of adsorption decreases. Optimum catalytic activity corresponds in general to some intermediate strength of adsorption between these two extremes.

Many different types of materials have been used as catalysts. In heterogeneous catalysis they are commonly separated into two broad categories— metals and nonmetals. In the first category the most commonly used metals are those in Group VIII and Group IB of the periodic table. In the second

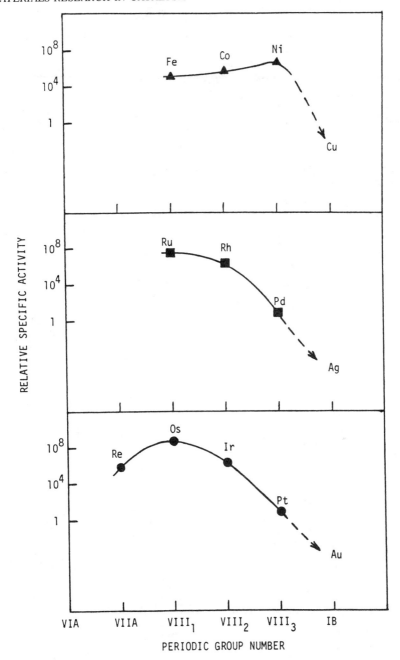

FIGURE 1 Catalytic activities of metals for the hydrogenolysis of ethane to methane. The activities were determined at a temperature of 478 K and at ethane and hydrogen partial pressures of 0.030 and 0.20 atm, respectively. From Sinfelt.[8,9]

category, oxides are the most common catalysts. Although there are major applications of materials in both of these categories in industrial catalysis, only metal catalysts are considered in any detail in this chapter. The area embodies a number of issues that are likely to be of broad interest in materials science. Furthermore, metal catalysts illustrate well the approaches that have been used in developing the science of catalytic materials.

METAL CATALYSTS

In one form of metal catalyst that is widely used commercially,[4] the catalyst particles consist of a porous refractory material and small metal crystallites or clusters dispersed throughout the particles (Figure 2). The term *carrier*, or *support*, is commonly used in referring to the refractory material, and the catalyst is known as a supported metal catalyst. In a small laboratory reactor the particles could be granules approximately 0.5 mm in diameter. In a commercial reactor the particle size would be somewhat larger, perhaps 2 or 3 mm, to avoid an excessive drop in pressure as the gas passes through the catalyst bed. The refractory material constituting the bulk of the particles is frequently an oxide such as alumina (Al_2O_3) or silica (SiO_2) with a structure consisting of a network of pores with an average diameter of about 100 angstroms. The metal clusters or crystallites reside on the walls of the pores and must therefore be smaller than the pores. In some cases the metal clusters are as small as 10 angstroms.

TYPICAL CATALYST PARTICLE
NETWORK OF PORES

SINGLE PORE
ENLARGED VIEW

METAL
CLUSTERS

FIGURE 2 Schematic drawing of a catalyst particle with a structure consisting of a network of pores with an average diameter of perhaps 100 Å. The particle consists of a refractory material such as alumina or silica, with small metal clusters residing on the walls of the pores. In some commonly used catalysts the metal clusters are as small as 10 Å.

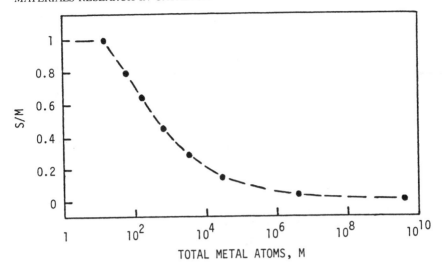

FIGURE 3   The ratio of surface atoms S to total atoms M in a metal crystal, as a function of M. The metal crystals are assumed to be cubes with the face-centered cubic structure.

In a typical application of such a catalyst, reactant molecules diffuse into pores of the catalyst and are adsorbed on the active metal clusters. The adsorbed molecules then undergo chemical transformations on the clusters to yield molecules of a different chemical species. These molecules are subsequently desorbed to yield molecules of product in the pores. The product molecules must then diffuse through the network of pores into the gas stream flowing through the space between the particles.

The rate of reaction obtained with a given mass of catalyst depends on the number of catalytic sites that are present at the surface. For a reaction occurring on the metal clusters in a supported metal catalyst, the rate per metal atom can be determined readily. However, it is the rate per surface metal atom that is of fundamental interest. To determine this quantity, we need to know the ratio of surface metal atoms S to total metal atoms M in the clusters. The ratio, S/M, will in general depend on the value of M. If we make the simplifying assumption that the clusters are present as cubes and that the atoms are arranged in the clusters in the same manner as in a large metal crystal, we can calculate the relation between S/M and M for a catalytically important metal such as platinum or nickel (Figure 3). The value of S/M, which is commonly called the metal dispersion, increases as M decreases, approaching unity when M becomes sufficiently small. Metal dispersions close to unity are commonly realized in precious-metal catalysts used for the production of antiknock components for gasoline. Such high dispersions imply that the metal clusters are extremely small, of the order of 10 angstroms. Alternatively, metal dispersions equal to unity would be obtained if the metal clusters were raftlike or platelike structures consisting of single layers of metal atoms on the carrier. This alternative would require a strong interaction between the metal and the carrier to impart stability to clusters with such shapes.

Chemisorption Measurements of Metal Dispersion

An experimental estimate of S/M can be made from a measurement of the amount of gas chemisorbed on the metal clusters. The chemisorption must be selective, readily saturating the surfaces of the metal clusters with a monolayer but not occurring on the metal-free surface of the carrier. The chemisorption of a gas such as hydrogen, carbon monoxide, or oxygen at room temperature has been used effectively for this purpose. Use of the method requires knowledge of the stoichiometry of the chemisorption process, that is, the number of molecules chemisorbed per surface metal atom. The ratio of the number of chemisorbed molecules to the total number of metal atoms present in the catalyst, coupled with knowledge of the chemisorption stoichiometry, makes it possible to determine the metal dispersion S/M.

In hydrogen chemisorption on the Group VIII metals, it is generally accepted that the hydrogen molecule dissociates, so that hydrogen atoms are adsorbed on the surface. Typical data on the chemisorption of hydrogen at room temperature on a platinum-on-alumina catalyst[11] are shown in Figure 4. The isotherm labeled A is the original isotherm determined on the "bare" catalyst surface. The bare surface was prepared by evacuation of the adsorption cell at high temperature (725 K) subsequent to the reduction of the catalyst in flowing hydrogen at 775 K. The catalyst was cooled to room temperature in a vacuum, hydrogen was passed over it, and isotherm A was measured. The adsorption cell was again evacuated at room temperature for 10 min (to approximately 10^{-6} torr), and a second isotherm, labeled B, was measured. Isotherm A represents the total chemisorption, and isotherm B represents the weakly chemisorbed fraction, since it is removed by simple evacuation at room temperature. Isotherm B includes adsorption on the alumina carrier. The difference isotherm, labeled A–B, is obtained by subtracting isotherm B from isotherm A and is independent of pressure over the range of pressures used in obtaining the isotherm. It represents the strongly chemisorbed fraction, that is, the amount that cannot be removed by evacuation at room temperature. The quantity H/M in the right-hand ordinate of Figure 4 represents the ratio of the number H of hydrogen atoms adsorbed to the number M of platinum atoms in the catalyst. If we assume a stoichiometry of one hydrogen atom per surface platinum atom in the case of the strongly chemisorbed fraction, the value of H/M determined from the dif-

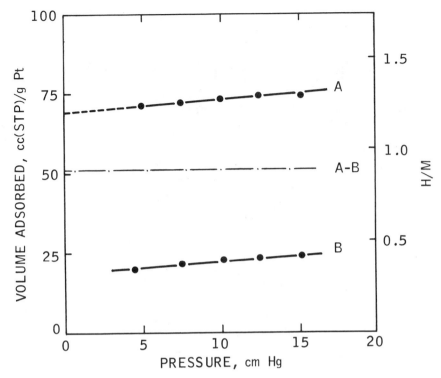

FIGURE 4 Typical hydrogen chemisorption at room temperature on a platinum-on-alumina catalyst containing 1 wt % platinum. Isotherm A is the original isotherm, and isotherm B is a second isotherm determined after evacuation of the adsorption cell for 10 min to a pressure of approximately 10^{-6} torr subsequent to the completion of isotherm A. The difference isotherm A–B, obtained by subtracting isotherm B from isotherm A, represents the strongly chemisorbed fraction. The quantity H/M is the ratio of the number of hydrogen atoms absorbed to the number of platinum atoms in the catalyst. From Via, Sinfelt, and Lytle.[11]

ference isotherm A–B corresponds to the ratio of surface platinum atoms to total platinum atoms in the catalyst. This ratio is about 0.9 for the catalyst in Figure 4.

High-resolution electron microscopy provides independent evidence of the highly dispersed nature of platinum in platinum-alumina reforming catalysts.[12] Such studies have shown that the platinum exists as very small crystallites or clusters of the order of 10 angstroms in diameter. Platinum clusters of this size necessarily have a large proportion of their atoms present in the surface. The fraction would be very close to the value of 0.9 derived from the chemisorption data in Figure 4.

The successful application of chemisorption methods in the characterization of platinum-on-alumina reforming catalysts led to their use with other supported metals, including most of the Group VIII metals.[10] This represents a major advance in the characterization of supported metal catalysts. With this capability, the activity of such a catalyst can be referred to the amount of metal in the surface rather than to the metal content of the catalyst as a whole. Data on the activities of different metal catalysts for a given reaction can therefore be compared in a more fundamental manner.

Characterization of Metal Catalysts by X-Ray Absorption Spectroscopy

Extended x-ray absorption fine structure (EXAFS) refers to the fluctuations in absorption coefficient commonly observed on the high-energy side of an x-ray absorption edge. The fluctuations of interest in EXAFS begin at approximately 30 eV beyond an absorption edge and extend over an additional range of 1,000–1,500 eV. The fine structure is observed in the absorption of x-rays by all forms of matter other than monatomic gases and was first considered theoretically by Kronig.[13–15] The possibilities of EXAFS as a tool for investigating the structures of noncrystalline materials, however, have been realized only recently. They have emerged as a result of advances in methods of data analysis[16,17] and experimental techniques, the latter primarily in the application of high-intensity synchrotron radiation as an x-ray source.[18]

EXAFS is concerned with ejection of an inner-core electron from an atom as a result of x-ray absorption. The ejected electron (photoelectron) is characterized by a wave vector $\mathbf{K}$, which is proportional to the square root of its kinetic energy. The kinetic energy of the photoelectron is the difference between the energy of the x-ray photons and a threshold energy associated with the ejection of the electron. A typical spectrum[19] for bulk platinum at 100 K is shown in Figure 5. The data cover a wide enough range of energy to include all three of the characteristic L absorption edges, L_{III}, L_{II}, and L_I, corresponding, respectively, to ejection of photoelectrons from $2p_{3/2}$, $2p_{1/2}$, and $2s$ states. At energies higher than the threshold value corresponding to a particular absorption edge, fluctuations occur in the absorption coefficient, which constitute the extended fine structure.

In the treatment of EXAFS data, the absorption coefficient in the region of the EXAFS is divided into two parts. One part is identical to the absorption coefficient for the free atom. The other part, which depends on the environment around the absorber atom, is the oscillating part constituting EXAFS. Division of the latter part by the former normalizes the EXAFS oscillations. The normalized oscillations are represented by the EXAFS function $X(\mathbf{K})$. Details concerning the determination of $X(\mathbf{K})$ from experimental EXAFS data are given in the literature.[11,17]

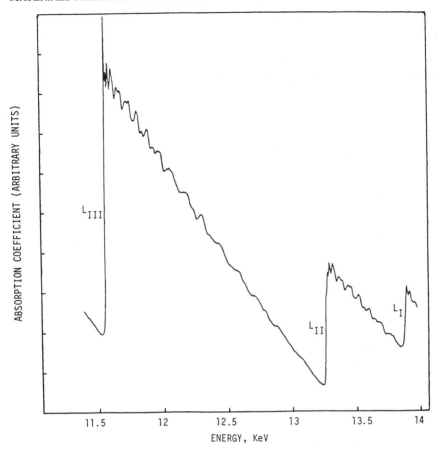

FIGURE 5 X-ray absorption spectrum of bulk platinum at 100 K in the region of the *L*-absorption edges. L_{III}, L_{II}, and L_I correspond, respectively, to ejection of photoelectrons from $2p_{3/2}$, $2p_{1/2}$, and $2s$ states. From Sinfelt, Via, and Lytle.[19]

Plots of the function $K^3 \cdot \chi(K)$ as a function of K are shown in the left-hand sections of Figure 6 for bulk platinum and for two platinum catalysts containing 1 weight percent platinum.[11] In one catalyst the platinum was dispersed on silica, and in the other it was dispersed on alumina. Chemisorption measurements on the catalysts indicated platinum dispersions in the range of 0.7 to 0.9. The data in Figure 6, which were obtained at a temperature of 100 K, are for EXAFS associated with the L_{III} absorption edge. Fourier transforms of $K^3 \cdot \chi(K)$ are shown in the right-hand sections of the figure. The Fourier transform yields a function $\phi(R)$, where R is the distance from the absorber atom.[20] Peaks corresponding to neighboring atoms are displaced

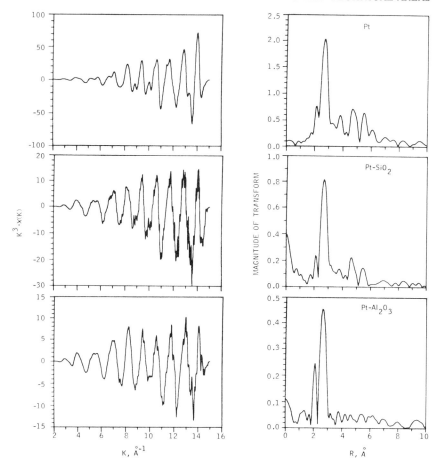

FIGURE 6   Normalized EXAFS data at 100 K and associated Fourier transforms for bulk platinum and for dispersed platinum catalysts containing 1 wt % platinum. From Via, Sinfelt, and Lytle.[11]

from true interatomic distances because of phase shifts. The feature in the transforms for the catalysts near $R = 0$ is an artifact introduced by asymmetry in the EXAFS function, which in turn is due to a limitation in ability to extract the background absorption from the total absorption. Improvements in the characterization of background absorption have largely eliminated this artifact in more recent work.

The EXAFS fluctuations for the dispersed platinum catalysts are substantially smaller than those for bulk platinum. Correspondingly, the magnitudes of the peaks in the Fourier transforms are also smaller (note that the scales in the figures are not the same for the dispersed platinum catalysts and bulk platinum). These features are a consequence of a lower average coordination number and a higher degree of disorder of the platinum atoms in the dispersed catalysts. The degree of disorder is characterized by a parameter σ, which is the root mean square deviation of the interatomic distance from the equilibrium value.

From the EXAFS data in Figure 6, values of average coordination number, interatomic distance, and disorder parameter σ can be obtained for the platinum clusters in the catalysts.[11] The average number of nearest-neighbor atoms around a platinum atom in a cluster is 7 for the Pt/Al_2O_3 catalyst and 8 for the Pt/SiO_2 catalyst. The values are significantly lower than the value of 12 for bulk platinum. This result is expected, since most of the platinum atoms in the clusters are surface atoms with lower coordination numbers than the atoms in the interior of a crystal. Also, atoms at corners and edges have lower coordination numbers than the interior atoms in surface planes of crystals and become increasingly important as the size of a metal crystal decreases. Nearest-neighbor interatomic distances in the platinum clusters differ from the value for bulk platinum by less than 0.02 angstrom, which is within the estimated uncertainty in the determination of distances. Although differences in distances are small, the value of the disorder parameter σ for the platinum clusters is greater by a factor of 1.4 to 1.7 than the value for bulk platinum.

Application of Nuclear Magnetic Resonance to Metal Catalysts

In recent years the author has been collaborating with Professor Charles Slichter and his students at the University of Illinois in the application of nuclear magnetic resonance (NMR) for the characterization of platinum catalysts and molecules chemisorbed on the catalysts. Following is a brief discussion of some experimental results on ^{195}Pt NMR line shapes for a series of air-exposed platinum-on-alumina catalysts of widely different platinum dispersions.[21] The results were obtained using the spin echo technique.[22]

Data are shown in Figure 7 for catalysts in which the percentage of surface atoms in the platinum clusters or crystallites—that is, the platinum dispersion—varies by an order of magnitude from 4 to 58. In the figure, each catalyst has a designation Pt-X-R, in which X is the platinum dispersion and "R" signifies "as received," that is, air exposed. The values of platinum dispersion were determined from hydrogen chemisorption isotherms. In Figure 7 the ordinate is the NMR absorption, and the abscissa is the ratio of the static field to the characteristic NMR frequency.[21] The NMR lines are broad, in marked contrast with the narrow NMR lines observed with liquids.

For the catalysts with low platinum dispersion (4 to 11 percent), there is a pronounced peak at $H_0/\nu_0 = 1.138$ kG/MHz. The resonance for bulk

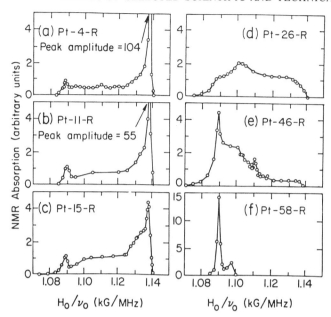

FIGURE 7   Shapes of NMR absorption lines at 77 K and at a frequency (ν_0) of 74 MHz for platinum-on-alumina catalysts of varying platinum dispersion. From Rhodes et al.[21]

platinum is observed at the same value of H_0/ν_0, which is 3.4 percent higher than the value at which the resonance is observed for H_2PtI_6, the standard reference typical of diamagnetic platinum compounds. The large displacement of the resonance for the bulk metal from the resonance for the diamagnetic platinum compounds is due to polarization of the spins of the conduction electrons in the metal. It is known as the Knight shift.[22] The peak characteristic of bulk platinum is due to atoms in the deep interior of the platinum crystallites. The small peak at H_0/ν_0 = 1.089 kG/MHz is identified with surface platinum atoms covered by chemisorbed species, which are present because the catalysts were exposed to the air. The position of the peak is in the region characteristic of diamagnetic platinum compounds, indicating that the conduction electrons of the surface platinum atoms are tied up in chemical bonds. The surface platinum atoms are therefore not metallic and do not exhibit a Knight shift. The broad structureless region of the NMR line between the bulk and surface peaks is attributed to platinum nuclei near the surface, the environments of which are sufficiently different to produce a range of Knight shifts. As the platinum dispersion increases, the surface peak at 1.089 kG/MHz becomes progressively larger, while the bulk peak at 1.138 kG/MHz becomes smaller.

No peak at 1.138 kG/MHz is evident for the catalysts with platinum dispersions of 26 to 58 percent. The catalysts with platinum dispersions of 46 and 58 percent exhibit pronounced surface peaks at 1.089 kG/MHz. The ratio of the area of the surface peak to the total area of the NMR line should be equal to the ratio of surface atoms to total atoms in the platinum clusters. In general, there was fair agreement between the value of this ratio obtained from the NMR data and the value obtained from hydrogen chemisorption data. In the determination of the area of the surface peak in cases where only the low-field side of the peak was well resolved from the line, the high-field side was drawn by assuming the peak was symmetric at about 1.089 kG/MHz.

When the adsorbed species are removed from the catalysts by a cleanup procedure involving alternate treatments with flowing hydrogen and oxygen at 573 K, followed by evacuation, the surface peak disappears from the NMR spectrum. The surface platinum atoms are then metallic, since their conduction electrons are no longer tied up in chemisorption bonds. The observation of the resonance for surface platinum atoms is therefore dependent on the presence of adsorbed species with which they form chemical bonds.

BIMETALLIC CATALYSTS

Bimetallic catalysts have played an important role in heterogeneous catalysis. They have been used extensively for fundamental investigations and have had a major technological impact, especially in the petroleum industry.[23]

Metal Alloys as Catalysts

A complicating feature in catalytic studies on metal alloys is the possibility of a difference between surface and bulk compositions. Evidence for such a difference in the case of nickel-copper (Ni-Cu) alloys is based on the observation that strong H_2 chemisorption does not occur on copper. The addition of only a few percent of Cu to Ni decreases the amount of strongly chemisorbed H_2 severalfold (Figure 8), an indication that the concentration of Cu in the surface is much greater than in the bulk.[24] Similar results have been obtained by several different groups of investigators,[24-26] and the findings are consistent with the results of studies of surface composition by Auger electron spectroscopy.[27] An important factor in determining surface composition is the nature of the gas in contact with the surface of an alloy. Thus, for nickel-gold (Ni-Au) alloys, Au concentrates in the surface in an inert atmosphere, whereas Ni is the predominant surface component in the presence of O_2.[28] If the interaction of a gas with one of the components is sufficiently strong and selective, the surface tends to become enriched in that particular component.

The emphasis in early studies on alloy catalysis was on the activity for a

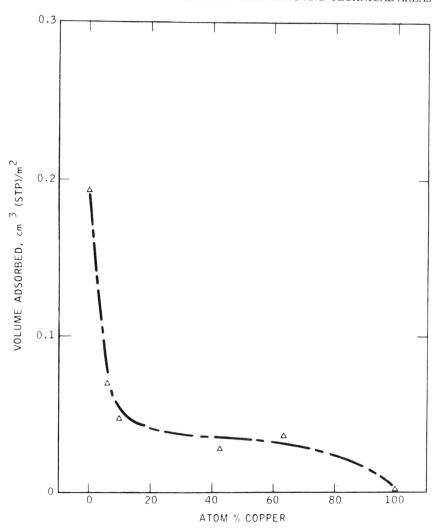

FIGURE 8 Hydrogen chemisorption on nickel-copper alloys at room temperature.[9,24] The data are for strongly chemisorbed hydrogen, i.e., the amount that cannot be desorbed at room temperature by evacuation for 10 min to a pressure of approximately 10^{-6} torr.

particular reaction, often a simple hydrogenation reaction of an unsaturated hydrocarbon. The possibility that the effect of alloying depends on the type of reaction was considered later.[24,29,30] A striking example of specificity with regard to the type of reaction is provided by work on Ni-Cu alloy catalysts in which two different reactions were investigated, the hydrogenolysis of ethane to methane and the dehydrogenation of cyclohexane to benzene. The latter type of reaction is important in the production of gasoline components in the petroleum industry.[23] The effect of Cu on the catalytic activity of Ni for cyclohexane dehydrogenation is very different from that found for ethane hydrogenolysis,[24] as shown by the data on a series of Ni-Cu alloys in Figure 9. In the case of ethane hydrogenolysis, adding only 5 atomic percent Cu to Ni decreases the catalytic activity by 3 orders of magnitude. With further addition of Cu, the activity continues to decrease. However, the activity of Ni for the dehydrogenation of cyclohexane is affected little over a wide range of Ni-Cu alloy compositions and actually increases on the addition of the first increments of Cu to Ni. Only as the catalyst composition approaches pure Cu is a marked decline in activity for this reaction observed.

Bimetallic Aggregates of Immiscible Components

The Ni-Cu alloys just discussed were prepared under conditions of complete miscibility of the two components. At this point, it is pertinent to consider a system such as ruthenium-copper (Ru-Cu), the components of which are essentially immiscible in the bulk. The crystal structures of the two metals are different, Ru having a hexagonal close-packed structure and Cu a face-centered cubic structure. Although the Ru-Cu system can hardly be considered as an alloy-forming system, it is possible to prepare bimetallic Ru-Cu aggregates that are similar to alloys such as Ni-Cu in their catalytic behavior. In such aggregates the Cu tends to cover the surface of the Ru.[31,32] Evidence for this structure comes from studies of hydrogen chemisorption capacity and ethane hydrogenolysis activity, both of which are markedly suppressed when even small amounts of Cu are present with the Ru. The interaction between the two components may be considered analogous to that which would exist in the chemisorption of Cu on Ru. The behavior of the Ru-Cu system for ethane hydrogenolysis is similar to that observed for Ni-Cu. In cyclohexane dehydrogenation to benzene, the two systems also behave similarly, in that Cu has only a small effect on dehydrogenation activity. However, pure Ru exhibits extensive hydrogenolysis of cyclohexane to alkanes of lower carbon number (mostly methane) in addition to dehydrogenation to benzene. Addition of Cu to Ru suppresses hydrogenolysis strongly relative to dehydrogenation, so that a marked increase in the selectivity to benzene is observed.

Thus copper can influence the selectivity of a Group VIII metal whether

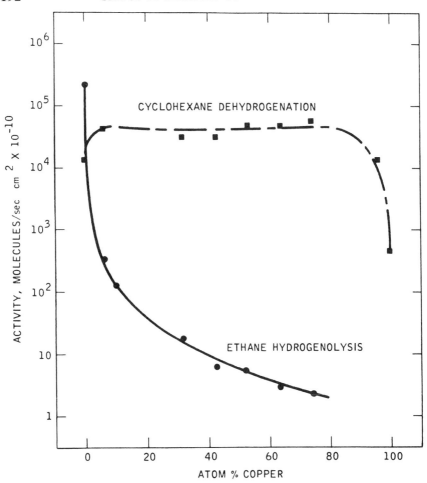

FIGURE 9 Effect of Cu composition on catalytic activity of Ni during the hydrogenolysis of ethane to methane and the dehydrogenation of cyclohexane to benzene.[8,9,24] The activities are reaction rates at 589 K.

or not it forms solid solutions with the latter in the bulk. The effect of the copper is associated with its presence in, or on top of, the surface layer of the active Group VIII metal. Selective inhibition of the hydrogenolysis activity of a Group VIII metal has also been observed when gold or silver is substituted for copper. In general, it has been observed that a Group IB metal suppresses the hydrogenolysis activity of a Group VIII metal and improves its selectivity for catalyzing such reactions as the dehydrogenation and isomerization of hydrocarbons. In accounting for the differences between hydrogenolysis and these other reactions, it has frequently been suggested that hydrogenolysis requires surface sites consisting of arrays of active metal atoms that are larger than the arrays required for the other reactions. The availability of large arrays of active metal atoms relative to small arrays decreases sharply when an inactive component such as copper is dispersed in, or on top of, the surface layer of the active metal. The possible role of an electronic interaction between the Group VIII and Group IB metal has also been considered.

Bimetallic Clusters

For industrial application of bimetallic catalysts, high metal surface areas are desirable. Highly dispersed bimetallic clusters can be prepared by impregnating a carrier with an aqueous solution of salts of the two metals of interest. The material is dried and then brought in contact with a stream of H_2 at elevated temperature to reduce the metal salts. This procedure results in the formation of bimetallic clusters even where individual metal components exhibit very low miscibility in the bulk.[23,32,33] Examples of such metal clusters that have been investigated are ruthenium-copper and osmium-copper supported on silica, in which the metal clusters cover about 1 percent of the surface of the silica. Size of the clusters ranges from about 10 to 30 angstroms in these systems.

As copper is incorporated with ruthenium or osmium in bimetallic clusters, the selectivity for conversion of cyclohexane to benzene is improved greatly (Figure 10); hydrogenolysis to alkanes is inhibited markedly, whereas dehydrogenation to benzene is relatively unaffected.[5,33] The behavior is similar to that described for unsupported Ru-Cu aggregates and therefore provides clear evidence for the interaction between Cu and the Group VIII metal on the carrier. As in the case of the unsupported materials, the copper in the bimetallic clusters is present at the surface.

When the initial research on bimetallic clusters such as ruthenium-copper and osmium-copper was conducted, the characterization of the clusters was limited to methods involving chemical probes because of the difficulty of obtaining information with physical probes. However, the situation changed markedly when it became evident that x-ray absorption spectroscopy was effective for investigating the structures of catalysts. Results of EXAFS studies on Ru-Cu and Os-Cu bimetallic clusters have provided strong evidence in support of the conclusions about structure derived from the studies with chemical probes.

The quantitative analysis of EXAFS data on bimetallic cluster catalysts has been limited to consideration of contributions of nearest-neighbor atoms to EXAFS.[34–39] In Figure 11, the EXAFS fluctuations represented by the solid line in all three fields of the figure are due to contributions from nearest-

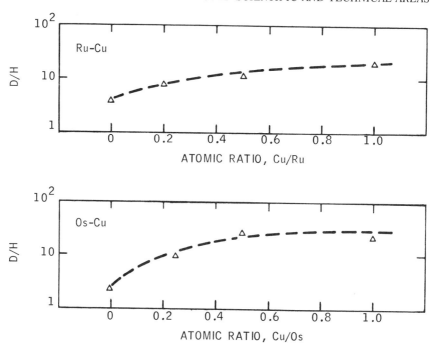

FIGURE 10 Selectivity of conversion of cyclohexane over silica-supported bimetallic clusters of ruthenium-copper and osmium-copper at 589 K, as represented by the ratio D/H,[5,33] where D is the rate of dehydrogenation of cyclohexane to benzene, and H is the rate of hydrogenolysis to alkanes.

neighbor backscattering atoms for a silica-supported osmium-copper cata-lyst.[35] The solid line was derived experimentally by inverting a Fourier transform of EXAFS data associated with the L_{III} absorption edge of osmium over a range of distances chosen to include only backscattering contributions from nearest-neighbor atoms. The points in the upper field (labeled A) of the figure represent values of an EXAFS function calculated using parameters for the osmium-copper clusters obtained from the data by an iterative least-squares fitting procedure. They provide a good illustration of the quality of fit achieved in the analysis. In the lower two fields of Figure 11, the points represent the separate contributions of nearest-neighbor copper and osmium backscattering atoms (fields B and C, respectively) to the osmium EXAFS for the osmium-copper catalyst.

In addition to the information that can be obtained from the EXAFS associated with an x-ray absorption edge, valuable information can be obtained from an analysis of the structure of the edge itself. From a study of L_{III} or L_{II} absorption threshold resonances, one can obtain information on

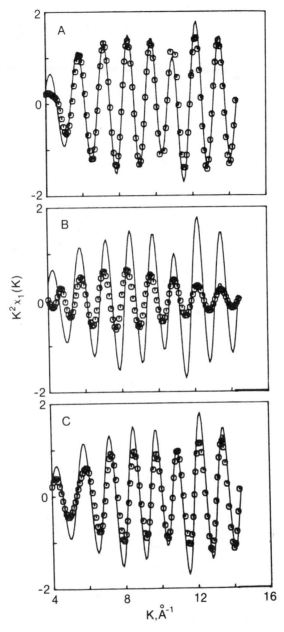

FIGURE 11 Contributions of nearest-neighbor copper and osmium backscattering atoms (points in fields B and C, respectively) to the EXAFS associated with the osmium L_{III} absorption edge of a silica-supported osmium-copper catalyst containing 2 wt % Os and 0.66 wt % Cu. (The points in field A show how the individual contributions combine to describe the experimental EXAFS represented by the solid line.) From Sinfelt et al.[35]

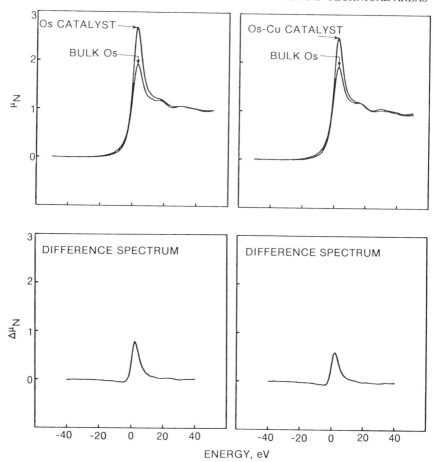

FIGURE 12   The effect of copper on the threshold x-ray absorption resonance associated with the L_{III} absorption edge of the osmium in a silica-supported catalyst. Upper left section compares the resonance for a silica-supported osmium catalyst containing 1 wt % osmium with that for pure metallic osmium, the extent of increase indicated in the lower left. A similar comparison is made on the right between osmium-copper clusters and pure metallic osmium. From Sinfelt et al.[35]

electronic transitions from a core level, $2p_{3/2}$ or $2p_{1/2}$, respectively, to vacant d states of the absorbing atom.[40,41] The electronic transitions are sensitive to the chemical environment of the absorbing atom.[42] In the case of silica-supported osmium-copper catalysts, the magnitude of the absorption threshold resonance associated with the osmium atom is decreased by the presence of the copper. This effect is illustrated in Figure 12 for the L_{III} absorption edge of osmium.[35] The absorption coefficient μ_N is a normalized coefficient.[42] In the upper half of the figure, the left-hand section compares the resonance for a silica-supported osmium catalyst containing 1 weight percent osmium with that for pure metallic osmium. The magnitude of the resonance is higher for the osmium clusters dispersed on the support, the extent of increase being indicated by the difference spectrum in the lower left-hand section of the figure. This effect is similar to that observed for iridium and platinum dispersed on alumina.[42] In the upper right-hand section of Figure 12, the magnitude of the resonance for silica-supported osmium-copper clusters is again higher than that for pure metallic osmium, the extent of increase being indicated again by the difference spectrum in the lower right-hand section of the figure. However, the increase in this case is about 30 percent lower than is observed when the supported osmium alone is compared with pure metallic osmium—that is, the area under the difference spectral line in the lower right-hand section is about 30 percent lower than the area under the corresponding spectral line in the lower left-hand section of the figure.

In the case of the catalyst containing osmium alone on silica, the osmium clusters behave as if they are more electron deficient than pure metallic osmium, that is, there appear to be more unfilled d states to accommodate the electron transitions from the $2p_{3/2}$ core level of the absorbing atom. In the silica-supported osmium-copper clusters, however, the osmium atoms appear to be less electron deficient than they are in the pure osmium clusters dispersed on silica. The presence of the copper thus appears to decrease the number of unfilled d states associated with the osmium atoms.

Up to this point the discussion of bimetallic clusters has been concerned with combinations of a Group VIII metal and a Group IB metal. Another type of bimetallic cluster of interest is a combination of atoms of two Group VIII metals, for example, platinum-iridium.[43-45] Dispersed platinum-iridium clusters can be prepared by bringing a carrier such as silica or alumina into contact with an aqueous solution of chloroplatinic and chloroiridic acids. After the impregnated carrier is dried and possibly heated to 525–575 K, it is exposed to flowing hydrogen at a temperature of 575–775 K. The resulting material contains platinum-iridium clusters dispersed on the carrier.

An x-ray absorption spectrum at 100 K showing the L absorption edges of iridium and platinum[36] is given in Figure 13 for a catalyst containing bimetallic clusters of platinum and iridium. The data were obtained over a wide enough range of energies of the x-ray photons to include all of the L absorption edges of iridium and platinum. Since the extended fine structure associated with the L_{III} edge of iridium is observable to energies of 1,200–1,300 eV beyond the edge, there is overlap of the EXAFS associated with the L_{III} edges of iridium and platinum in the case of a catalyst containing both of these elements. Separating the iridium EXAFS from the platinum EXAFS in the region of overlap is therefore necessary in the analysis of the data.[36] Briefly, the results of the analysis on interatomic distances indicate

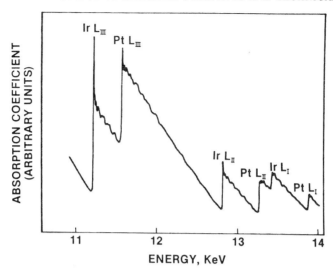

FIGURE 13   X-ray absorption spectrum at 100 K in the region of the *L* absorption edges of iridium and platinum for a catalyst containing platinum-iridium clusters. From Sinfelt, Via, and Lytle.[36]

that the average composition of the first coordination shell of atoms (nearest neighbors) surrounding a platinum atom is different from that surrounding an iridium atom. The catalyst appears to exhibit platinum-rich and iridium-rich regions.

One might visualize a distribution of metal clusters with different compositions, some of which are platinum-rich and others of which are iridium-rich. Both the platinum-rich and iridium-rich clusters would contain substantial amounts of the minor component on the basis of the distances derived from the EXAFS data. Alternatively, one can visualize platinum-rich and iridium-rich regions within a given metal cluster. This possibility seems reasonable on the basis of surface energy considerations. According to this view, the platinum-rich region would be present at the surface, since platinum would be expected to have a lower surface energy than iridium. In support of this expectation, recent work on platinum-iridium films indicates that platinum concentrates in the surface.[46]

When the ratio of surface atoms to total atoms is equal to 0.5 for clusters containing 50 percent each of platinum and iridium, one can visualize a situation in which essentially all of the platinum is present in the surface and all the iridium in the interior. There would then be a close resemblance to the ruthenium-copper clusters considered earlier. When the ratio of surface atoms to total atoms approaches unity, the notion of complete or nearly complete segregation of the platinum in a surface layer and of iridium in a central core cannot be accommodated if the clusters are spherically symmetrical. The notion can, however, be accommodated without difficulty if the clusters have a two-dimensional, raftlike shape rather than a spherical shape. One can then visualize a central iridium or iridium-rich raft with platinum atoms around the perimeter. In highly dispersed catalysts of the type visualized here, the effect of the platinum on the catalytic properties of the iridium, and vice versa, would presumably be a consequence of the interaction between the two components at the boundary.

Catalysts containing platinum-iridium clusters dispersed on alumina are of interest in the reforming of petroleum fractions for production of high-octane-number gasoline components. They are more active and exhibit much better activity maintenance than the platinum-alumina catalysts originally used in reforming.[23,43] In parallel with the development of platinum-iridium catalysts in the Exxon laboratories, another reforming catalyst containing platinum and rhenium (a Group VIIA metal) was under development in the laboratories of the Chevron Corporation. During the 1970s, platinum-iridium and platinum-rhenium catalysts were introduced widely in catalytic reformers. The use of these catalysts was a key factor in making unleaded gasoline feasible.

OTHER CATALYTIC MATERIALS

Metals are key components of catalysts for a number of well-known and important chemical processes. The same can also be said for various nonmetallic materials.

A particularly impressive example is the class of materials known as aluminosilicates, which are widely used in the catalytic cracking of petroleum fractions. In the cracking process, large hydrocarbon molecules are converted into smaller molecules. The resulting hydrocarbons provide components for products such as gasoline and heating oil. The cracking activity of aluminosilicates is due to the presence of acidic sites in the surface.[47] The existence of these sites is readily demonstrated by the affinity of basic molecules such as ammonia, pyridine, or quinoline for the surface of aluminosilicates. In typical cracking catalysts, the structure may be viewed as consisting of tetrahedrally coordinated silicon and aluminum atoms linked through the sharing of oxygen atoms at the corners of SiO_4 and AlO_4 tetrahedra. For aluminum-containing tetrahedra bonded at all four corners to silicon atoms in tetrahedral coordination, there is an excess of one unit of negative charge. This arises because a trivalent aluminum atom has been substituted for tetravalent silicon in a silica structure. Consequently, there must be present a compensating positive charge to provide electroneutrality. A proton coordinated to the structure satisfies this requirement and is strongly acidic in its behavior.

The first aluminosilicates used as cracking catalysts were amorphous; that is, the primary crystallites of the materials were too small to be observed by the usual x-ray diffraction procedures for obtaining structural information. They included naturally occurring clays, which were acid treated, and synthetic aluminosilicates. Such materials were used as cracking catalysts for almost three decades, beginning in 1936 with the first commercial application of the Houdry catalytic cracking process.[48]

In the early 1960s crystalline aluminosilicates (zeolites) were introduced in catalytic cracking. The primary structural units of these materials are still SiO_4 and AlO_4 tetrahedra, but larger secondary units are now clearly distinguishable. The secondary units are composed of the primary tetrahedra, and exist in the form of regular polyhedra, rings, or chains. Various types of zeolite structures are obtained by linking these secondary units together in different ways. In the zeolites commonly used in catalytic cracking, which are known as Y-zeolites, there are internal cavities of uniform size. The cavities are interconnected through well-defined openings or windows, giving rise to an intracrystalline pore structure. The diameters of the internal cavities and interconnecting windows are approximately 12 and 8 angstroms, respectively. Catalysis occurs within the intracrystalline pore structure.

Crystalline aluminosilicates have been responsible for dramatic improvements in the cracking process. The amount of gasoline produced from a gas-oil fraction is much higher than can be obtained with amorphous aluminosilicate catalysts.[49] The octane number of the gasoline is also higher, because of higher contents of aromatics and isoparaffins. The much higher activities of the zeolite cracking catalysts relative to the amorphous aluminosilicates[50] stimulated investigations into the acidities of these new materials. Results obtained by a variety of methods indicated that the density of Brönsted acid sites was much higher for the Y-type zeolites used in cracking than for amorphous aluminosilicates.[51] The higher selectivity to aromatics and isoparaffins indicates that hydrogen transfer reactions occur more readily with zeolites as catalysts.[52] The excellent performance of zeolites in catalytic cracking has intensified research on these materials. The research has led to new forms of zeolites and to new catalytic applications.[49,53,54]

Other examples of oxide catalysts of great industrial importance are the bismuth molybdate systems used in the production of acrylonitrile and the cobalt molybdate catalysts used in the desulfurization of petroleum fractions.[55] The former generally contain additional components such as K_2O and P_2O_5 and use silica as a support. The cobalt molybdate catalysts are sulfided in actual operation and contain alumina as a supporting material. These examples constitute only a small fraction of the oxide materials that have found application in catalysis.

Another group of materials with potential interest as catalysts includes various carbides, nitrides, and borides of the transition metals.[56] Such materials have the beneficial feature of high thermal stability and at the same time offer the possibility of having catalytic properties of a kind normally associated with precious metals.[57,58] The further exploration of these materials in catalysis would appear to be worthwhile. An important aspect of research in this area is the development of methods for preparation of materials with high surface areas.

CONCLUSIONS

Catalysts are fascinating materials, embracing many different chemical compositions. The elucidation of their structures and surface properties provides exciting challenges for scientists. The development of new methods for probing catalytic materials has greatly extended our capabilities for investigation at a microscopic level. Such methods provide information to complement that obtained from more traditional studies of chemisorption, kinetics, and reaction mechanisms. The synthesis of new materials for application as catalysts is a continuing activity, with a great deal of opportunity for the future. On a long-term basis, the outlook for the field of catalysis is excellent.

NOTES

1. J. H. Sinfelt, Perkin Medal address in Chem. Ind., No. 11, pp. 403–406 (June 4, 1984).
2. G. Bylinsky, Fortune, pp. 82–88 (May 27, 1985).
3. J. H. Sinfelt, Science **195**, 641 (1977).
4. J. H. Sinfelt, Sci. Am. **253** (3), 90 (1985).
5. J. H. Sinfelt, Rev. Mod. Phys. **51** (3), 569 (1979).
6. M. Boudart, *Kinetics of Chemical Processes* (Prentice-Hall, Englewood Cliffs, N.J., 1968), p. 61.
7. H. Voge and C. R. Adams, Adv. Catal. **17**, 151 (1967).
8. J. H. Sinfelt, Adv. Catal. **23**, 91 (1973).
9. J. H. Sinfelt, Catal. Rev. Sci. Eng. **9** (1), 147 (1974).
10. J. H. Sinfelt, Prog. Solid State Chem. **10** (2), 55 (1975).
11. G. H. Via, J. H. Sinfelt, and F. W. Lytle, J. Chem. Phys. **71**, 690 (1979).
12. G. R. Wilson and W. K. Hall, J. Catal. **17**, 190 (1970).
13. R. de L. Kronig, Z. Phys. **70**, 317 (1931).
14. R. de L. Kronig, Z. Phys. **75**, 191 (1932).
15. R. de L. Kronig, Z. Phys. **75**, 468 (1932).
16. D. E. Sayers, F. W. Lytle, and E. A. Stern, Phys. Rev. Lett. **27**, 1204 (1971).
17. F. W. Lytle, D. Sayers, and E. Stern, Phys. Rev. B **11**, 4825 (1975).
18. B. M. Kincaid and P. Eisenberger, Phys. Rev. Lett. **34**, 1361 (1975).
19. J. H. Sinfelt, G. H. Via, and F. W. Lytle, Catal. Rev. Sci. Eng. **26** (1), 81 (1984).
20. D. E. Sayers, F. W. Lytle, and E. A. Stern, Adv. X-Ray Anal. **13**, 248 (1970).

21. H. E. Rhodes, P.-K. Wang, H. T. Stokes, C. P. Slichter, and J. H. Sinfelt, Phys. Rev. B **26**, 3559 (1982).

22. C. P. Slichter, *Principles of Magnetic Resonance,* 2nd ed. (Springer, New York, 1980).

23. J. H. Sinfelt, *Bimetallic Catalysts: Discoveries, Concepts, and Applications* (Wiley, New York, 1983).

24. J. H. Sinfelt, J. L. Carter, and D. J. C. Yates, J. Catal. **24**, 283 (1972).

25. P. van der Plank and W. M. H. Sachtler, J. Catal. **7**, 300 (1967).

26. D. A. Cadenhead and N. J. Wagner, J. Phys. Chem. **72**, 2775 (1968).

27. C. R. Helms, J. Catal. **36**, 114 (1975).

28. F. L. Williams and M. Boudart, J. Catal. **30**, 438 (1973).

29. J. H. Sinfelt, A. E. Barnett, and G. W. Dembinski, U.S. Patent 3 442 973 (1969).

30. J. H. Sinfelt, A. E. Barnett, and J. L. Carter, U.S. Patent 3 617 518 (1971).

31. J. H. Sinfelt, Y. L. Lam, J. A. Cusumano, and A. E. Barnett, J. Catal. **42**, 227 (1976).

32. J. H. Sinfelt, Acc. Chem. Res. **10**, 15 (1977).

33. J. H. Sinfelt, J. Catal. **29**, 308 (1973).

34. J. H. Sinfelt, G. H. Via, and F. W. Lytle, J. Chem. Phys. **72**, 4832 (1980).

35. J. H. Sinfelt, G. H. Via, F. W. Lytle, and R. B. Greegor, J. Chem. Phys. **75**, 5527 (1981).

36. J. H. Sinfelt, G. H. Via, and F. W. Lytle, J. Chem. Phys. **76**, 2779 (1982).

37. G. Meitzner, G. H. Via, F. W. Lytle, and J. H. Sinfelt, J. Chem. Phys. **78**, 882 (1983).

38. G. Meitzner, G. H. Via, F. W. Lytle, and J. H. Sinfelt, J. Chem. Phys. **78**, 2533 (1983).

39. G. Meitzner, G. H. Via, F. W. Lytle, and J. H. Sinfelt, J. Chem. Phys. **83**, 353 (1985).

40. N. F. Mott, Proc. Phys. Soc. London **62**, 416 (1949).

41. Y. Cauchois and N. F. Mott, Philos. Mag. **40**, 1260 (1949).

42. F. W. Lytle, P. S. P. Wei, R. B. Greegor, G. H. Via, and J. H. Sinfelt, J. Chem. Phys. **70**, 4849 (1979).

43. J. H. Sinfelt, U.S. Patent 3 953 368 (1976).

44. J. H. Sinfelt and G. H. Via, J. Catal. **56**, 1 (1979).

45. R. L. Garten and J. H. Sinfelt, J. Catal. **62**, 127 (1980).

46. F. J. Kuijers and V. Ponec, Appl. Surf. Sci. **2**, 43 (1978).

47. G. A. Mills, E. R. Boedeker, and A. G. Oblad, J. Am. Chem. Soc. **72**, 1554 (1950).

48. E. Houdry, W. F. Burt, A. E. Pew, Jr., and W. A. Peters, Petroleum Refiner, **17** (11), 574 (1938).

49. H. Heinemann, Catal. Rev. Sci. Eng. **23** (1 & 2), 315 (1981).

50. J. N. Miale, N. Y. Chen, and P. B. Weisz, J. Catal. **6**, 278 (1966).

51. B. C. Gates, J. R. Katzer, and G. C. A. Schuit, *Chemistry of Catalytic Processes* (McGraw-Hill, New York, 1979), p. 80.

52. P. B. Weisz, Chem. Technol. 498 (1973).

53. G. T. Kerr, Catal. Rev. Sci. Eng. **23** (1 & 2), 281 (1981).

54. J. A. Rabo, Catal. Rev. Sci. Eng. **23** (1 & 2), 293 (1981).

55. Note 51, pp. 366–379, 411–422.

56. R. B. Levy, in *Advanced Materials in Catalysis,* edited by J. J. Burton and R. L. Garten (Academic Press, New York, 1977), pp. 101–127.

57. J. M. Muller and F. G. Gault, Bull. Soc. Chim. Fr. **2**, 416 (1970).

58. R. B. Levy and M. Boudart, Science **181**, 547 (1973).

The Role of Chemistry in Materials Science

GEORGE M. WHITESIDES, MARK S. WRIGHTON,
and GEORGE PARSHALL

Chemistry has always been an indispensable contributor to materials science. Materials are synthesized from chemical precursors and assembled using processes requiring chemical transformations. Of the six major classes of products produced by the chemical industry—fuels, commodity chemicals, polymers, agricultural chemicals, pharmaceuticals, and specialty chemicals—two contribute directly to materials science.[1] Synthetic organic polymers constitute a major class of materials, and specialty chemicals (e.g., paints, corrosion inhibitors, lubricants, adhesives and adhesion promoters, electronics chemicals) are essential components of many assembled materials systems. Until recently, chemistry has been relatively inactive in other major areas of materials: metallurgy has attracted little activity from chemists, and only in the last few years has chemistry again become involved in ceramics.

The importance of chemistry to materials science has been masked by at least two factors. First, the most obvious contribution of chemistry to materials—large-volume organic polymers—is now a mature technology. These substances are perceived (incorrectly) as being scientifically unexciting. The very scale of these large-volume materials and the evolutionary nature of changes in the technology for their production and use have masked the recent emergence and application of exciting new classes of polymeric materials.[2,3] Both large-volume commodity polymers and small-volume specialty polymers are subsumed under the general term "polymers," and the interest and potential of the latter is overshadowed by the volume and importance of the former.

Second, the many small components required for the operations of materials systems—e.g., adhesives, lubricants, corrosion inhibitors, mold release agents, surfactants, imaging systems—are indispensable but almost invisible in the final systems. Overall, chemistry is perceived as playing a supporting role in materials science, and a relatively unexciting one at that. This situation will change. Materials science is facing problems for which existing systems do not offer satisfactory solutions. The great strength of materials science has rested in its ability to process, combine, and fabricate final systems from existing materials (e.g., metals, polymers, ceramics). The potential for major innovation through improved processing of existing materials is not decreasing, but many important problems cannot be solved simply by processing. The strength of chemistry is its ability to design, synthesize, and produce new materials. The current requirement in materials science for new classes of materials capable of meeting high-performance specifications has stimulated great interest in chemistry. Both the intellectual and practical commercial aspects of materials design and production are becoming major foci of research and development in chemistry.[4]

This chapter outlines representative recent contributions of chemistry to materials science, suggests areas of materials science to which chemical research might directly contribute in the immediate future, and speculates about the long-range impact of chemical research in producing new types of materials systems and new concepts for materials science. It is not a comprehensive survey of the relations between chemistry and materials science. Rather, it offers informed opinions concerning areas in which new chemistry might lead to new materials and ultimately to new, technologically significant materials systems.

THE CURRENT ROLE OF CHEMISTRY IN MATERIALS SCIENCE

The production of a final assembled object can be broken down into three major processes (Figure 1). The components of the system—polymers, metals, ceramics, and functional agents—are prepared or synthesized from raw materials. These components are then processed into materials having desired properties and shapes, and, finally, are assembled into the final product. Chemistry contributes to all these stages but plays its largest role in the first—the synthesis of individual components. The importance of the adhesives, protective coatings, lubricants, and other products used in later stages of the process is often overlooked. One major change expected in the future is the more active involvement of chemistry in the later stages of the transformation from raw materials to final product.

Ceramics processing is an example of a field of opportunity for chemists. In ceramics processing, a ceramic powder is typically suspended in an aqueous or nonaqueous medium with the help of wetting agents and dispersants. A polymeric binder is added to convert the dispersion to a thick paste. Once the "green" ceramic paste has been cast or molded, the polymeric binder is extracted or pyrolyzed to leave a hard, brittle ceramic residue in the final

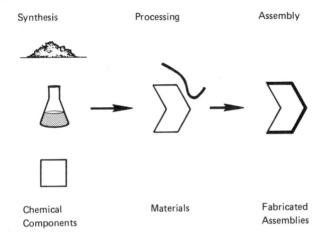

Synthesis   Processing   Assembly

Chemical   Materials   Fabricated
Components   Assemblies

FIGURE 1   The materials production process.

shape. High-temperature sintering and densification yield the finished ceramic product, somewhat smaller than the "green" object. Both the binder pyrolysis and the sintering process are subject to catalysis by chemical processes that are totally empirical in character. Major opportunities for improvements such as reduction in pyrolysis and sintering temperatures and control in crystallite structure in the final object await better understanding of the chemistry.

In fact, there are three distinct ways in which chemistry may contribute to materials science: first, in the design of chemical additives (coupling agents, lubricants, corrosion inhibitors, barrier films) to facilitate processing, assembly, and performance of the final products; second, in the synthesis of major chemical components (high-performance matrix resins, nonlinear optical materials, ceramic precursors) that result in desirable properties and promote processing in the final pieces; third, in providing new chemical starting materials and reactions for use in processing.

It is useful to consider the contributions of several traditional disciplines to materials science (Figure 2) and to anticipate new contributions from each. The strength of chemistry is its ability to manipulate matter at the molecular level: it synthesizes starting components in materials science, provides techniques for analyzing molecular and atomic structures, and generates the understanding required to manipulate properties by changing structure at the molecular level. Physics is particularly successful in rationalizing the delocalized and cooperative properties of materials, and it provides new analytical and processing techniques. Engineering contributes techniques for design, processing, and assembly of fabricated structures, and an understanding (or,

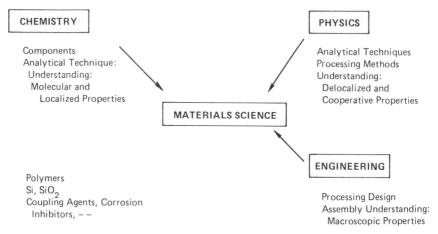

FIGURE 2   Contributions of various disciplines to materials science.

in some cases, empirical modeling) of important macroscopic materials properties.

The general character of the contributions from chemistry to materials science is not likely to change. As chemistry turns increasingly to investigations of the solid state, however, and becomes more active in connecting the molecular structure of starting components with the macroscopic properties of final assemblies, the capability of chemistry to contribute throughout materials science will increase. The major classes of substances derived explicitly by chemical synthesis and processing, and used in materials science, have been organic polymers. Polymers are low-density, processable materials having desirable properties such as high tensile strength or elasticity. These are among the properties one can expect from new organic materials. The great power of organic chemistry is its versatility: many organic compounds with different properties can be synthesized. It is this versatility—the ability to manipulate molecular-level structure and produce materials with desired properties—that offers hope for the generation of fundamentally new types of materials.

The disadvantages associated with organic materials have been low stability at high temperatures, high sensitivity to oxidation, and low electrical and thermal conductivity. Although it is unlikely that the temperature stability and oxidation resistance of even new organic materials will ever reach those of ceramics and stable metals, strategies for improving these properties are well understood in theory and are being actively explored experimentally.[5]

Perhaps as important as the potential development of new organic components for materials systems is the opportunity afforded by other classes of chemicals—inorganics, organometallics, and biologicals. Their potential utility to materials science has only begun to be explored. Moreover, their combinations with one another and with more traditional organic materials offer opportunities for entirely new types of systems.

Two examples suggest the current role of chemistry in materials science. The first concerns the production of carbon-fiber-reinforced composite structures; the second illustrates the importance of organosilicon chemistry in materials science.

Carbon-Fiber-Reinforced Composites

Carbon-fiber-reinforced composite materials are increasingly substituted for metals in situations where the ratio of weight to strength is a critical issue. The largest current use of these materials is in military aircraft, but their use is being extended to commercial aircraft and to other structural applications as well. The contributions of chemistry to this technology include the production of both the carbon fiber and the matrix resin as shown in Figure 3 with polyether ether ketone (PEEK). The production of carbon fiber involves many chemical steps: conversion of propylene to acrylonitrile (a

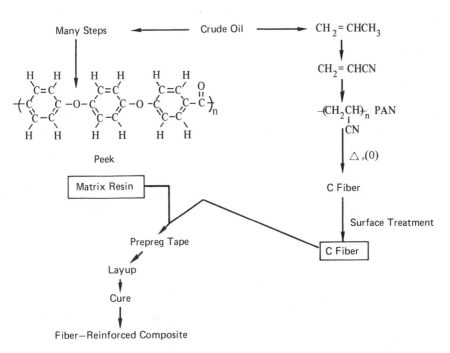

FIGURE 3 The chemistry of fiber-reinforced composites, as shown with polyether ether ketone (PEEK).

commodity chemical), conversion of acrylonitrile to a special grade of polyacrylonitrile (PAN), spinning of this polymer into fiber form, and careful oxidation and heat treatment of the fiber under tension to produce carbonized fiber. The corresponding pathway from crude oil to PEEK is too complex to trace in detail, but is shown generally in Figure 3. This type of polymer—a high-performance engineering polymer—represents a major accomplishment in molecular design and chemical synthesis and processing. The combination of PEEK with carbon fiber to form the prepregnated (prepreg) tape from which complex aeronautical shapes are commonly constructed also depends strongly on chemistry. A major problem in this process is to achieve intimate contact between the fiber and the matrix polymer; the resin is viscous and the fibers are fragile. The electrochemical surface treatment applied to the carbon fiber before wetting it with the resin is essential to the success of the final composite.

Chemistry has been little involved in the later stages of the process—layup of the prepreg tape and cure of the resulting multilayer system to the final object. However, it is precisely in such areas that chemistry may be able to contribute most effectively in the immediate future. The major mode of stress- or impact-induced failure of fiber-reinforced composites is fracture occurring at the interface between the layers of tape and at the interface between the fiber and the matrix polymer.[6] Examination of these interfaces and development of chemical treatments and additives to strengthen them is just beginning. Such studies offer probably the best avenue to improvement of the performance of composites generated by this highly evolved materials technology. It is superfluous to point out the complexity and the sophistication of the chemical technology already used to produce matrix polymers and reinforcing fibers for composites. More to the point is the fact that much greater sophistication can and will be applied to certain aspects of each. Further, the chemical aspects of the later stages in this process—especially the molecular tailoring of the many interfaces between the components of these systems—offer extraordinary opportunity both for the development of new interfacial science and for the design, synthesis, and production of chemical reagents to control the properties of these interfaces in useful ways.

Organosilicon Chemistry

A second representative example of the role of chemistry in present-day materials science is provided by the chemistry of derivatives of silicon (Figure 4). The central column in the figure outlines the current process used to prepare the highly purified silicon that provides the basic materials for the production of semiconductor devices. This process depends upon the conversion of the raw material (silicon dioxide) to a volatile form (silicon tetrachloride) that can be purified by distillation. An alternative version of this

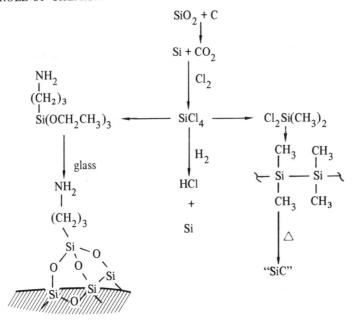

FIGURE 4 Chemistry of derivatives of silicon. Center column shows the process for preparing the highly purified silicon used in semiconductor devices. At left is the conversion of $SiCl_4$ to triethoxypropylaminosilane, used in the production of glass fiber–reinforced composites. At right is the route to development of silicon carbide fibers. $SiCl_4$ is converted to dimethyldichlorosilane and then to the polymer $Si(CH_3)_2$. The resulting structure, SiC, remains unclear.

scheme involving silane (SiH_4) as the penultimate volatile silicon compound is being developed.

An alternative technology, critical for materials science, that depends upon the production of silicon derivatives is based on the conversion of $SiCl_4$ in several steps to triethoxypropylaminosilane $[(CH_3CH_2O)_3SiCH_2CH_2CH_2NH_2]$ (shown in left-hand part of Figure 4). This compound reacts with hydroxyl groups present on the surface of glass, silicon, and related materials and attaches the amine-terminated silane covalently to these surfaces. This surface modification is a component in the production of, among other things, glass-fiber-reinforced composites. Without the silane surface modification, adhesion between the glass fiber and the matrix is poor, and the resulting composites have unsatisfactory mechanical properties.[7]

The right-hand part of Figure 4 sketches a new technology in development. Silicon tetrachloride can be converted to dimethyldichlorosilane and then to a polymer having elemental composition $Si(CH_3)_2$ by using the techniques of organometallic chemistry. Thermal rearrangement of this polymer, spinning into a fiber, and controlled oxidation and heat treatment provide the most thoroughly developed route to materials loosely called "silicon carbide fibers." The detailed structure of this "SiC" remains unclear. It appears to be a ceramic glass having approximately this composition, and the mechanical properties of these fibers are not yet those of silicon carbide whiskers. Nonetheless, this sophisticated combination of organometallic chemistry, polymer chemistry, and fiber technology typifies a major activity at the border between chemistry and materials science—that is, the generation of useful ceramic forms from organometallic precursors.

PROBLEMS IN MATERIALS SCIENCE AND
POTENTIAL SOLUTIONS THROUGH CHEMISTRY

The preceding examples illustrate the role of chemistry in materials science. Chemistry is critical at the front end of the materials chain in providing components and reagents; its involvement (although not necessarily its importance) declines in the processing and assembly steps. Does existing chemical science have the potential to solve important problems in existing materials processes? Are there classes of problems for which one might expect useful solutions in the short term (less than five years)?

Any near-term solution to problems with a commercial process must involve modification of existing technology rather than development of fundamentally new ones. Opportunities to develop specific chemical components and reagents that add value and performance to existing materials systems abound, and many of these opportunities seem well within the reach of existing chemical technology. However, the most important issue in these types of problems is often as much one of management as of science or technology. The market for an additive—for example, a coupling agent or adhesion promoter—that adds value to a materials system may be small, even if the value added is large. Thus it may not be worth the effort of a commodity-oriented chemical company to develop such an additive for sale to others, and it is often outside the competence of a typical specialty chemical company to evaluate performance of additives in complex materials systems. The users most competent to judge the value of such new additives and to take advantage of the value they add—the materials processors themselves— may not be willing or competent to carry out the chemistry required. University chemistry laboratories are typically not familiar with problems in materials science, and again, are unable either to test the performance of compounds they might make or to arrange for commercialization of successful materials. Thus, although the exploration of problems depending on the design, synthesis, and production of specialty additives for materials systems seems practical in technical terms, it is unclear how or where this type of research should be conducted. Government laboratories and university-industry collaborative groups seem possibilities. A few specific problems and the possible role of chemistry in their solution will illustrate some of the issues.

Multilayer Substrates for Electronics

The fabrication of high-performance microelectronic devices depends increasingly on a sophisticated technology in which individual components are located on complex substrates containing the necessary power distribution lines and interconnects. These substrates comprise multiple layers of ceramic (alumina), metal, and thin-film organic insulators. The fabrication of these substrates is made difficult by a number of problems, prominent among which is that of ensuring adhesion between the different components. These components commonly exhibit widely divergent coefficients of thermal expansion and fundamentally incompatible surface chemistries. Current adhesion promoters and coupling agents used in these devices are not entirely satisfactory, and the mechanisms of interfacial failure are being explored. This area represents an important opportunity for chemistry—the development of new series of coupling agents designed and optimized to improve adhesion between the ceramic, organic, and metallic components of these multilayer substrates.

The packaging of microelectronic components, which are commonly assembled on fiberglass-reinforced epoxy circuit boards, presents many other significant problems. As the density of circuit interconnects on these boards increases along with requirements for flexibility and durability, the intrinsic limitations of such boards become more evident. For instance, delamination resulting from adhesive failure at the epoxy-fiberglass interface during drilling of interconnect holes can cause short-circuiting between leads and consequently is a serious problem in large, high-density circuit boards. In the near term, development of improved, water-resistant coupling agents to improve adhesion between fiberglass and epoxy will improve this technology. In the long term, development of homogeneous substrates or composite substrates that have fewer problems with delamination will be important.

The production of ceramics for microelectronics presents additional problems. The most commonly used ceramic in microelectronics is alumina. It has a high dielectric constant which reduces the speed of electrical signal transmission. Ceramics with a lower dielectric constant would be preferable, but none of the present alternatives is as easily processed as alumina. The development of new, processable, low-dielectric-constant ceramics using organometallic ceramic precursors and sol-gel methods is attractive.

The microelectronic packaging requirements for low-temperature sintering, low dielectric constant, and controlled thermal expansion cannot be met by conventional ceramic materials such as alumina. New multiphase ceramic composites offer many of the needed properties, but the relationships between structure and property are highly empirical. Chemistry can make an enormous contribution by providing new materials and by making possible rational design of composite materials with preselected properties.

Even when conventional materials such as alumina possess adequate electronic properties, they often have unacceptable particle characteristics and levels of impurities. The electronic ceramics industry is moving toward chemically synthesized ceramic powders in which sol-gel[8] and other innovative techniques yield materials that disperse, form, and sinter more readily and yield more acceptable physical properties.

High-Performance Composite Structures

Tailoring the properties of the interface between reinforcing component and matrix is a major application of chemistry to improving the performance of composites. Failure in multilayer fiber-reinforced composite structures often occurs either at the fiber-matrix interface or at the matrix-matrix interface. The surface treatments now used to modify the surface properties of reinforcing fibers in composites are largely empirical. Coupling agents and adhesion promoters operate by principles that are poorly understood and fail by mechanisms that are only partially understood. The practicality of developing fundamentally different types of adhesion promoters is high if the principles of adhesion promotion in these systems is better understood.

An example of the need for improved performance of a fiber-composite interface can be seen in efforts to develop ceramic-metal composites for use in automobile engines.[9] Because of the poor adhesion between the dissimilar materials in these composites, the designer of an aluminum connecting rod reinforced with alumina fibers must deal with the fact that aluminum metal does not wet aluminum oxide. This problem has been partially solved in an empirical way, but a better understanding of surface chemistry would be a major step toward a more satisfactory solution. The payoff would be broad commercial use of lightweight aluminum connecting rods in automobile engines to achieve greater fuel economy and improved acceleration.

New Electronic Materials

Chemistry already plays an important role in the fabrication of microelectronic devices. For example, photoresist technology and etch processes are crucial in achieving state-of-the-art integrated circuits. Understanding of the basic chemistry underlying the achievement of very-large-scale integration (VLSI) lags somewhat behind the technological achievements so far.

However, it is clear that emphasis on the chemistry of electronic materials will yield important advances in the next generations of devices.[10–14]

Part of the basis for an increasingly important role for molecular chemistry is that the size of individual devices now approaches the size of large molecules that chemists are accustomed to characterizing. An even more significant consideration is that new electronic materials and devices will be needed in certain technological applications. Most notably, the fabrication of semiconductor microelectronic devices from molecular precursors may emerge as the method of choice for such devices as infrared detectors and semiconductor lasers.

The use of organometallic substances as precursors to semiconductor materials of device quality is obviously an area where chemists' knowledge can be profitably applied. In particular, the purity of the materials and their handling and storage pose unprecedented problems because of the performance demanded of microelectronic devices. There is a clear need for chemists to become involved in the science of semiconductor devices, to appreciate the materials properties required. For instance, remarkable progress has been made in the fabrication of certain gallium-arsenide–based devices through application of chemistry, but a more thorough understanding of semiconductor growth is required to exploit metal-organics in chemical vapor deposition growth processes.

Molecular chemistry and associated particle-assisted (photon, electron, and ion) deposition processes represent another area where molecular chemists can contribute directly to the fabrication of electronic devices. The fundamentals of laser chemistry of small molecules can be addressed by chemists and may well lead to new ways of fabricating complex devices. By taking advantage of various nonlinear phenomena, it is possible to produce structures that are smaller than the wavelength of the light used to cause deposition of a solid material, and there is the prospect of nanometer-sized structures from focused ion or electron beams.

Although hybrid electronic circuitry depends heavily on ceramics—ceramic resistors, capacitors, dielectrics, and metal-glass composite conductors—the potential exists for a new, parallel, polymer-based technology in which binders, dielectrics, and other components are made from polymers rather than ceramics. In the low-technology end of consumer electronics, such polymer-based systems are well developed. Conductors are fabricated from silver-polymer pastes and resistors from carbon-polymer composites. Although this technology will probably never reach the high end of the electronics market (aerospace, for example), it has enormous potential for modestly sophisticated electronic circuitry. Despite needs for improved stability and reliability of polymer-based systems, the ease and simplicity of fabrication offer opportunity for more varied and less expensive circuit designs.

Polymeric Precursors to Ceramics

Recently, great interest has emerged in synthesizing polymers that can be processed (into fiber, for example) at low temperature and subsequently converted to high-performance ceramic objects.[9,15–17] One notable system has already been mentioned, namely, the formation of high-performance SiC fibers. Emphasis has been placed on forming Si_3N_4 from polymer precursors. Interestingly, the molecular materials requirements (and problems) are similar to those in the fabrication of semiconductor devices from molecular precursors in that high purity is required in the final materials. In the case of the Si_3N_4 fibers, it is important to prepare oxygen-free materials in order to realize the maximum materials performance. Like many of the precursors to important electronic materials, the precursors to ceramics are often sensitive to oxygen and water. Therefore, unusual synthesis, storage, and transfer techniques are required.

Materials in Energy Conversion

Chemistry is central to present energy systems. The diversity of energy systems ranges from the lead-acid batteries in automobiles to nuclear reactors to combustion of fossil fuels. Chemistry has contributed heavily to the science and technology of energy production and storage: electrochemical principles, separations chemistry for enrichment of uranium, catalytic chemistry involved in refining petroleum products, and combustion chemistry.[18–25] For the foreseeable future, the production of energy will involve many materials problems which chemistry should be able to solve.

In electrical energy storage, for example, recent discoveries of polymeric electronic conductors[21] may lead to the development of new kinds of energy storage systems having high energy density coupled with the advantages of high discharge rate and the ability to undergo many complete charge-discharge cycles. New electrical energy storage systems are needed for the development of electric vehicles, but more near-term applications of polymer batteries are likely to emerge from advantages associated with rechargeability and the high discharge rate.

Development of large-scale solar energy systems (based on the excitation of electrons) for the direct generation of electricity or production of chemical fuels is a possibility, but many materials problems must be solved before a large-scale technology can be realized.[22] In the last decade, chemistry has contributed significantly to the development of semiconductor-based photoelectrochemical cells that can convert sunlight to electrical energy or to chemical energy in the form of H_2 from the reduction of H_2O with an efficiency exceeding 10 percent. Advances in solar photovoltaics and solar-driven chemical fuel formation depend on the ability to synthesize photosensitive materials that cover many square miles of surface. Approaches to semiconductor fabrication involving molecular precursors may be most appropriate for such large-scale synthesis.

Catalytic chemistry is important in the production of gasoline. In the future it is likely that catalytic chemistry will continue to play a crucial role, independent of whether inexpensive fusion or solar electricity generation systems become available. There will remain a need for chemical fuels. Catalysts will be important at interfaces between solids and liquids to accelerate the interconversion of electrical and chemical energy. Devices such as fuel cells, for example, require the use of catalysts to achieve practical rates of conversion from chemical to electrical energy. If inexpensive electricity becomes available, from any source, there will be the need to develop redox catalysts for electrolyzers that will be used to produce chemical fuels.[23] Chemistry can contribute significantly to the solution of problems in heterogeneous redox catalysis, through synthesis, characterization, and theoretical modeling.

NEW MATERIALS, PROCESSES, AND STRATEGIES FROM MOLECULAR SCIENCE

The chemistry of materials is now an active field in molecular science. Major activity in this field can be expected in both industrial and university communities. The motivations of these two communities are different, but both bring important skills. The chemical industry is motivated by declining profitability of the existing commodity and agricultural chemical markets, and by the high value of materials produced for high-technology applications in electronics and defense. The profitability of these areas for a traditional chemical company is unclear, but probably irrelevant in the short term to the amount of research that will be devoted to generating new products for these areas. The chemical industry brings to materials science several important capabilities in developing economical processes for the production of chemical substances, especially polymers. For example, catalysis has been applied with great success to the development of commodity chemicals but has not been widely applied to processes leading directly to materials. The industry has organized complex, multidisciplinary development groups needed to span the range from chemical synthesis to materials testing. And, it has the financial resources required for commercial development.

University research is motivated by a growing interest in the solid state, in surface and interfacial phenomena,[26,27] and in cooperative effects occurring in solids and at surfaces. University science has generated much information in organometallic chemistry, electrochemistry, and inorganic chemistry, little of which has been applied to the development of new materials. It has available new theoretical techniques for relating molecular structure and materials properties. It provides the connections between chemistry, materials science, and apparently unrelated areas such as molecular biology. What new molecular science will chemistry provide for use in materials science in the future? Among the topics of high current activity in chemistry are the following:

New Polymers A wide variety of polymers are now being developed for use in an impressive range of engineering plastics. The commercialization of many of these materials is held up in part by difficulties in their processing, and in part by uncertainty about markets. New inorganic and organometallic polymers are being explored, and increasing activity is being focused on functional polymers (that is, polymers showing properties such as piezoelectric and ferroelectric response).

Interface-Modifying Agents The application of chemistry to the development of agents that modify interfaces has been mentioned in connection with microelectronics and composites. Related principles of molecular design and synthesis are directly applicable to the generation of new barrier films, corrosion inhibitors, and agents to control wetting, surface reflectivity, and many other phenomena.

Functional Systems Chemistry is increasingly used to generate new types of membranes for gas separation and electrochemistry. New technologies are being developed for the preparation of highly monodispersed particles in wide ranges of sizes.

Optically Responsive Systems Organic materials show more promise in applications such as information storage and optical communications, which require nonlinear optical effects, than many of the traditional inorganic materials. Perhaps this promise arises because damage induced by high radiation intensities is able to heal spontaneously.[28] Organic and organometallic materials also have the great advantage that their optical properties can be easily tailored. Their disadvantages are thermal instability and sensitivity to oxidation.

Electroactive Systems A range of organic conductors has been developed, and organic superconductors have recently been identified. Although none of these materials is likely to compete with conventional metallic conductors and superconductors in the near future, the information derived from their synthesis and study should be useful in the synthesis of weakly conducting materials for other applications, such as static charge dissipation and electromagnetic shielding.

Biocompatible Materials Practical economic considerations stemming from rising costs of health care for an aging population, coupled with the great increases in fundamental understanding of biological systems, now make it practical to design materials for applications requiring biocompatibility. Such applications include joint, tooth, tendon, and ligament replacements, vascular grafts, contact lenses, artificial skin, implantable insulin pumps and monitors, extracorporeal shunts, and related systems.

High-Purity Chemicals A key consideration in the fabrication of microelectronic devices is the purity in the chemical components used. The development of volatile organometallics promises to provide new routes to high-purity sources of elements for use in chemical vapor deposition and related materials processing techniques. Solvents and inert gases are important components of current and future processes.

Chemistry also has important contributions to make in materials processing. Probably the most important single area for the immediate future is a scientifically unglamorous but economically and politically critical one—the development of environmentally acceptable processes. Chemical industries—both commodity and pharmaceutical—are facing this problem first. Many techniques learned in these industries for safe, low-pollution processing and for safety testing and cost-benefit analysis should be transferable to manufacturing in materials science. Other prospective new materials processes include the following:

Economical Syntheses Many materials (for example, rigid-rod polymers such as polybenzthiazole) are known that have highly attractive properties as components in materials systems but are not currently produced in significant quantities partly because no economical routes for their synthesis now exist. As the chemical industry turns increasingly to materials science for new markets, the techniques of economical catalytic synthesis should be applied to make available these types of materials.

Molecular Control of Processes Several processes (especially chemical vapor deposition) are widely used in materials processing but are poorly understood at the molecular level. Chemists are now studying the detailed kinetics and molecular mechanisms of these processes, with the objective of better control. Practical benefits from these studies will be the development of processes that will operate at higher pressure, lower temperature, with faster growth rates, and that will yield more uniform products.

Self-Assembling Systems The importance of composite structures in materials science is beyond question. An activity of increasing significance, both intellectually and practically, in chemistry is the development of techniques for generating systems that spontaneously self-assemble into microscopically heterogeneous domains—that is, to molecular-level composites. The most highly developed of these systems are phase-separated block copolymer systems. They combine desirable properties characteristic of the individual polymeric blocks but can be processed as homogeneous materials. Self-assembling or supramolecular chemistry is being actively studied in areas of chemistry from surface science (Langmuir-Blodgett–like self-assembling monolayer films) to micelles and liposomes.

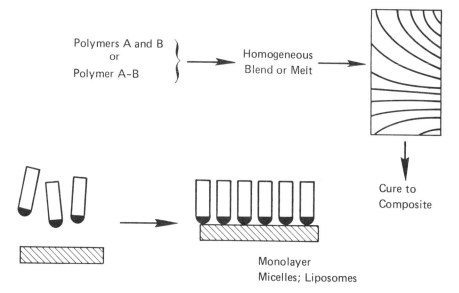

FIGURE 5   Representative examples of molecular spontaneous self-assembly.

A long-term objective of this type of work is summarized schematically in Figure 5. Polymer blends or block copolymers can be handled and formed as homogeneous blends or melts. After standing, they would phase-separate into well-defined domains with spatial arrangements appropriate for a composite structure. Appropriate curing would convert one component of the two-phase system to the equivalent of the stiff fiber reinforcement in conventional composites; the second component would remain the equivalent of the matrix resin; the interface between these two phases would transmit stress between them. The result would be the formation of an *in situ* composite in which, in principle, it would be possible to achieve geometries for the "reinforcing phase" that would be impossible using existing composite technology, and in which the perfection of the structure, the ease of its assembly, and the control of its fiber-matrix interface would be greater than could be achieved using existing technology.

RELEVANCE OF BASIC CHEMICAL RESEARCH TO MATERIALS SCIENCE

One contribution that chemistry makes to materials science is the ability to control composition and structure at the atomic and molecular levels. This ability is highly developed for molecules with molecular weight less than

2,000 (pharmaceuticals, complex natural products), moderately developed in several highly evolved routes to certain classes of macromolecules (synthetic polymers produced by condensation and addition polymerizations), and relatively undeveloped in preparations of other systems (most types of solids, thin films, and surfaces). The development of rational techniques for controlling the extended, molecular-level structure of the solid state (in both two and three dimensions) is one of the most interesting challenges now facing chemistry. The intellectual relation between molecular chemistry and materials science can be summarized in two questions:

• What are the relations between atomic- and molecular-level structure (elemental composition, bond connectivity) and macroscopic properties (e.g., tensile modulus, thermal and electrical conductivity, second-order optical response) of materials?

• What new compounds or compositions of matter will provide new properties or facilitate processing and assembly of materials? How can these new compounds be synthesized?

As these questions are answered in specific materials systems, those systems and their properties will fall under rational synthetic control and eventually under economic synthetic control.

The areas of intellectual excitement in chemistry today are the areas in which new synthetic materials will probably first emerge. A selected list includes

• Solids whose properties can be rationally controlled by varying molecular and electronic structure (organic conductors, optically responsive materials, materials with nonlinear optical effects, ferromagnetics);

• Surfaces and thin films, especially those relevant to catalysis by metals and metal oxides, and those that are active in electron transport;

• Solids having large internal surface or volume, such as zeolites, layer structures, pillared clays, and intercalates;

• Self-assembling structures, such as ordered monolayer films, liposomes, liquid crystals, micelles, and ordered two-phase systems.

Several other areas of chemistry that are, in principle, important to materials science are either inactive or in a state in which development is steady but few new ideas are being introduced. These fields are less active than those mentioned previously, either because of the perceived difficulty of working in them or because they are not currently fashionable. Examples include the synthesis of hard, tough, or thermally conducting solids; the rational synthetic control of the crystal structure of organic, inorganic, and organometallic solids; and the study of adhesion and tribology. As the chemistry community's interest in materials science grows, these fields will develop.

BIOLOGY: A STIMULUS TO CHEMISTRY AND MATERIALS SCIENCE

As a final note, it is worthwhile briefly to consider the role another molecular science—biology—might play in the future of materials science. Biology and biochemistry and their several subfields, especially molecular genetics, immunology, endocrinology, neurobiology, and enzymology, have developed explosively. Although much of this development is arguably irrelevant to materials science, some threads of biology do have major long-term relevance as sources of new materials and processes (Figure 6) and as stimulating intellectual concepts (Figure 7).

One of the true scientific revolutions of this century has been the development of molecular genetics. Among the practical applications of this knowledge is the ability to produce a virtually limitless number of proteins, both natural and unnatural, in large quantities. Thus, for the first time, proteins can be considered as components of materials systems, although it is not known which proteins and structures are appropriate for what purposes. None of these questions can be answered at present. Proteins are, however, a class of macromolecular species with potentially great versatility; the development of protein structure-property relationships could be of great practical importance in materials science.

At the same time, more mundane but possibly more immediately useful advances in classical microbiology have made available new polysaccharides

Materials
   Proteins (rDNA)
   Polysaccharides
   Biological Lubricants
Third World Production

Molasses $\longrightarrow$ $(\text{-CHCH}_2\text{C-O-})_n$ with CH_3 and O

Barnacle Cement; Silk

Processes
   Microbial Corrosion
   Antifouling

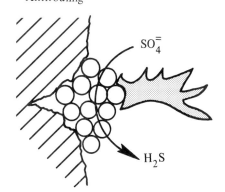

$SO_4^=$

H_2S

FIGURE 6   Biologically derived materials and processes relevant to materials science.

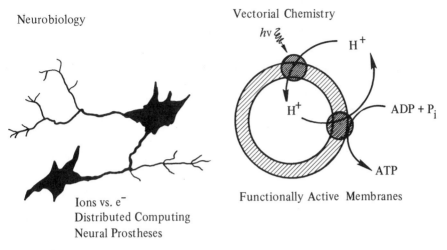

Neurobiology

Vectorial Chemistry

Ions vs. e⁻
Distributed Computing
Neural Prostheses

Functionally Active Membranes

FIGURE 7   Examples of biological structures representing concepts not now exploited in materials science.

and certain other classes of biologically derived polymers. Some of these materials are useful in biomaterials applications (for example, polylactic acid has been developed for biodegradable sutures, and hyaluronic acid is a valuable lubricant for use *in vivo*); others provide engineering plastics (polyhydroxybutyrate/propionate) whose impact may ultimately be greater in Third World nations lacking a petrochemical base than in developed countries. Finally, one should not forget that it is not yet possible to duplicate the properties of many useful and interesting biomaterials, for example, barnacle cement and spider silk.

The interaction between conventional materials and living systems involves a different type of activity. For example, microbiological action contributes significantly to corrosion of metals in marine and underground environments, and marine colonization and fouling limit the use of all materials in marine environments. By understanding the physiological, metabolic, and molecular mechanisms responsible for such processes, it may be possible to limit their impact on materials systems.

Biology also offers hints of important processes and concepts currently alien to practical chemistry and materials science (Figure 7). These biologically derived concepts may, in fact, never be used directly in materials science, but their existence provides an intellectual stimulus and an opportunity to reexamine familiar hypotheses. The nervous system is one obvious example. Control and computation in mammalian systems is conducted by processes relying on information transmission using a bizarre hybrid system containing ionic conductivity and chemical diffusion as major components; the logic of the brain is based on still mysterious processing, storage, and retrieval algorithms. All of these processes are unarguably slower, more delicate, and more limited than semiconductor-based methods, but the biological systems are nonetheless able to deal with certain tasks such as pattern recognition, training, and associative recall with a facility that is difficult to duplicate with existing silicon-based devices. Will new types of materials be required to model these processes and to accomplish similar results? Can existing materials be assembled in new configurations to duplicate them?

A less familiar example is provided by vectorial chemistry. Energy is stored in biological systems in two forms: reactive molecules and in concentration gradients across cell membranes. There are no purely chemical processes that duplicate the biological processes that convert the energy generated by dissipation of a concentration gradient into useful work. The concepts on which these conversions rest involve systems containing areas of active membrane, and promise to stimulate efforts to develop similar active membrane systems for other purposes. These systems may eventually appear as problems and opportunities in materials science.

CONCLUSIONS

Chemistry and materials science have been considered largely separate disciplines, to the disadvantage of both. In the past decades researchers in both fields have been profitably occupied in separate spheres: chemists with the products of the classical chemical economy (fuels, commodity chemicals, polymers, agricultural chemicals, pharmaceuticals, specialty chemicals) and materials scientists with the core of classical materials (metals, glasses, and ceramics). Many of these areas are now scientifically and technologically mature. New problems require new solutions, and new science yields new technology. The push toward high-strength, lightweight, durable materials has stimulated interest in composite structures. The importance of microelectronics, and the specialized requirements of the U.S. Department of Defense, have focused attention on new classes of materials. Environmental constraints and competition from other nations have rendered many existing processes obsolete or unacceptable. In chemistry, a range of types of information—in catalysis, polymers, organometallics, synthetic methods—awaits sophisticated application to the solid state. The boundary between chemistry and materials science is beginning to blur, but the pace of evolutionary change is too slow. Materials scientists should learn what chemistry has to offer; chemists must actively seek to understand and solve the problems in materials science.

ACKNOWLEDGMENT

This work was supported in part by the National Science Foundation, grants CHE-82-05142, DMR-83-16979, and CHE-83-20096.

NOTES

1. H. A. Wittcoff and B. G. Reuben, *Industrial Organic Chemicals in Perspective*, Parts 1 & 2 (Interscience, New York, 1980).
2. H. R. Allcock and F. W. Lampe, *Contemporary Polymer Chemistry* (Prentice-Hall, Englewood Cliffs, N.J., 1981).
3. F. A. Bovey and F. H. Winslow, editors, *Macromolecules: An Introduction to Polymer Science* (Academic Press, New York, 1979).
4. Committee to Survey Opportunities in the Chemical Sciences, National Research Council, *Opportunities in Chemistry* (National Academy Press, Washington, D.C., 1985).
5. P. M. Hergenrother, ChemTech **14**, 496 (1984).
6. J. L. Kardos, J. Adhesion **5**, 119 (1973); J. L. Kardos, ChemTech **14**, 430 (1984); J. L. Kardos, Polym. Prepr., Am. Chem. Soc., Div. Polym. Chem. **24**, 185 (1983).
7. E. P. Plueddemann, *Silane Coupling Agents* (Plenum, New York, 1982).
8. J. L. Woodhead and D. L. Segal, Chem. Br. **20**, 310 (1984).
9. H. J. Sanders, Chem. Eng. News **62** (28), 26–40 (1984).
10. R. D. Dupuis, Science **226**, 623 (1984).
11. R. Solanki, C. A. Moore, and G. J. Collins, Solid State Technol. **28**, 220 (1985).
12. K. A. Jones, Solid State Technol. **28**, 151 (1985).
13. R. M. Osgood and T. F. Deutsch, Science **227**, 709 (1985).
14. S. M. Sze, editor, *VLSI Technology* (McGraw-Hill, New York, 1983).
15. R. F. Davis, H. Palmour III, and R. L. Porter, editors, *Emergent Process Methods for High Technology Ceramics* (Plenum, New York, 1984).
16. R. R. Ulrich and L. L. Hench, editors, *Ultrastructure Processing of Ceramics, Glasses, and Composites* (Wiley, New York, 1984).
17. R. W. Rice, Ceram. Bull. **62**, 889 (1983).
18. R. H. Baughman, J. L. Bredas, R. R. Chance, R. L. Elsenbaumer, and L. W. Shacklette, Chem. Rev. **82**, 209 (1982).
19. D. F. Shriver and G. C. Farrington, Chem. Eng. News **63** (20), 42–57 (1985).
20. H. R. Allcock, Chem. Eng. News **63** (11), 22–36 (1985).
21. R. L. Greene and G. B. Street, Science **226**, 651 (1984); M. R. Bryce and L. C. Murphy, Nature **309**, 119 (1984).
22. S. M. Sze, *Physics of Semiconductor Devices*, 2nd ed. (Wiley, New York, 1981).
23. M. H. Chisholm, editor, *Inorganic Chemistry: Toward the Twenty-First Century*, ACS Symposium Series, No. 211 (American Chemical Society, Washington, D.C., 1983).
24. A. Heller, Science **223**, 1141 (1984).
25. M. S. Wrighton, J. Vac. Sci. Technol. A **2**, 795 (1984).
26. R. D. Vold and M. J. Vold, *Colloid and Interface Science* (Addison-Wesley, Reading, Mass., 1983).
27. A. W. Adamson, *Physical Chemistry of Surfaces*, 3rd ed. (Wiley, New York, 1976).
28. D. J. Williams, editor, *Nonlinear Optical Properties of Organic and Polymeric Materials*, ACS Symposium Series, No. 233 (American Chemical Society, Washington, D.C., 1983).

Advanced Ceramics

ALBERT R. C. WESTWOOD and STEPHEN R. WINZER

During the past five years, ceramics has undergone a revolution almost as dramatic as the more familiar one in electronics. Novel approaches to preparing and processing ceramic solids have been developed, ingenious ways of circumventing the age-old problem of brittleness have been introduced, and new markets have begun to open up in such areas as sensors, orthopedics, photonics, and heat engines.

Today's advanced ceramics represent developments well beyond the imagination of even the few farsighted scientists of 25 years ago who first perceived the remarkable potential of ceramic solids and established "ductile" engineering ceramics as a suitable objective for materials researchers to pursue. It was with this goal in mind that an interdisciplinary Conference on the Mechanical Properties of Engineering Ceramics was held at North Carolina State University in March 1960. Earl Parker and co-workers[1-3] had just confirmed that ionic crystals could exhibit considerable ductility, as Joffe and others[4,5] had first demonstrated in the 1920s. They had decided that ionic solids were intrinsically ductile but readily embrittled by notches, surface films, and internal barriers to dislocation motion. Accordingly, the 1960s saw, for example, the alloying of oxides and of carbides[6] to increase the ductility of ceramic solids by influencing their interatomic bonding and, hence, ease of cross slip. But it proved impossible to overcome notch brittleness, that is, to arrest a crack once initiated by some preexisting flaw or by a dislocation pileup at some obstacle such as a grain boundary[7] (see Figure 1).

The late 1950s also saw initiation of the Basic Sciences and Electronics Divisions of the American Ceramic Society. By 1960, papers were being published on phase equilibria and sintering behavior in multicomponent oxide

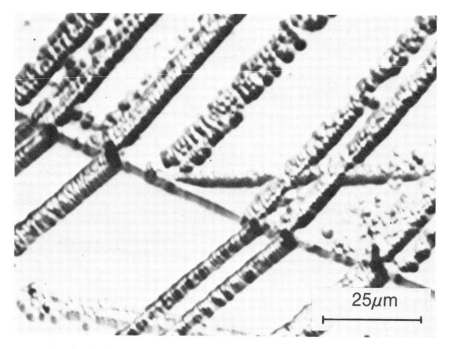

FIGURE 1   Cracks formed at the boundary of an MgO bicrystal, caused by piling up of edge dislocations. From Westwood.[7]

systems, SiC as a candidate material for the leading edge of wings on hypersonic aircraft, the dielectric behavior of zirconates and simple niobates, and the use of garnets and ferrites for computer memories.[8] However, most papers were still concerned with refractories for furnace walls and with enamels and whitewares—the mainstays of the ceramics industry at that time. Parker[9] succinctly summed up the state of affairs 25 years ago when he said in his closing remarks to the North Carolina State meeting, "The most important thing we have learned in this conference is how little we really know about complex ceramic materials. . . . Each speaker, talking for something like half an hour, or even less, was running out of things to say by the time he was finished."

The years 1960–1980 have served as the long period of slowly increasing investment in research and development and technical advances that often precedes the S-curve development of a new industry. We are now entering the initial growth phase of the advanced ceramics industry, in which scientific understanding and developments are exploited in diverse areas, completely new applications are appearing, and companies are beginning to compete for market share. This chapter briefly reviews some of the ways in which the

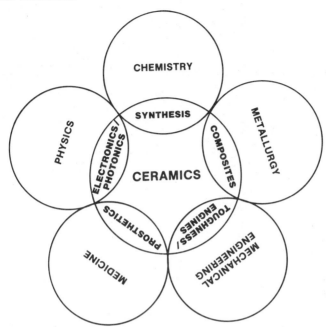

FIGURE 2 Interactions of ceramics science with other technical fields.

field of ceramics has influenced, or been influenced by, other technical fields, especially chemistry, physics, metallurgy, medicine, and mechanical engineering. Thus, the focus of this chapter might be termed "ceramics at the interfaces" (see Figure 2).

CERAMICS AND CHEMISTRY: CERAMIC SYNTHESIS

Traditionally, ceramics have been used in chemistry as catalysts, catalyst substrates, and corrosion-resistant reaction vessels. Today, ceramics are beginning to be used as chemical-specific sensors for the detection of oxygen, hydrogen, carbon monoxide, and more complex organic species such as propane or isobutane.[10] They also are being used as durable containers for active chemical and nuclear wastes, the new lead-iron phosphate glasses being a thousand times more resistant to leaching than standard borosilicate glasses (see Figure 3).[11]

Chemistry, on the other hand, has profoundly influenced the emergence of advanced ceramics. Through the development and application of novel chemical routes for the synthesis of micron-sized inorganic powders, or through rediscovery of "ancient" routes, it has become feasible to produce

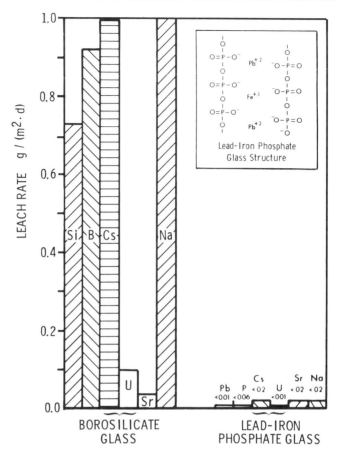

FIGURE 3   Improved resistance of lead-iron phosphate glass to aqueous corrosion (90°C for 30 days) over conventional borosilicate glass. From Sales and Boatner.[11] Reprinted, with permission, from B. C. Sales and L. A. Boatner, Science **226**, 45 (1984). © 1984 by the American Association for the Advancement of Science.

raw materials of sufficient purity and size consistency for the preparation of advanced ceramics.

Conventional chemical approaches for making fine particulate solids involve colloidal suspension followed by removal of the solvent. But if the suspension is simply dried by heating or evaporation, coarse crystals or agglomerates usually result. An alternative route is through sol-gel chemistry, first used in 1864 by Thomas Graham to make silica gel. It involves three steps: (1) producing a concentrated solution of a metallic salt in a dilute acid (the sol); (2) adjusting the pH, adding a gelling agent, and evaporating the liquid to produce a gel; and (3) calcining the gel under carefully controlled atmospheric conditions to produce fine particles of the requisite ceramic. This approach is especially useful for oxide-based ceramics such as Al_2O_3, ZrO_2, and TiO_2.

An alternative sol-gel process for producing colloidal dispersions is the hydrolysis of metal alkoxides, the products of reactions between alcohols and metal oxides. The advantages of this approach are that alkoxides can be purified by distillation and that the subsequently precipitated hydroxides tend to be pure, uniform, spherical, submicron-sized particles that, upon sintering, retain their uniformity and fine grain size (see Figure 4).[12]

Sol-gel processes have been used to produce a variety of glass and ceramic fibers, including high-purity SiO_2 fibers for optical waveguides. Starting with $Si(OEt)_4$ as a precursor, fibers with optical attenuations of 6 dB/km have been made.[13] Research is now under way to produce non-oxide fibers for infrared waveguides. Kamiya and co-workers[14,15] have also spun TiO_2-SiO_2 and ZrO_2-SiO_2 fibers exhibiting extremely low coefficients of expansion and high thermal stability.

Barium titanate films 200 angstroms thick have been prepared by dip coating, though whether their dielectric properties are suitable for electronic applications was not reported.[16] Vanadium pentoxide gels have been prepared for antistatic coatings[17] and tungstate gels for optical display materials.[18]

Other developments include the production of UO_2 spheres for nuclear applications.[19] These are made by dropping spray-formed sol spheres through a heated column of inert liquid. Gelation occurs during the fall, after which the spheres (30–1,200 μm in diameter) are collected and fired to near-theoretical density. This process has also been applied to the encapsulation of radioactive waste.

The principal problems with the sol-gel route are economic (a sol-gel silica glass can cost $20/lb), long processing times, and product porosity, although porosity can be advantageous in the production of porous structures, such as catalyst supports. A comprehensive review of sol-gel processing has been published by Mackenzie.[20]

Another route particularly appropriate for the production of such ceramic fibers as SiC and Si_3N_4 involves the thermal degradation of polymers. Again this is not a new discovery; polysilazanes were pyrolyzed to form Si_3N_4 as long ago as 1881.[21] More recent work by Baker, Grisdale, and Winslow[22] in the 1950s led to the production of silicon-carbon bodies, but the field really came of age in the mid-1970s with the pioneering work of Yajima,[23] which permitted Nippon Carbon to bring SiC fibers to the marketplace. Their process involves heating polydimethylsilane in an autoclave to yield a polycarbosilane with a molecular weight of approximately 2,000. This is melt-spun into polymer fibers of 10–20 μm in diameter, and the fibers are then partially oxidized by heating in air at 200°C to give them sufficient

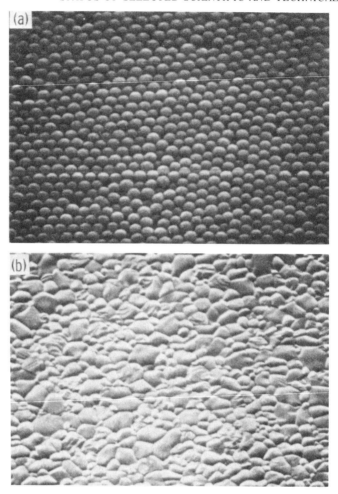

FIGURE 4   (a) TiO_2 powder, about 0.35 μm in diameter, produced by the hydrolysis of metal alkoxides. (b) TiO_2 ceramic of >99 percent theoretical density made from powder above. Average grain size is 1.2 μm. From Barringer and Bowen.[12] Reprinted with permission.

strength to retain their shape at the pyrolizing temperature of 1,200–1,400°C. The resulting SiC fibers are similar in dimensions to the original polymer fiber, and can be woven into mattes. Various ceramic materials have now been produced by the polymer degradation route, including BN, AlN, Si_3N_4, Si-Ti-C, and $SiC-B_4C$.[24,25]

Other routes for producing ceramic particles involve vapor-phase reactions. For example, researchers at the Massachusetts Institute of Technology and

Rutgers University have produced fine particles of SiC and Si_3N_4 by reacting SiH_4, NH_3, and C_2H_4 in a CO_2 laser beam. The powders produced are typically less than 0.1 μm in diameter.[26] In other work, water vapor has been reacted with aerosol droplets of alkoxides to produce either pure or mixed oxide powders of the order of 1 μm in diameter.[27]

Although the approaches just described are technically promising, their cost-effectiveness remains a problem. Thus it is sometimes worthwhile for the industrial scientist to revisit a long-established approach and see if improved mechanistic understanding can reveal some new opportunity for improving its efficiency. For example, it is known that silica and carbon can interact through the gaseous phase SiO, which adsorbs on the carbon and reacts to produce SiC and CO. If the carbon particles are small, this reaction can be controlled so that the size and shape of the product SiC particle is strongly determined by that of its carbon precursor. In this way, SiC particles 1 μm in diameter have been produced at 1,600°—500°C below traditional SiC production temperatures.[28] Estimates indicate that this approach, scaled up, could produce submicron-sized SiC for sale at $5 to $7 per pound.

CERAMICS AND METALLURGY: METAL-MATRIX COMPOSITES

The classic challenge to the metallurgist has been to increase the strength and stiffness of metallic alloys without significantly reducing their ductility. Considerable success has been achieved with respect to strength, and ferrous alloys exhibiting yield strengths greater than 1,800 MPa and fracture toughness of 80 MPa $m^{1/2}$ are now available. But economical ways of increasing alloy stiffness have been more difficult to come by. Over the past 20 years, the development of metals reinforced with graphite or ceramic fibers has been vigorously pursued, yet the resulting materials remain expensive, and the production of complex shapes from them is difficult. Joining fiber-reinforced metal components also presents problems.

However, new approaches to improving specific stiffness are emerging, driven by the need for lightweight space structures. One such approach has resulted in the new aluminum-lithium alloys now coming to market. These alloys exhibit a specific modulus more than 20 percent greater than that of aluminum. Another approach, using rapid solidification technology, has produced aluminum-base materials of complex nonequilibrium chemistry with strengths greater than 600 MPa, ductilities greater than 9 percent at 20°C, and substantial strength retention to about 350°C. One might conjecture, however, that the intrinsic chemical instability of such materials could lead to unpredictable behavior during complex operating conditions involving elevated temperatures, cyclic stressing, and active environments.

A third approach, now under development at Martin Marietta Laboratories, is based on the intrinsic *stability* of ceramic particles and their known ability to increase stiffness when present in sufficiently small size (about 1 μm), high concentration, and homogeneous distribution. Invented by an interdisciplinary team, the new materials, termed XD alloys, exhibit specific moduli up to 40 percent greater than the base metal.[29] The process by which these alloys are produced is proprietary, but the prospects for such materials appear very encouraging because, once formed, they can be processed (for example, cast, rolled, extruded, or welded) by conventional means.

To date, the XD process for producing ceramic-stiffened metallic materials has been demonstrated for Al, Cu, Fe, Mg, Ni, Pb, and Ti alloys, and also for Ti and Ni aluminides. Their outstanding properties apparently result not only from the uniform dispersion of fine ceramic particles but also from the "cleanliness" of the ceramic particle–metal interface, a result not readily achieved in conventional powder metallurgy processing. Figure 5 compares the modulus of XD-Al alloys with SiC-reinforced Al, and Figure 6 shows the improved high-temperature performance of XD-7075 Al over the conventional 7075 alloy. Other demonstrated advantages of XD-aluminum alloys

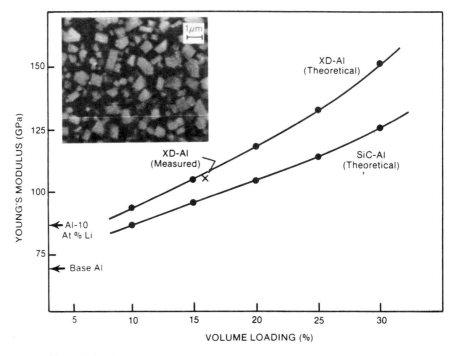

FIGURE 5 Relation between Young's modulus and concentration of ceramic phase for XD-Al and SiC-Al alloys. Insert shows typical microstructure of XD-Al material. From Christodoulou, Brupbacher, and Nagle.[29]

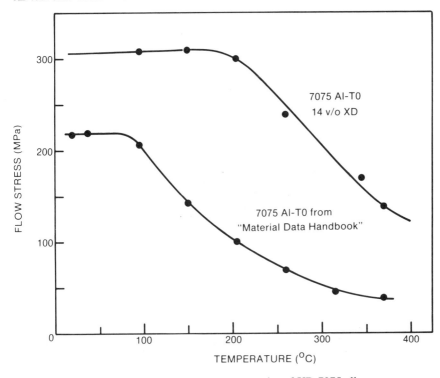

FIGURE 6   Improvement of high-temperature properties of XD-7075 alloy over conventional alloy. From Christodoulou, Brupbacher, and Nagle.[29]

include superior weldments (because of the stability of the ceramic phase), more than a 10-fold increase in resistance to wear, greater resistance to fatigue due to crack branching, and production and processing costs much less than those of SiC-Al, with an eventual selling price of less than $10 per pound. Although XD alloys are not inexpensive, their improved performance may lead to their early use in space structures, transatmospheric vehicles, and piston rods.

Other interesting developments are occurring in the field of *in situ* precipitated composites. The possibilities for such materials include metal-matrix structures containing 10^8 high-strength reinforcing ceramic whiskers per cubic inch or, conversely, ceramic matrices containing high densities of metal fibers,[30] for example, tungsten fibers in ZrO_2.[31] Applications include novel magnetic and electronic devices, such as the electron emitter, photovoltaics and capacitors, anisotropic heat conductors, superconducting materials, catalysts, and advanced superalloy-based structural materials.

CERAMICS AND MECHANICAL ENGINEERING: TOUGH STRUCTURAL CERAMICS

The major problem to be overcome before ceramics can be seriously considered for structural applications is that of notch brittleness. Great progress has been made in this direction over the past few years, and future toughness K_{IC} values in excess of 20 MPa m$^{1/2}$ are now beginning to be achieved through various toughening approaches. These approaches include reducing the size and concentration of preexisting crack initiators (such as microcracks and pores) by decreasing grain sizes to the micron range and increasing densities to 99 percent or so, and introducing various synthetic crack-retarding entities, some of which are illustrated in Figure 7. Of these approaches, the incorporation of crack-closing particles is receiving the most scientific attention. Such transformation-toughened ceramics contain dispersed small particles of a metastable phase that transform crystallographically when the strain field of a crack passes through or near them. In this way some of the energy of the crack is absorbed. If the transforming particles

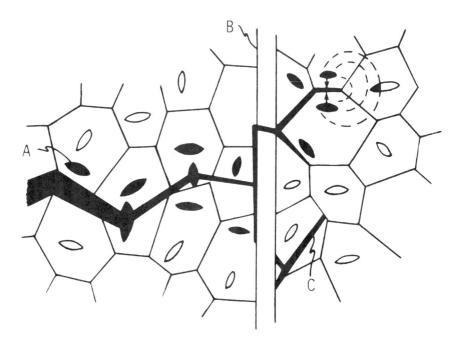

FIGURE 7 Crack-retarding entities used to produce toughness in ceramics: (a) phase-transforming particles, e.g., ZrO_2 (tetragonal) $\rightarrow$ ZrO_2 (monoclinic); (b) fibers with weak fiber-matrix interfaces; and (c) other cracks.

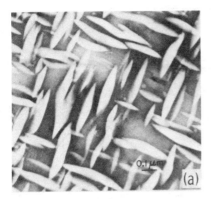 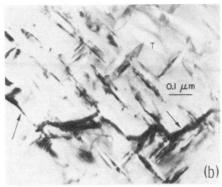

FIGURE 8 Partially stabilized ZrO_2 (a) unstressed, showing coherent tetragonal precipitate particles; and (b) stressed by indenter, revealing transformed monoclinic particles near indentation (arrows) and untransformed tetragonal particles elsewhere. From Porter and Heuer.[32] Reprinted with permission.

also increase in volume, they can apply a compressive stress to the crack tip, reducing its effective driving force. Further crack-retarding interactions occur at the particle-matrix interface, and within the particle itself.

The best known example of this behavior occurs in partially stabilized ZrO_2 (PSZ). In this case a two-phase ZrO_2 is produced by partially stabilizing the tetragonal ZrO_2 phase through additions of up to 10 percent Y_2O_3, MgO, or other oxide. A typical structure is shown in Figure 8.[32] Note the relatively high volume, crystallographic orientation, and small size (0.5–2 μm) of the tetragonal phase. When a crack cuts through this material, the tetragonal (T) phase transforms locally into a monoclinic (M) structure, and toughening occurs by the mechanisms described above. Polycrystalline PSZ exhibits strengths of 500–1,500 MPa and fracture toughnesses of about 12–16 MPa $m^{1/2}$ at room temperature. PSZ can also provide strengths of up to 700 MPa at 1,500°C.[33]

Noncubic ZrO_2 particles can be incorporated into other ceramic substances, such as polycrystalline alumina, and recent studies[34] have investigated the influence of stabilizer element (Y_2O_3) concentration on the stress required to initiate the T $\rightarrow$ M transformation in ZrO_2 particles in the vicinity of a crack tip, and so on its fracture toughness. The value of K_{IC} at room temperature for Al_2O_3–20% [$ZrO_2(Y_2O_3)$] increases from 4 MPa $m^{1/2}$ to greater than 10 MPa $m^{1/2}$ as the Y_2O_3 content is decreased from 3 to 1 mole percent (see Figure 9). Fracture toughness also increases with number of ZrO_2 particles that transform per unit volume of the crack-tip stress region. Thus, for a given Y_2O_3 content, K_{IC} increases with volume fraction of T-ZrO_2 particles. However, for each concentration of Y_2O_3, K_{IC} reaches some maximum, and

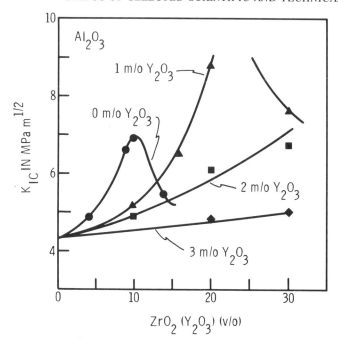

FIGURE 9 Fracture toughness as a function of composition for Al_2O_3-$ZrO_2(Y_2O_3)$ composites. From Becher.[34] Reprinted, with permission, from P. F. Becher, Acta Metall. (in press), © 1986 by Pergamon Press, Ltd.

the stress required to transform a ZrO_2 particle increases with Y_2O_3 content. Thus the maximum in K_{IC} occurs at higher ZrO_2 concentrations as the Y_2O_3 content increases, as is evident from Figure 9. The value of K_{IC} also increases as testing temperature is decreased, for example, from 7 MPa $m^{1/2}$ at room temperature to greater than 14 MPa $m^{1/2}$ at $-195°C$ (78 K) for Al_2O_3–[18.5 mole percent ZrO_2–1.5 mole percent Y_2O_3].

Another method of toughening ceramics is to incorporate fibers or whiskers, and encouraging progress has been made with this approach, too. For example, the fracture toughness of a lithium aluminosilicate glass containing approximately 50 percent SiC fibers ranged from about 17 MPa $m^{1/2}$ at room temperature to 25 MPa $m^{1/2}$ at 1,000°C, at which temperature the matrix began to soften appreciably.[35] Whiskers of SiC can also produce useful and relatively temperature-insensitive increases in the toughness of polycrystalline Al_2O_3. Moreover, conventional ball milling and sintering (to 95 percent theoretical density) procedures can be used in fabrication. For example, Al_2O_3 composites containing 20 volume percent SiC whiskers (7 μm diameter × 30 μm long) typically exhibit K_{IC} values of 7–9 MPa $m^{1/2}$ at room temperature (see Figure 10), and values as high as 12 MPa m$^{1/2}$ are now being reported.[36] In contrast to PSZ ceramics, these values are retained to about 1,000°C (see Figure 11), as are strengths in the range of 800 MPa. Composites of Al$_2$O$_3$ reinforced with SiC whiskers compete well with the glass ceramic-matrix materials containing fine SiC fibers (see Figure 10) and have the advantages of being less sensitive to orientation than fiber-reinforced solids and easier to manufacture.

Such materials are now used to make tough cutting tools and wear-resistant spray nozzles. But potentially the most explosive future application for tough ceramics is, of course, auto engine components. All-ceramic engines of the conventional piston-gasoline type are not considered likely, because of design limitations and because substantial fuel savings are not foreseen.[37] It seems more likely that the next 5–10 years will see the gradual introduction of various engine parts, such as those shown schematically in Figure 12. Glow plugs and turbocharger rotors already have been introduced, with different ceramic materials having been used for different parts. The increased use of ceramic coatings is also foreseen.[38]

In the longer term (5–15 years), ceramic-dependent adiabatic diesel and

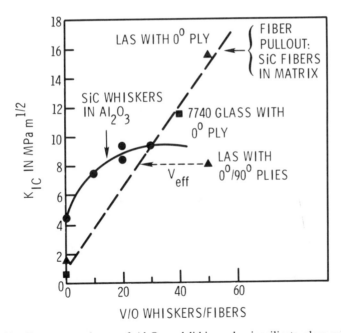

FIGURE 10 Fracture toughness of Al$_2$O$_3$ and lithium aluminosilicate glass reinforced, respectively, with SiC whiskers and fibers. Courtesy of Paul F. Becher, Oak Ridge National Laboratories, Oak Ridge, Tennessee.

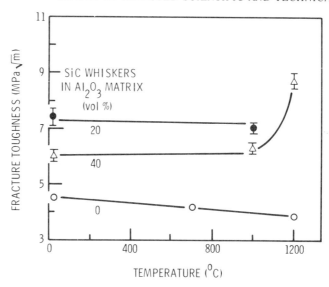

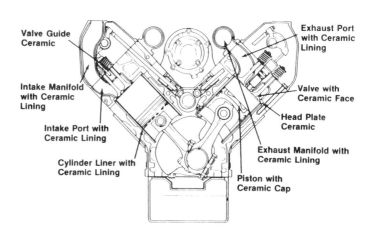

FIGURE 12   Potential uses of advanced ceramic components in auto engines.

gas turbines will be marketed. The objective will be to eliminate radiators, water, oil, various pumps, and so forth to produce engines that are lighter, more efficient, and less polluting because of higher operating temperatures. Ceramics now being developed for such applications include SiC, Si_3N_4 (for turborotors, valves, piston caps, etc.), PSZ (for combustion chamber components), and aluminum silicates (for regenerator cores). However, the auto engines of the mid-1990s will certainly use more complex ceramics than these, probably ceramic alloys with toughness and durability optimized by thermomechanical treatments, and with surfaces processed (glazed) to minimize the potential consequences of small flaws introduced by abrasion or erosion.

CERAMICS AND MEDICINE: PROSTHETICS

Ceramics are extremely resistant to corrosion by body fluids and can be formed with surface characteristics that closely simulate those of natural bone. Thus their use in surgical applications is increasing.[39] Materials now being used or evaluated include alumina, calcium and aluminum triphosphates, hydroxy apatites, and various glasses. Interesting developments include Kyocera Corporation's use of single-crystal sapphire to produce products ranging from hip prostheses to dental implants and Corning Glass Works' introduction of a castable glass ceramic that is machinable and contains a pure mica that provides a natural translucency to false teeth. This material is stronger than a tooth's own enamel.

Porous aluminas are being developed that permit infiltration of connective tissues to depths of 100 μm. Bioglass, introduced in 1972 by Hench, Splinter, and Allen[40] and based on the system $Na_2O–CaO–CaF_2–P_2O_5–SiO_2$, forms a chemical bond with bone. It can be used by itself if strength is not an issue, or as an interface between body tissues and a stronger steel implant. Cerevital, a product of the German firm E. Leitz Wetzlar, is a glass ceramic with a composition similar to that of Bioglass, and also has been used to coat implants of metal femoral head devices. The bond formed is stronger than the bone itself.

Trisodium phosphate, various calcium phosphates, and polylactic acid/carbon compounds are finding increasing use as resorbable bioceramics. These materials provide a porous ceramic that forms a temporary scaffold or space filler in human tissue. Initially its small pore size gives strength, but gradually the ceramic dissolves, and the space is filled with bone or tissue.[41] The chemistry of these compounds can be adjusted to match the kinetics of the regeneration process. Rapid advances expected in this field include the integration of miniaturized implantable sensors and power sources to produce "active" prosthetic devices.

CERAMICS AND PHYSICS: ELECTRONIC AND PHOTONICS COMPONENTS

Electronic applications now constitute the major market for advanced ceramics used as substrates, capacitors, piezoelectrics, and resistors, for example. Emerging rapidly, however, is photonics, and the growth of this field has been greatly accelerated by the introduction of low-loss optical fibers for broadband data transmission. High-silica fibers containing less than 10 parts per billion of hydroxyl and doped with phosphorus, germanium, and boron oxides can now provide losses of less than 1 dB/km in the 1.5-μm range. Materials with much lower losses (less than 10^{-2} dB/km), and operating in the 2–4-μm range, will be needed for the next generation of transoceanic cables, and it seems likely that they will be made from fluoride-based materials. Potentially, such materials could reduce losses to 10^{-3}– 10^{-4} dB/km, in principle permitting transmission across the Atlantic, or the Pacific, without repeater stations.[42]

Today's most advanced communication systems are hybrids of digital electronic and optical devices, and this situation is likely to persist for the next 10 years or so. Subsequently, however, the emergence of vastly more efficient and totally photonic systems will be based on integrated optical devices somewhat analogous to today's integrated circuits.[43] Ceramics such as $LiNbO_3$ and $LiTaO_3$, in single-crystal form, are of current interest as materials for optical modulators, switches, splitters, and other waveguide devices, functioning usually through the change in refractive index induced by an electric field. Newer materials such as $SrBaNb_2O_6$ and $NaBaNb_2O_6$ exhibit electro-optic coefficients 2 to 5 times greater than those of $LiNbO_3$, and so will permit more compact devices, providing that problems in growing single crystals of these materials can be overcome.

Another area of interest to ceramists is the multilayer technology being developed for packaging VLSI electronic devices. Figure 13 shows a recent example of the state of the art, namely, the multilayer multichip module (MCM) developed by IBM Corp.[44] This consists of about 23 layers of alumina, co-fired with molybdenum metallization. Interconnects between layers are achieved by punching holes and filling them with molybdenum frit before firing. Such modules can include more than 300,000 vias and 500 cm of integral wiring for power and data transmission to and through the chip. Such a module typically carries nine chips, each equivalent to 700 circuits. Today, modules containing more than 40 layers are being introduced, and the trend is toward the use of lower-melting-point lead borosilicate glasses, $Pb_2Fe_2Nb_2O_6$ layers as capacitors, RuO_2 layers for resistors, and copper or gold interconnects. Such MCMs can be fired at temperatures below 1,000°C.

Just as the composites approach can be used to extend the strength and toughness of ceramics, so it can be used to develop superior or completely

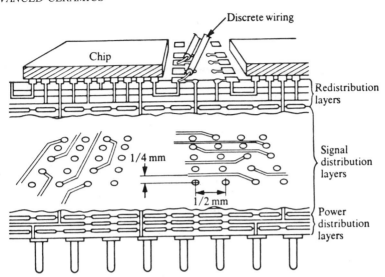

FIGURE 13   Schematic of multilayer multichip module (MCM) developed by IBM Corp., approximately 50 mm square and containing 23 layers of alumina. From Seraphim and Feinberg.[44] © 1981 by International Business Machines Corporation; reprinted with permission.

new electronic or magnetic properties for ceramic materials. The key concept here is connectivity[45]—that is, the manner in which the component phases are self-connected in three dimensions and whether they are electrically connected in parallel or series. Ten connectivity patterns exist for a two-phase solid, and by use of relationships derived from the study of such patterns, materials with specific properties can be designed. For example, the $BaTiO_3$ barrier-layer capacitor has at the grain boundaries an $NaNbO_3$ phase that is connected in three dimensions. The $BaTiO_3$ grains are not interconnected, so this is termed a 3-0 composite. Normally, the polarization of $BaTiO_3$ capacitors saturates at high voltages, with the dielectric constant decreasing by as much as a factor of 2.[45] But separating the grains of the ferroelectric $BaTiO_3$ with the thin layer of antiferroelectric $NaNbO_3$ compensates the saturation effect to provide a flat voltage response.[46] Using the same approach, Skinner, Newnham, and Cross[47] have shown how piezoelectric composites with figures of merit 10 to 100 times those of one-phase PZT ceramics could be made by embedding rods of PZT in a polymer.

THE FUTURE

This chapter has reviewed the progress made in ceramics over the past 25 years. What of the next 25 years? Predictions are always difficult and usually err on the conservative side because they underestimate scientific ingenuity, capitalist entrepreneurism, and the breakthroughs in understanding or processing capability that open up completely unexpected paths of development. Given such caveats, it is expected that multicomponent, self-reinforced ceramic alloys, heat treated to optimize properties, protected by compressive layers applied by ion bombardment or laser glazing, and joined by lasers, electron beams, or novel cements, will become respected members of the engineers' portfolio of useful structural materials by the year 2000.[37]

By 2010,[48] photonics will have become a dominant technology based on integrated ceramic devices. Coated-fiber sensors will translate electrical, magnetic, and pressure variations into optical signals for real-time processing. Massively parallel "thinking" computers, based on photonics, will be extensively used. Ultra-large-scale integrated electronic chips will be based on doped ceramic materials. Various types of optoelectronic, acousto-optic, and other types of sensors, modulators, and switches based on complex ceramic compositions will be widely used in automated and robotic systems at home and in industry. Bioceramic prostheses will be in common use, and nuclear energy will be the power source of choice, with advanced ceramics used in fuels, structures, and disposal operations.

ACKNOWLEDGMENTS

It is a pleasure to acknowledge useful discussions with numerous colleagues during the preparation of this paper. Especially valuable were those with members of the Metals and Ceramics Division at the Oak Ridge National Laboratory, including J. Stiegler, V. J. Tennery, P. F. Becher, C. J. McHarge, and G. S. Painter; and with associates at Martin Marietta Laboratories, notably K. W. Bridger, L. Christodoulou, and J. Skalny (now with W. R. Grace and Co., Columbia, Maryland).

NOTES

1. A. E. Gorum, E. R. Parker, and J. A. Pask, J. Am. Ceram. Soc. **41**, 161 (1958).
2. T. L. Johnston, R. J. Stokes, and C. H. Li, Philos. Mag. **4**, 1316 (1959).
3. E. R. Parker, in *Mechanical Properties of Engineering Ceramics*, edited by W. W. Kriegel and H. Palmour (Interscience, New York, 1961), p. 65.
4. A. Joffe, N. W. Kirpitschewa, and M. A. Lewitsky, Z. Phys. **22**, 286 (1924).
5. W. Ewald and M. Polany, Z. Phys. **28**, 29 (1924).
6. R. G. Lye, G. E. Hollox, and J. D. Venables, in *Anisotropy in Single Crystal Refractory Materials*, edited by F. W. Valdiek and S. A. Mersol (Plenum, New York, 1986), p. 445.
7. A. R. C. Westwood, in *Mechanical Properties of Engineering Ceramics*, edited by W. W. Kriegel and H. Palmour (Interscience, New York, 1961), p. 89.
8. E. Albers-Schoenberg, Ceram. Bull. **30**, 136 (1960).
9. E. R. Parker, in *Mechanical Properties of Engineering Ceramics*, edited by W. W. Kriegel and H. Palmour (Interscience, New York, 1961), p. 595.
10. N. Ichinose, Bull. Am. Ceram. Soc. **12**, 1581 (1985).
11. B. C. Sales and L. A. Boatner, Science **226**, 45 (1984).

12. E. A. Barringer and H. K. Bowen, J. Am. Ceram. Soc. **65**, C-199 (1982).
13. K. Susa, I. Matsuyama, S. Satoh, and T. Suganuma, Electron. Lett. **18**, 499 (1982).
14. K. Kamiya, S. Sakka, and Y. Tatemichi, J. Mater. Sci. **84**, 614 (1976).
15. K. Kamiya, S. Sakka, and Y. Tatemichi, J. Mater. Sci. **15**, 1765 (1980).
16. J. Fukushima, K. Kodaira, and T. Matushita, Bull. Am. Ceram. Soc. **55**, 1064 (1976).
17. C. Guestaux, Kodak Patent FR Patent No. 2 429 252 (1980); and Kodak Patent FR Patent No. 2 318 442 (1977).
18. J. Livage, J. Phys. (Paris) **42**, C4-981 (1981).
19. P. A. Haas et al., Ind. Eng. Chem. Prod. Res. Dev. **19**, 459 (1980).
20. J. D. Mackenzie, in *Ultrastructure Processing of Ceramics, Glasses and Composites,* edited by L. L. Hench and D. R. Ulrich (Wiley, New York, 1984), p. 15.
21. P. Schutzenberger and H. Colson, C. R. Acad. Sci. **92**, 1508 (1881).
22. W. O. Baker, R. O. Grisdale, and F. H. Winslow, U.S. Patent No. 2 697 029 (1954).
23. S. Yajima, Philos. Trans. R. Soc. London, Ser. A **294**, 419 (1980).
24. For reviews see Bull. Am. Ceram. Soc. **62**, August (1983).
25. K. J. Wynne and R. W. Rice, Annu. Rev. Mater. Sci. **14**, 297 (1984).
26. Reported by R. D. McIntyre, Mater. Eng., June 1983, p. 19.
27. E. Matijevic, Acc. Chem. Res. **14**, 22 (1981).
28. D. C. Nagle, L. Struble, and K. W. Bridger, Martin Marietta Laboratories, Baltimore, Md., 1982 (unpublished).
29. L. Christodoulou, J. M. Brupbacher, and D. C. Nagle, Martin Marietta Laboratories, Baltimore, Md., 1984–1985 (unpublished). Patents applied for.
30. F. D. Lemkey, in *Industrial Materials Science and Engineering,* edited by L. E. Murr (Dekker, New York, 1984), p. 441.
31. J. K. Cochran, A. T. Chapman, R. K. Feeney, and D. N. Hill, in *Proceedings of International Electron Devices Meeting* (Institute of Electrical and Electronics Engineers, New York, 1980), p. 462.
32. D. L. Porter and A. H. Heuer, J. Am. Ceram. Soc. **60**, 183 (1977); **62**, 298 (1979).
33. R. W. Rice, ChemTech, **13**, 230 (1983).
34. P. F. Becher, Acta Metall. 1986, in press.
35. J. J. Brennan and K. M. Prewo, J. Mater. Sci. **17**, 2371 (1982).
36. P. F. Becher, T. N. Tiegs, J. C. Ogle, and W. H. Warwick, in *Fracture Mechanisms of Ceramics,* edited by R. C. Bradt et al. (Plenum, New York, 1986), in press.
37. A. R. C. Westwood and J. Skalny, in *Cutting Edge Technologies* (National Academy Press, Washington, D.C., 1984), p. 117.
38. W. J. Lackey, D. P. Stinton, G. A. Cerny, L. L. Fehrenbacher, and A. C. Shaffhauser, in *Proceedings of the International Symposium on Ceramic Components for Heat Engines,* Hakkone, Japan, October 1983 (National Technical Information Service, Springfield, Va.).
39. J. W. Boretos, Ceram. Bull. **64**, 1098 (1985).
40. L. L. Hench, R. J. Splinter, and W. C. Allen, J. Biomed. Mater. Res. Symp. **2**, Pt. 1, 117 (1971).
41. F. Pernot, P. Baldet, F. Bonnel, J. Zarzycki, and P. Rabischong, in *Ceramics in Surgery,* edited by P. Vincenzini (Elsevier, New York, 1983), p. 177.
42. R. W. Lucky, The Bridge, **15** (2), 2 (1985).
43. Charles River Associates, Inc., *Technological and Economic Assessment of Advanced Ceramic Materials: Integrated Optic Devices.* Vol. 4, Report No. 684 (Boston, August 1984).
44. D. P. Seraphim and L. Feinberg, IBM J. Res. Dev. **25**, 622 (1981).
45. R. E. Newnham, D. P. Skinner, and L. E. Cross, Mater. Res. Bull. **13**, 525 (1978).
46. D. A. Payne, Ph.D. thesis, Pennsylvania State University, 1973.
47. D. P. Skinner, R. E. Newnham, and L. E. Cross, Mater. Res. Bull. **13**, 599 (1978).
48. A. R. C. Westwood and J. Skalny, Adv. Ceram. Mater. **1**, 21 (1986).

Organic Polymers

JOHN D. HOFFMAN and ROBERT L. MILLER

Compared to metallurgy and ceramics, the field of organic polymers is new. For example, the now widely used polymer polyethylene was discovered in Britain only a little more than 50 years ago. New polymers continue to be introduced every year at a significant rate, and new applications in both science and commerce inevitably follow. The number of new polymers is sufficient to justify books on the subject.[1]

This review considers some of the opportunities and challenges related to organic polymers. It not only covers what polymers are but also develops the nature of certain opportunities. Chemical properties and physical properties (which are becoming very important) are illustrated, both in experiment and in theory. Our goal in part is to remove some of the mystique that sometimes surrounds the subject of organic polymers and polymer science and to put these substances in proper perspective in the larger world of materials generally. The need for understanding the processing of polymers is one of the main themes of the review, as is the nature of certain exciting new theoretical developments.

Roles of the molecular theories and of fundamental research are broadly illustrated throughout. The very strong interaction of polymers with other materials and their significant contribution to application technology in other fields are shown. To balance this, instances are mentioned where polymer science and technology owe a debt to other areas of materials research and development, and examples are given where polymers indeed have their limitations. Although this review covers organic polymers, it does not intrude far into the field of biotechnology, which would require a separate review of its own. Emphasis is given to major new trends, such as the use of polymers

FIGURE 1 Schematic representation of a polymer chain adsorbed on a surface. The black dots represent polymer-surface bonding.

in composites, and the special properties that can be achieved from polymer blends.

Figure 1 shows one aspect of the sometimes unique behavior of polymers. It depicts a typical long, concatenated polymer chain adsorbed on a surface. The chain consists of similar chain units (monomers) and is flexible. This illustration is important because it shows that, to desorb the entire polymer molecule, all of the little "feet" in the long molecule that are attached to points on the surface must be lifted from the surface simultaneously. From a probability point of view this is difficult even when the occasional attachments involve relatively weak van der Waals forces, and it is still more difficult if the attachments involve chemical bonds. The figure thus indicates one reason that polymers make such good surface coatings: Once adsorbed, they can be very difficult to detach. Polymer molecules will adsorb on a surface in seconds but may take weeks to detach fully, even in the presence of pure solvent; in poor solvents or in the absence of solvents, they virtually never detach. For short chains this is not the case; from a statistical point of view they come off rapidly in solvents because of the relatively low number of attachments. This simple illustration shows that the treatment of polymers deals with a property not ordinarily thought of as an important materials parameter, namely, *molecular length*, or, in more customary terms, *molecular weight*.

MORPHOLOGY AND PROPERTIES

Crystalline Polymers

In the field of organic polymers, a wide range of chemical structures is readily available. As a beginning, consider the remarkable variety of properties and morphologies one can obtain with a specific single polymer chain, i.e., with "constant chemistry." For this purpose we emphasize polyethylene, $—(CH_2—CH_2)_n—$, which is a very simple chain. The examples will be single crystals, lamellar spherulitic structures, and high-strength fibers— all with the same molecule (common polyethylene), but with different *processing*.

Consider the following experiment: in ordinary xylene at, say, 135 to 138°C, a small amount of linear polyethylene (0.001 to 0.01 percent) is dissolved, and the solution is cooled to around 70 to 80°C. Chains with a

_____

FIGURE 2 Shadowed electron micrograph of a ridged, chain-folded, polyethylene single-crystal lozenge with a hollow pyramidal center formed from dilute solution. Crystal was sedimented on glycerine to prevent damage. Scale bar, 1 μm. From Bassett, Frank, and Keller.[3] Reprinted with permission.

molecular weight of 50,000 (corresponding to a chain length of about 455 nm) are suitable. Crystals, such as the one shown in Figure 2, will form and precipitate. This is a polyethylene *single crystal*! That such beautiful crystals could be formed from a polymer came as a surprise to most researchers. In now classical work, Keller[2] elucidated the basic nature of these crystals. Figure 2 is an electron micrograph of such a crystal taken by Bassett,[3] formerly one of Keller's students. Although a full discussion of polymer single crystals is beyond the scope of this review, salient features are presented. A somewhat idealized structure of such a crystal[4] is shown in Figure 3, in which each continuous, accordion-like line represents a single long polyethylene chain. It has been well established that the polymer molecules are chain-folded as shown. The diagonal striations seen in Figure 2 are the (310) slip planes indicated in Figure 3. The thickness l of a crystal is, say, 9 to 20 nm and is dependent on the crystallization temperature, as suggested by nucleation theory.[4] (Nucleation theory, invented by metallurgists, is highly useful in explaining the formation and thickness of these polymer single crystals.)

Such crystals began a revolution in polymer physics, namely, as a consequence of the chain-folding phenomenon. Modern techniques such as infrared spectroscopy[5] and neutron scattering[6,7] suggest that the fold perfection in such crystals is about 75 percent—nature does in fact make mistakes in putting together a crystal consisting of such long molecules. (The concept

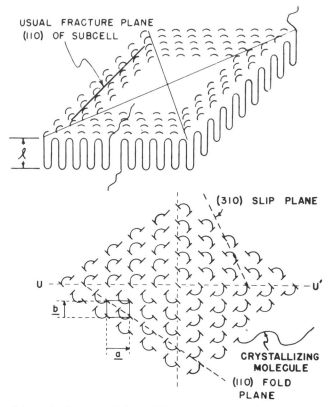

USUAL FRACTURE PLANE
(110) OF SUBCELL

(310) SLIP PLANE

U ———— U′

CRYSTALLIZING
MOLECULE
(110) FOLD
PLANE

FIGURE 3   Schematic diagram of chain-folded polyethylene single crystal. The ortho-
rhombic subcell with dimensions a and b typical of many of the η-paraffins is shown in
the lower diagram. From Hoffman, Davis, and Lauritzen.[4] Reprinted with permission.

of chain folding—even in single crystals—was adamantly resisted by some
of the doyens in the field. In the end, the concept proved too useful and well
supported to be ignored.)

Polymer single crystals are not of great commercial importance, although
strong mats resembling a sheet of paper can be prepared from them. Their
importance is that they started a whole new line of thought concerning the
morphology and basic character of crystalline polymers and, moreover, provided new insights into structure-property relationships for crystalline and
semicrystalline polymeric materials. Many (but not all) of the polymers of
commerce are potentially crystallizable, and in practice do frequently exhibit
crystalline, or more often semicrystalline, properties. Depending on intended
use, the crystallinity can be either useful or detrimental. More frequently it

is useful. For example, the crystalline regions are relatively effective barriers to diffusion of gases and small molecules. Hence the use of semicrystalline polymers—e.g., polyethylene—in applications such as food wrapping. Also, the crystalline regions may act as physical, rather than chemical, cross-links in forming a three-dimensional network that imparts mechanical stability. Yet, when melted again they may be processed or even reprocessed.

Ordinary commercially crystallized polyethylene, such as food and freezer wrapping material, is crystallized from the melt. Under such conditions, objects such as those shown in Figure 4 are frequently seen under a polarizing optical microscope.[8] These are called spherulites (by analogy with mineralogical spherulites) and appear superficially to be exceedingly different from a single crystal such as that shown in Figure 2. The four fields in Figure 4 represent three different molecular weights of polyethylene (18,000; 30,000; and 60,000). The first three were crystallized isothermally at the temperature indicated; the fourth was quench-crystallized. Molecular weights studied varied from 3,600 to 807,000, that is, chains varying from 32 nm to 7,300 nm in length. Commercial polyethylene crystallized in an unstrained manner contains typical spherulites as do other crystallizable polymers, such as nylon, which is a polyamide.

What is the structure of a spherulite and what is the relation, if any, with single crystals such as that in Figure 2? Figure 5 shows some of the structural details of a polymer spherulite. It consists of lamellae or blades radiating from a central point, which is usually a piece of dirt (more elegantly, a "heterogeneous nucleus"). The lamellae are again chain-folded, somewhat like a single crystal, although not as perfectly. In spherulites, however, there are interlamellar links that make it stronger, and there are branch points that allow the spherulite to be a three-dimensional object. Nevertheless, the basic structural unit is similar, but not exactly equal, to that of the single crystal.

The lamellar nature of polymer spherulites in melt-crystallized polymer was first recognized by Eppe, Fischer, and Stuart[9] in Germany shortly after Keller's original work in England[2] on single crystals from dilute solution. The bands seen in Figure 4D arise from the cooperative twisting of adjacent lamellae.[10] This lamellar nature is more clearly seen in Figure 6,[11] which is an electron micrograph of a microtomed section of a spherulite of polyethylene. The lamellae are being viewed edge-on and have the appearance of the edges of a fanned deck of cards.[12] The lamellae in Figure 6 are about 30 nm thick, and the polyethylene sample is a good polymer fraction with about the same molecular weight as the single crystal of Figure 2. (A "fraction" is a polymer specimen for which special techniques have been employed to ensure that the polymer chains are about the same length; most polymers, as synthesized, have a broad distribution of lengths.) Impurities and the shorter polymer chains are normally excluded from such lamellae.[13] Some of the shorter chains may subsequently crystallize; the remainder of the

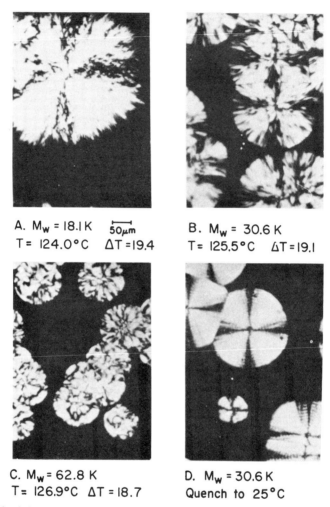

A. M_w = 18.1 K   50μm
T = 124.0°C   ΔT = 19.4

B. M_w = 30.6 K
T = 125.5°C   ΔT = 19.1

C. M_w = 62.8 K
T = 126.9°C   ΔT = 18.7

D. M_w = 30.6 K
Quench to 25°C

FIGURE 4   Spherulites in specimens of intermediate-molecular-weight polyethylene at $\Delta T > 17.5°C$, optical micrograph, crossed Nicol prisms. A, B, and C show coarse-grained nonbanded spherulites resulting from isothermal growth, $\Delta T > 17.5°C$. Micrograph D shows typical banded spherulites obtained in specimen 30.6 K by rapid quenching (30.6 K means molecular weight = 30,600). From Hoffman et al.[8] Reprinted with permission.

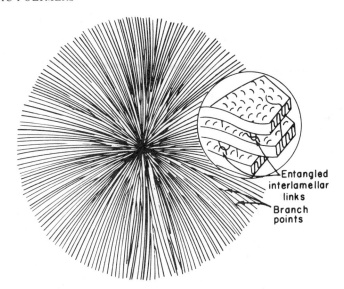

Entangled
interlamellar
links
Branch
points

FIGURE 5 Schematic diagram of polymer spherulite with chain-folded lamellae. The spherulite consists of chain-folded lamellae radiating from a central point. The polymer chain axes in lamellae are more or less perpendicular to the radius of the spherulite. Branching causes the spherulite to become spherical in shape after sufficient growth. Noncrystallizable material (not shown) when present accumulates between lamellae and at the outer boundary. Twist of the lamellae when present causes rings in optical extinction pattern (compare Figure 4D). Interlamellar links and entanglements can cause incomplete crystallization in high-molecular-weight polymers. From Hoffman, Davis, and Lauritzen.[4] Reprinted with permission.

excluded material contributes to the noncrystalline (amorphous) component of the spherulite.

Spherulites from branched polyethylene, i.e., polyethylene with adventitious pendant —CH_3 and —CH_2CH_3 groups, do not display as clear a lamellar picture. Polyethylene spherulites, then, present an interesting morphology in which 15 to 20 percent of the material in the objects in Figure 4 is amorphous and the remainder is like that of a single crystal. The amorphous material is largely between the lamellae, and part of it is in the form of interlamellar links. Since composites are discussed later, note that the polymer spherulite is a *self-assembled composite*. That is one of the reasons polymers such as polyethylene and nylon are useful. They are natural composites, held together in part by interlamellar links, the reinforcement coming from the crystal lamellae. The composite is formed by the process of crystallization itself, an interesting result. Self-assembly is mentioned again below.

Another mode of solution crystallization is possible while still holding the chemistry constant. Solutions, such as those used to prepare polyethylene single crystals, can be crystallized under shear. Vigorous stirring is sufficient, and this process works best if the chains are long. Here a high molecular weight is desirable, and a more concentrated solution (approximately 0.1 to 1.0 percent) is to be used. Under these conditions a strikingly different morphological entity is obtained, as shown in Figure 7 (lying on a graphite substrate).[14] The central thread is a very strong fiber. Work of this nature was first performed by Pennings and Kiel[15] in Holland (which highlights the international character of the significant advances in this field). A break in the central thread can be seen roughly in the middle of the lower unit—it was stressed too much while being subjected to the beam in an electron microscope. The shear direction during crystallization was parallel to the central threads. Such entities are called "shish kebabs" and display the structure shown in Figure 8[16]—a tremendously strong central fiber of primarily extended-chain conformation decorated with (again) chain-folded lamellae. The chain-folding part is not as perfect as it is in a single crystal, but the extended-chain perfection in the central fiber is high. The important point here is that shish kebabs are enormously strong—at least half the strength of the carbon-carbon bond and, in relation to their weight, stronger

FIGURE 6   Electron micrograph of microtomed section of spherulite in melt-crystallized polyethylene showing lamellar nature. Lamellae are about 30 nm thick. Sample was stained with a chlorosulfonic acid/uranyl acetate treatment. From Keller.[11]

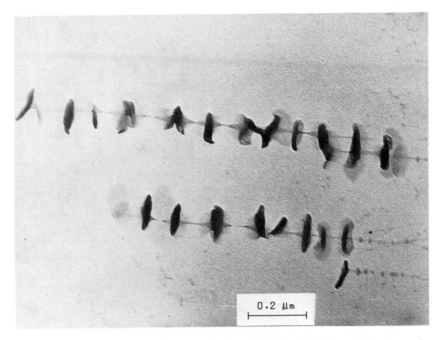

FIGURE 7   Electron micrograph of polyethylene "shish kebabs" formed by shear of a moderately concentrated solution. Note the break in the central thread in the lower unit. From Clark.[14]

than steel. The strength, of course, is due to the "shish." Although shish kebabs themselves are not commercially important, they have been the impetus behind worldwide efforts to produce fibers, sheets, and rods commercially whose strengths take advantage of the molecular orientation of the shish kebab structure. This area of processing is known to polymer scientists as *stress-induced crystallization* (SIC).

Briefly, one the approaches used to exploit the shish kebab effect is that of *solid-state extrusion* of polymers in the absence of solvents (for a recent review, see note 17). Figure 9 shows the results for polyethylene.[18] The thick, opaque rod at the upper right of this figure consists of common, spherulitic, melt-crystallized polyethylene, as discussed earlier. The extrusion process breaks up the spherulitic structure and produces optically clear fibers, as depicted in the lower portion of the figure. Such processes are being commercialized in laboratories in many countries, for example, by the Allied Corporation in the United States. The structure of such extruded polymers proposed by Zachariades and Porter[19] is shown schematically in Figure 10 (others have presented similar pictures). The resemblance to the

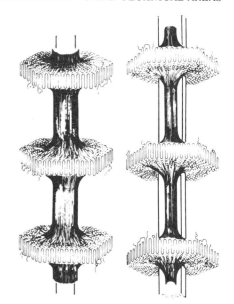

FIGURE 8 Models showing molecular nature of "shish kebabs" of polyethylene produced by stress-induced crystallization in solution. Strong core fibril is extended-chain; "kebabs" are imperfect chain-folded crystals. From Pennings, van der Mark, and Kiel.[16] Reprinted with permission.

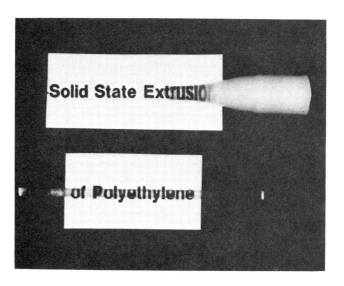

FIGURE 9 Example of the optical clarity achieved by solid-state extrusion of a normally opaque spherulitic rod of semicrystalline polyethylene. From Porter.[18]

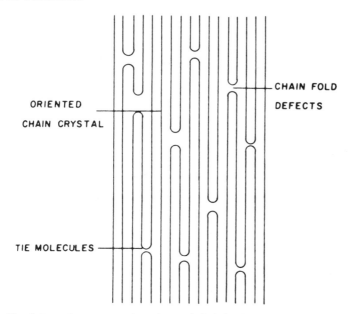

FIGURE 10   Schematic representation of extended-chain, lamellar block crystal structure produced by extrusion of spherulitic melt-crystallized polyethylene. From Zachariades and Porter.[19] Reprinted with permission.

structure of the shish kebab in Figure 8 is clear—mostly concatenated chains in the core fibril (the ''shish'') with perhaps some residual folds. Whatever the fine details, the important point is that the structure consists primarily of long molecules that are parallel over long distances. Only in that way can the enormous tensile strength and high modulus of such materials be explained.

A considerable amount of the progress cited here depended on electron microscopy. Polymer science has made its definite contributions, but it owes a considerable debt to those scientists and engineers who made the electron microscope a practical laboratory instrument.

Table 1 lists the mechanical properties (modulus) of several common materials (the modulus of a material is the initial slope of its stress-strain curve). The first material is a soft metal (aluminum), followed by glass fibers, and so on, ending with polyethylene in different forms. Moduli vary from 70 to 420 GPa, with that of extruded polyethylene fibers being essentially equal to that of steel. Theoretically, the modulus of polyethylene should be about 300 GPa; experimentally, the best achieved to date is about 220 GPa. Also shown in Table 1 is the specific modulus, which is the modulus divided by the density. On a weight basis, then, the polymeric fibers are impressive,

TABLE 1   Comparison of Mechanical Properties

Material	Modulus (stiffness) GPa*	Specific Modulus (modulus/density) MJ/kg
Aluminum	70	26
Glass fibers	72	29
Cast iron	140	20
Steel	200	26
Carbon fiber	420	210
Kevlar 49	132	92
Polyethylene		
Spherulitic	1	1
Fiber (experimental)	220	220
Fully oriented fiber (theoretical)	>300	>300

*GPa = 145,000 psi.

SOURCE: D. J. Meier.[20]

and one can understand why polyethylene, an inexpensive raw material, should be the subject of such interest. However, there is a negative aspect to this product. Although the longitudinal strength is high, the strength in the transverse direction is not spectacular; such materials tend to fibrillate readily.

Thus, with a single type of polymer chain, three different morphological structures can be prepared (with vastly differing mechanical properties), depending on the *processing* variables chosen. This story, with variations, is repeated for many crystallizable polymers, such as the polyamides (nylons) and the polyesters.

Polymers do have their problems, not the least of which is instability at high temperatures. Here, they do not challenge metals or ceramics, although some are amazingly stable. When rendered highly thermally stable by the introduction of suitable chemical chain units, they tend to be more difficult to process. But, in many applications, often in conjunction with metals or ceramics, they are the material of choice. An additional problem with polymers is connected with their disposal as waste. However, many objects made from them can be either reused or recycled, but "mixtures" of them are hard to deal with and sorting for recycling is a definite problem.

The structure-processing-property theme may be expanded by changing the chemistry. Consider the case of polypropylene, $—[CH_2—CH(CH_3)]_n—$, which is "polyethylene" with a pendant methyl group on every other carbon atom. Solid-state extrusion in the manner described earlier produces uniaxially oriented material analogous to that shown in Figure 9, with again a presumably similar molecular picture. Alternatively, somewhat different processing yields biaxial orientation, which provides a superior product for certain applications. That this is not trivial is demonstrated by tests in which two polypropylene plates, each 3 mm thick, have stopped a .38-caliber normally loaded revolver bullet. This is a convincing demonstration of the impact strength possibilities of polymers; their ability to absorb large quantities of energy under certain specified conditions can be spectacular.

This discussion can be summarized as follows: (1) processing variables have a remarkable effect on the properties of polymers, even when the polymer chemistry is the same; (2) changes in the chemistry provide a greatly enhanced range of properties and opportunities. These are important themes whose initial impetus was largely from basic scientific studies, much of which started in Europe. Keller and his discovery of chain folding in single crystals[2] and Pennings and Kiel and their beautiful experiments on oriented fibers[15] are examples. To these must be added the role of distinguished chemists who discovered new synthesis routes to more uniform chain structures, such as Ziegler of Germany and Natta of Italy (discussed in the next section). Clearly, fundamental research in this field has contributed to applied technology, and vice versa.

If the emphasis in the foregoing discussion seems to be too much on polyethylene, it is worth observing that polyethylene is the largest-selling polymer from both poundage and monetary standpoints. The 1985 yearly production was roughly 7 million metric tons. The profits (or losses) were mostly in dollars, pounds, yen, marks, francs, lira, or guilders.

Amorphous Polymers

The story does not end with crystalline polymers. There are amorphous polymers of great importance that must be considered briefly and that introduce phenomena not encountered when discussing ordinary molecules. One such phenomenon is *tacticity,* a certain detail of the chain microstructure. Another is a fundamental physical phenomenon called the *glass transition,* which is still being studied and is exceptionally important in both physical and chemical properties. A third phenomenon concerns new insight into diffusion and into how polymer molecules *move.* The mode of motion of a long, snake-like molecule can differ from the diffusion of, say, an atom in a metallic alloy.

The simplest chemical structure of polypropylene was indicated earlier; it is essentially polyethylene with a methyl group attached to every other carbon atom. That makes every other carbon atom in the chain chiral (i.e., asymmetric), with the result that there are three classes of polypropylene structure, depending on the chiral relationship of each pendant methyl group with its neighbors. These three forms are illustrated in the lower part of Figure 11. When all chiral atoms have the same chirality, the polymer is called isotactic,

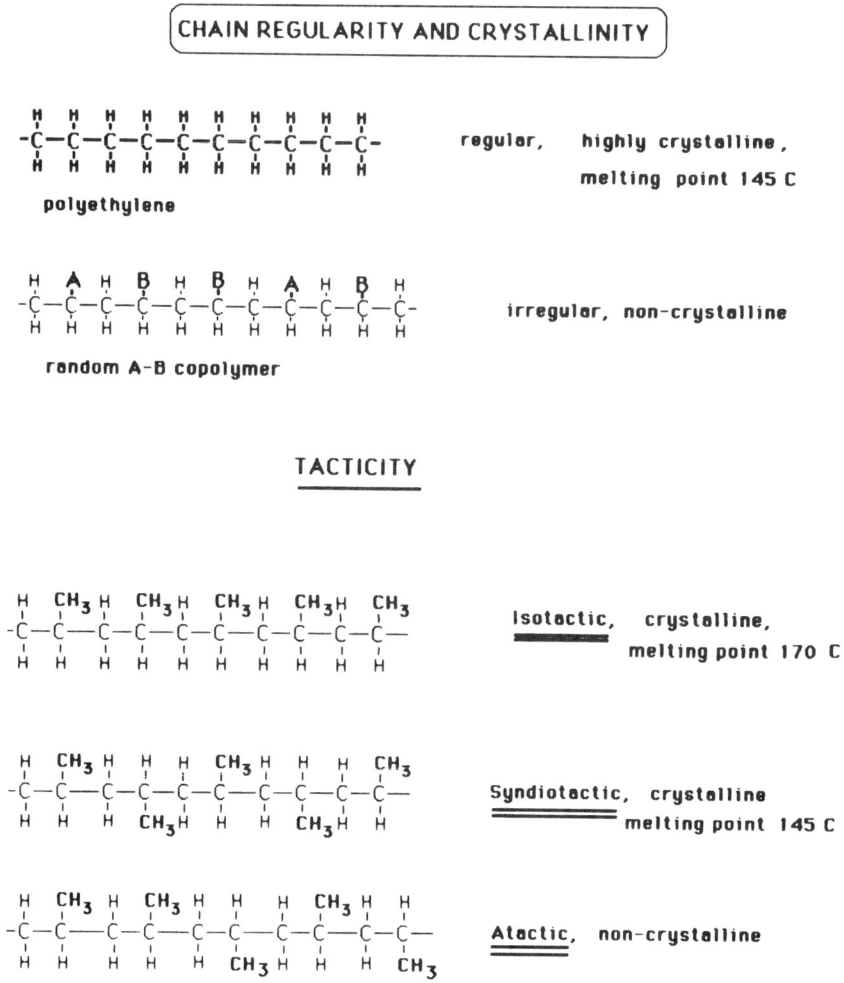

CHAIN REGULARITY AND CRYSTALLINITY

regular,   highly crystalline,
melting point 145 C

polyethylene

irregular, non-crystalline

random A-B copolymer

TACTICITY

Isotactic,   crystalline,
melting point 170 C

Syndiotactic,   crystalline
melting point 145 C

Atactic,   non-crystalline

FIGURE 11   Schematic representation of the effect of polymer chain regularity on ability to crystallize and on properties of the resulting crystals. From Meier.[20]

is crystalline, and has a moderately high melting point. When the chirality alternates regularly, as in the next line of the figure, the polymer is called syndiotactic, is also crystalline, and has a moderate melting point. When the chirality of successive atoms is random, as in the last line of the figure, the polymer is called atactic and it is noncrystalline (amorphous). That is, the stereoregular polymers crystallize and the stereoirregular ones do not. The whole subject of stereoregularity in polymers was elucidated by Ziegler et al.[21] and Natta et al.[22] Regularity of structure is a requirement for crystallization of polymers, as indicated also in the upper part of Figure 11, in which the regular structure of polyethylene is compared with the irregular structure produced by randomly coupling two different vinyl-type monomers. The ability or inability to crystallize is used to illustrate the importance that details of chemical structure (the microstructure) have on resulting physical properties. Chemically regular chains may crystallize; irregular chains cannot. This is an additional chain property that has expanded the range of opportunities for the use of organic polymers.

In amorphous polymers such as ordinary (atactic) polystyrene, an all-pervasive phenomenon of great importance occurs wherein properties change notably over a small temperature range. A change in slope in a volume-temperature plot (also in an enthalpy-temperature plot) occurs at a moderately well-defined temperature, known as the glass transition temperature, T_g, as illustrated in the left-hand side of Figure 12. This is formally a second-order transition in the Ehrenfest sense, although nonequilibrium rate effects attend it on all real occasions. Although this change of slope in itself appears to be subtle, there is a large change in mechanical properties as a sample goes through the glass transition. For example, the mechanical modulus decreases dramatically above the glass transition temperature, as indicated in the right-hand side of Figure 12: Below this temperature the material is brittle; above it, it is rubbery. (Remarkable changes in other properties also take place near T_g, such as in the dielectric loss.) This behavior also occurs in the amorphous regions of semicrystalline polymers.

As indicated earlier, the usual melt-crystallized specimen of polyethylene is partly crystalline and partly amorphous. Consequently, polyethylene exhibits amorphous properties (such as the glass transition) from the interlamellar regions, crystalline properties from the lamellae, and composite properties from the self-assembled combination. It is important to know about the glass transition, which should be thought of in the practical sense as an *engineering* property. Modulus behavior of a polymer is a major factor determining its behavior in use. Changes in modulus can be dramatic; frequently the modulus

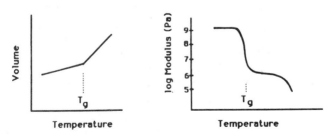

FIGURE 12   Schematic representation of the change in properties of an amorphous polymer at the glass transition temperature, T_g. From Meier.[20]

decreases by orders of magnitude above the glass transition temperature. Such behavior is also exhibited by some simple molecules and inorganic glasses, but the glass transition is of exceptional importance in polymeric materials.

The structure of amorphous polymers is often represented as entangled threads[23] according to Flory's[24] concept of polymer chains in the liquid being entangled random coils. Some polymer chains are somewhat stiffer than others, and some co-alignment of chain segments can occur in these (stiff, rod-like polymer chains can form "liquid crystals"). This picture may in some respects be approximate, but it is by far the best depiction currently available, especially for highly flexible chains. Such a picture raises two questions: (1) How does such a molecule move in such an entangled situation? and (2) What is the nature of the glass transition that appears in such systems at sufficiently low temperatures?

Figure 13 shows one way of looking at the first question.[25] The answer is that the polymer molecule moves by a process of curvilinear diffusion, called *reptation*. This is a new concept, due to de Gennes[26] and to Doi and Edwards,[27] that is appearing more and more in considerations of polymer dynamics and that is extremely important. In essence, the long molecule creeps along lengthwise, thus moving its center of mass in an effective manner.

Consider the uppermost molecule shown in Figure 13; surrounding molecules are not shown. It can be characterized by a mean-square end-to-end distance, $\langle R^2 \rangle$, a mean-square contour length, $\langle L^2 \rangle$, and a center-of-mass, CM. Consider that after a time the molecule has moved to the lower position, in which the center of mass has moved to the second position. There are two ways this can be treated, as indicated in the figure. One (on the right) is to consider the center of mass diffusion, which is related to the ordinary diffusion coefficient of the molecule as a whole and is given by the relationship shown in the upper right, where D_{cm} is the diffusion coefficient of the change of center of mass. This is a well-known formula by which the mean-square end-to-end distance, $\langle R^2 \rangle$, is related to the time, t_r, for the center of mass to move a distance equal to $\langle R^2 \rangle$. The time is defined as shown, and D_{cm} can be obtained by ordinary diffusion techniques.

Alternatively, this problem can be considered from the standpoint of reptation (left-hand side). Here, the molecule moves by lengthwise translation. If the diffusion coefficient is defined in units of lengthwise motion, the time, t_r (which is the time to move one contour length), can be written in terms of the mean-square contour length, $\langle L^2 \rangle$, as shown. However, the two times are equal, and the diffusion coefficient for curvilinear motion, D_r, can be expressed as shown in the first box. This quantity can be determined since all quantities on the right-hand side are measurable. This is another of de Gennes' results,[26] as adapted in Figure 13 by DiMarzio,[25] and yields values

$\mathcal{L}$ = CONTOUR LENGTH ; R = END-TO END DISTANCE

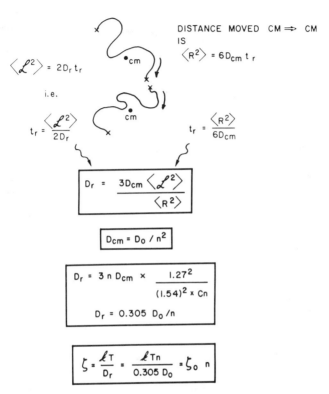

FIGURE 13 Schematic diagram of process of polymer chain movement. The right-hand side shows the center of mass diffusion; the left-hand side, reptation. See text for definition of symbols. From DiMarzio.[25]

of the curvilinear diffusion coefficient for reptation, D_r. For most organic polymers, $\langle L^2 \rangle \gg \langle R^2 \rangle$ with the result that reptational diffusion will be greatly enhanced relative to ordinary diffusion. Reptation is an effective mode of moving the center of mass of a polymer molecule.

One purpose of discussing motion in terms of reptation is to be able to explain how the polymer crystal discussed earlier could be formed out of an entangled melt. The answer is indicated schematically in Figure 14, in which the not-yet-crystallized portion of the polymer molecule is shown within a "reptation tube" from which the molecule is "reeled in" by the force of crystallization and forms chain folds on the crystal surface.[28] The concept of reptation is absolutely necessary to understand how a polymer chain can

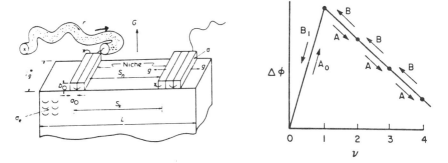

FIGURE 14   Model for coherent surface nucleation. The heavy arrow in the left-hand diagram represents motion of the polymer chain in the melt being "reeled" through the reptation tube onto the crystal surface by the force of crystallization. The right-hand diagram shows the barrier model for surface nucleation. From Hoffman.[28] Reprinted with permission.

crystallize out of an entangled melt within a reasonable time. No special "pre-structures" in the liquid are required to permit crystallization from the melt. Naturally, the longer the reptation tube (that is, the longer the molecule), the more difficult is the reeling-in[29] process. Figure 14 explains pictorially why crystallization becomes more difficult at higher molecular weights. Over and beyond its application to crystallization, reptation has a significant potential impact that is discussed below.

The origin and nature of the glass transition in amorphous substances in general and amorphous polymers in particular have been the subject of much study. In the polymer case, Gibbs and DiMarzio showed in a statistical mechanical treatment[30] that it is highly plausible that a true second-order thermodynamic transition underlies it. This thermodynamic transition temperature, denoted T_2, is below the observed T_g because of rate effects. Enormous periods of time would be required to approach T_2 experimentally. When discussing the underlying physical cause of the glass transition, Gibbs[31] likened the system of polymer molecules to an assembly of tree branches; the polymeric system on contraction and chain stiffening with lowering temperature resembles a compacted brush pile at T_2 incapable of much further compaction or overall "twig" (i.e., "polymer chain") motion at lower temperatures. The time effects near T_g were associated with the onset of increasing chain stiffness and degree of compaction as the system approached T_2. All this may be accepted as a highly reasonable general picture for amorphous polymers, but it leaves the ceramists and metallurgists to devise somewhat different analogies for inorganic and metallic glasses, just as one must do for organic glasses formed by supercooling simple molecules such as glucose and isoamyl bromide.

In glass transition the time effects near T_g follow an activation energy law far different from the customary Arrhenius law. For example, the fluidity ϕ (i.e., the inverse of the viscosity η) for simple liquids at high temperatures follows the Arrhenius form

$$\phi \simeq \phi_0 \, e^{-E^*/RT},$$

where E^* is the activation energy for viscous flow. However, in the subcooled state in the general vicinity of T_g, an amorphous polymer always exhibits the behavior

$$\phi \simeq \phi_0 \, e^{-U^*/R(T - T_\infty)},$$

where U^* is also an activation energy and T_∞ a temperature from 20°C, say, to 50°C below T_g. Thus the fluidity acts near T_g as if it would vanish at the finite temperature T_∞! Put another way, embrittlement sets in rapidly in a rather short range of temperature. Is T_∞ to be identified with the Gibbs-DiMarzio T_2? It is tempting to say yes, but the truth is that we do not know. The authors are aware of no completely satisfactory derivation of the $\exp[-U^*/R(T - T_\infty)]$ empirical law. "Free volume" concepts can be used to deduce a form like it, but pressure experiments (where constant volume can be maintained over a range of temperature) make trouble for this approach. This law is probably in the general class of time-dependent cooperative effects. We note also that the semiempirical law that polymer scientists refer to as the Williams-Landel-Ferry (WLF) equation,[32] was known independently by glass technologists as the Fulcher equation and by others. Further elucidation of the glass transition, especially the basis of its related time effects, stands as a challenge to ceramic, metal, and polymer scientists alike.

CURRENT APPLICATIONS

The following discussion of some current applications of polymers is presented (1) to retire the myth that polymers are *not* often the material of choice, (2) to show how polymeric materials support other major materials-intensive technologies interactively, (3) to indicate how polymers contribute to human benefit, (4) to demonstrate that progress is based on scientific foundations, and (5) to indicate how polymers work in conjunction with other materials. It is not often realized how pervasive polymers have become in daily life and in science and technology. We are inured to seeing plastic food wrappings and similar applications of polymers but are not often aware of a more complete set of applications.

There are, of course, many current applications of polymers, from contact lenses to containers. Following is a brief discussion of four applications:

piezoelectric polymers, polymer precursors for ceramics, photoresists for silicon chip technology, and *implants in the human body.*

Piezoelectric Polymers

One of the most prominent materials exhibiting piezoelectricity is a crystalline, processible polymer: polyvinylidene fluoride, $—(CH_2—CF_2)_n—$. It is a simple polymer—"polyethylene" again but with fluorine atoms replacing the protons every other carbon atom. Its three known molecular chain conformations are shown in Figure 15 in space-filling molecular models. The diagrams below the models show the carbon and fluorine atoms (protons omitted for clarity) as viewed down the chain. At each substituted carbon atom there is a large net electric dipole moment due to the highly polar $—CF_2—$ group. These three molecular conformations pack into a total of five known crystallographic phases (polymorphs). Projections on (001) of the two most important of these are shown in Figure 16, i.e., forms I (β) and II (α). Form II crystallizes from the quiescent melt and form I is obtained by stretching form II films at low temperatures (60–150°C). Each polymer chain has a net dipole moment indicated in the figure by an arrow. Clearly, the chain dipole moments cancel in form II, whereas they reinforce in form I. Application of a high electric field ("poling") reorients the dipoles of the crystal phase preferentially in the direction of the field, and they remain

FIGURE 15   Space-filling atomic models of the three known chain conformations of polyvinylidene fluoride in the crystalline state. From G. T. Davis, National Bureau of Standards.

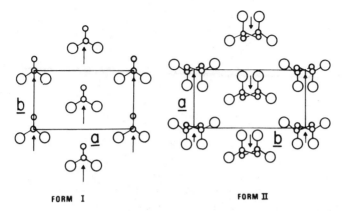

FORM I   FORM II

FIGURE 16 Projection of polyvinylidene fluoride chains onto the *ab* plane of the unit cell for polymorphic forms I and II. Large circles represent fluorine, small circles represent carbon, and the hydrogens have been omitted. Arrows indicate net dipole moment normal to chain axis. From Davis et al.[33] Reprinted with permission.

aligned upon removal of the field.[33] This interesting form of processing makes the material piezoelectric and apparently also ferroelectric.[33,34] Since polyvinylidene fluoride is moldable, transducers are readily fabricated.

In a related vein, many polymers show conductivity when they are doped (both n and p). Examples are shown in Figure 17. When these are doped, electrons can move freely along the polyconjugated paths. So far as we know, commercial applications are yet to be achieved but are surely to be expected. The activity in this field is considerable, and a conscientious review of it would be lengthy.

The detailed discussion concerning molecular conformations and crystal structures of polyvinylidene fluoride was included in part to illustrate that

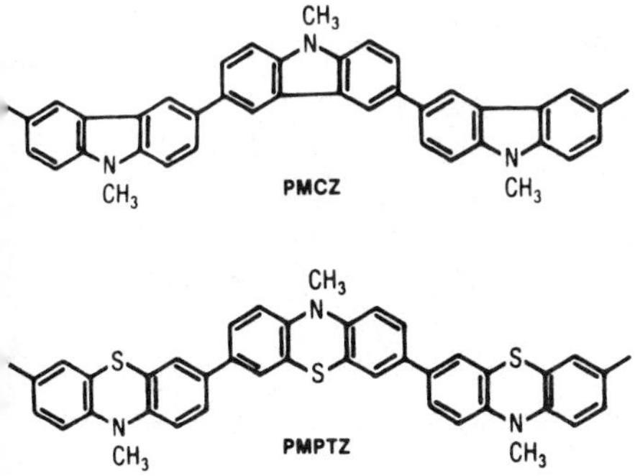

FIGURE 17 Line formulae of two processible polymers that are conducting when suitably doped. PMCZ is poly(*N*-methyl-3,6-carbazoyl); PMPTZ is poly(*N*-methyl-3,7-phenothiazinyl).

there is an enormous body of information on the crystal structure of polymers. Hundreds of crystal structures are known.[35] Here again polymer science owes a debt, this time to those who developed the principles of x-ray crystallography. The polymer scientists have since added nuances of their own to deal more effectively with special problems related to polymers.

Polymer Precursors for Ceramics

It is often difficult to produce molded objects (complex shapes) from ceramics because of their hardness and the extremely high temperatures that are required. A sometimes easier approach uses metal-organic polymer precursors that are processible and that are then converted to a ceramic body of the desired shape by appropriate pyrolysis (firing) techniques. Consequently, polymeric ceramic precursors are a potential source of coatings (for corrosion resistance, abrasion resistance, electrical insulation, and optical transmission/reflectance), of powders and sintering aids in the preparation of special-purpose bulk ceramics, and of fibers for high-temperature, high-strength composites. Again, the international character of research and technology in this field is evident.

The first example (Figure 18) is a process developed by the Japanese company, Nippon Carbon, to make the fiber called Nicalon®. The dimethylpolysilane polymer at the left is converted to a polycarbosilane. Both polymers are tractable and can be melt-spun to make fibers in a manner roughly analogous to the spinning of nylon. After curing, pyrolysis of the polycarbosilane fiber yields an extremely good silicon carbide (SiC) fiber (with the side products indicated). Objects molded or fabricated from the polymer precursor will, after pyrolysis, be silicon carbide ceramics. Note that SiC itself is difficult to shape. In this example, the SiC fiber was obtained by combining polymer technology and knowledge of how polymers degrade under heat. Study of Nicalon SiC fibers was conducted by the Celanese

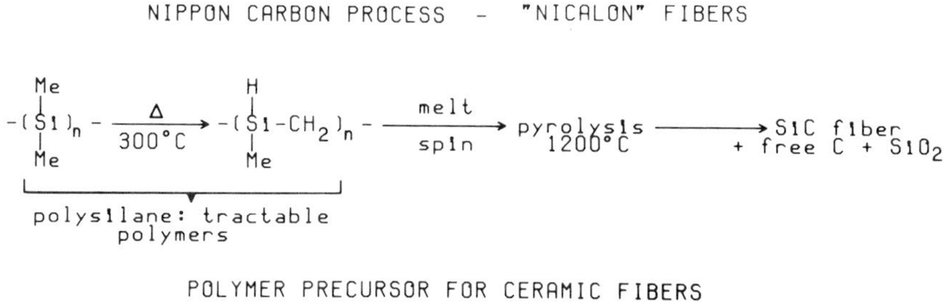

NIPPON CARBON PROCESS — "NICALON" FIBERS

FIGURE 18 Schematic representation of the process to prepare Nicalon ceramic fibers from polymeric precursor.

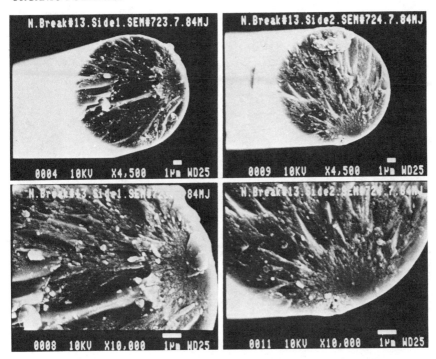

FIGURE 19   Typical fracture surfaces of a Nicalon ceramic fiber (matched ends), showing a classical fracture surface with initiating flaw, mirror, and the rougher surface indicative of catastrophic crack propagation. From L. C. Sawyer, Celanese Research Company.

Research Company and by Dow Corning under a contract with the Defense Advanced Research Projects Agency. Fracture surfaces of a 10-μm Nicalon fiber are shown in Figure 19 (a matched pair of ends). Each picture shows a classical Griffiths fracture surface with initiating flaw, mirror (smooth area around the flaw through which the crack traveled in a controlled fashion), and the rougher surface indicating catastrophic crack propagation. The cleaner and purer the fiber, the stronger and more reliable is the material. With appropriate care, the heterogeneities that initiate crack propagation can be minimized and excellent-strength SiC fibers formed.

The Dow Corning precursor is a polydisilylazane, a mixed polymer with monomer segment concentrations. After pyrolysis, one has a mixed-composition silicon carbide–silicon nitride (SiCN) fiber about 10 μm in diameter. By changing the polymer chemistry, cleverly synthesizing this molecule, spinning it as a tractable polymer, and pyrolyzing it, Dow Corning has made superior materials with tensile strengths of approximately 300 kpsi. This is an important area of emerging technology.

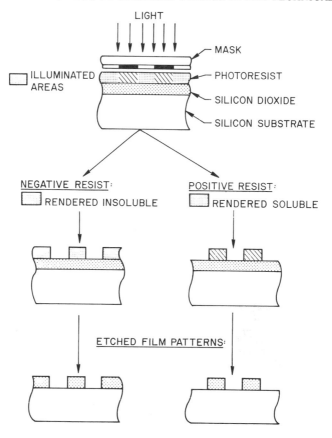

FIGURE 20 Polymers in silicon chip technology. Exposure and development of positive and negative polymeric resists with the subsequent etching of substrate films using the resists as etch masks. From D. W. McCall, AT&T Bell Laboratories.

Silicon Chip Technology

Briefly, virtually every silicon (also gallium arsenide) chip now in use was made using positive or negative photoresists that are polymeric in character. The process is shown in Figure 20. The photoresists control the areas of the chip that are made into conductors or insulators in subsequent evaporation operations; they are absent in the final product. Silicon chip technology would not have been developed without a major contribution of polymer science (much of it chemistry) and technology. This is another example where polymer science and technology assist other materials efforts.

The outstanding computer and communication industries in the United States owe much to polymeric photoresists.

Implants in the Human Body

Figure 21 is a picture of a hip implant, a good solution to a problem through the intelligent use of a combination of different classes of materials. Currently, two different polymers and a metal are used. The hip cup is made of ultrahigh-molecular-weight polyethylene (again!), which is put in the pelvis and virtually never fails. The shaft is vitalium metal. It is difficult to

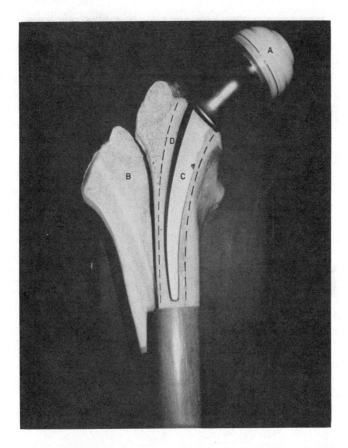

FIGURE 21 Hip implant employing a combination of materials: A, ultrahigh-molecular-weight polyethylene hip cup; B, bone; C, metal shaft; D, polymethyl methacrylate binder of metal shaft to femur. The dashed lines denote the boundaries between binder and bone. Photo by J. D. Hoffman of exhibit in possession of Polymers Division, National Bureau of Standards.

find a noncorrosive metal that is acceptable to the human body, although the vitalium generally works out well. The vitalium shaft is cemented to the femur with methyl methacrylate monomer, which is then polymerized *in situ* *during* the implant operation on the patient. The problem of controlling the polymerization reaction under these conditions can be imagined. Too rapid a polymerization means too much heat generation, which can be injurious, and too slow a polymerization can fail to give sufficient physical strength before the operation is complete. But the use of the methyl methacrylate, derived in part from dental technology, does indeed work. This method of attachment of the metal to the femur introduces a possible mode of failure— the metal shaft working loose in the polymethyl methacrylate binder. Improvements are undoubtedly possible, but these hip implants are a great boon to those who need them.

One measure of the importance of this application of polymer science and technology is the 130,000 hip implants per year using polyethylene. Because many of these are put into younger persons, it is appropriate to be concerned with failure analysis. The high molecular weight of this material, while subduing the crystallinity somewhat, goes a long way toward increasing impact strength and wear resistance. With its ultrahigh molecular weight and good toughness, this inert and reasonably tractable material has a very important application. The scientific foundations of such implants are impressive: studies of polymer chemical kinetics, polymer degradation, mechanical strength and wear, metal stress corrosion, and clinical uses all had to be done. This is a good example of the combined use of metals and polymers for human benefit.

The range of physical properties achievable by intelligent use of chemistry and an understanding of property-structure relationships is considerable, as we have seen. One more example will serve to elucidate this point further. By the appropriate choice of "ring opening" monomers, Bailey et al.[36] have shown that it is possible to make practical polymers that either contract (which is the usual case) or expand upon polymerization. Moreover, in a well-defined middle ground of composition, neither expansion nor contraction occurs. Such behavior is interesting to contemplate, and projected uses include dental applications where low-to-moderate expansion is desirable. Also to be considered here is the possibility of potting delicate electronic components to protect them from mechanical damage and hostile environments.

MAJOR NEW APPLICATION THRUSTS

In this section some expectations for future uses of polymers are discussed. Undoubtedly we have overlooked many possibilities, but the field is rich enough to permit many surprises. There will be improved composite structures that are readily manufacturable and of predictable lifetime. There will be improved blends (polymer alloys) that are also readily manufacturable and have a predictable lifetime. Much has been accomplished on blends, but a lot remains to be done. Lightweight batteries and high-quality aspheric lenses will become available. Clearly, camera manufacturers have already made advances here for their current models of small cameras. Corrosion resistance will be improved. The possibility of self-assembling polymeric chips may be farfetched but cannot be ignored. Practical polymers from direct biological conversion of inexpensive feedstocks (e.g., waste) are clearly possible—polyhydroxybutyrate, which in many respects rivals polyethylene in its physical properties, is currently obtained in this manner. *Escherichia coli* and some other bacteria can manufacture good, very pure polymers of known molecular weight and molecular weight distribution. This, of course, is what an important part of biotechnology is all about.

Blends: Block Copolymers and Polymer Alloys

Two extremely important subjects illustrate succinctly the current technology, current knowledge, and directions of future advances. First, there are blends, which may be either block copolymers (two or more chemically different polymer chains connected together by a chemical bond) or polymer alloys (two or more chemically different polymers that are mechanically mixed).

The manner of blending the two different polymers strongly affects the resultant properties—for example, the important property of impact strength (as mentioned earlier). Figure 22 shows this for blends of thermoplastic polystyrene (S) and polybutadiene (B). With mechanical mixtures (simple blends), impact strengths show little or no improvement. However, if the proper kind of block copolymer is made with chemical linkages between the two types of chains, superior impact strengths are achieved. The different types of copolymer that can be made are listed in Table 2 together with approximate tensile strengths. One can see that most of the possible copolymers offer little improvement in properties. However, with one of the possible triblock copolymers (S-B-S) there is a marked increase in tensile strength as well as in impact strength (Figure 22). The reason for this behavior is shown in Figure 23, in which the morphologies of S-B diblock and S-B-S and B-S-B triblock polymers are represented. In this figure, the butadiene (B) portion is shown by the solid lines and the styrene (S) portion by the broken lines. In each case there is an aggregation of one species (the styrene). Only in the case of the S-B-S block copolymer, however, does this aggregation create a three-dimensional network, which in turn leads to the improved toughness and tensile strength. This is another example of the effect of molecular architecture on properties, in this case on the important property of strength.

Polystyrene – Polybutadiene Blends

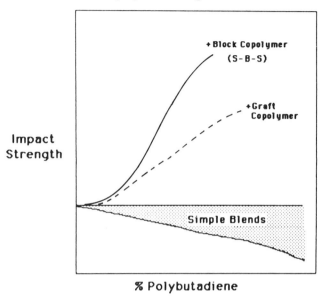

% Polybutadiene

FIGURE 22   Schematic representation of the effect of composition on properties of rubber-modified thermoplastics. S = polystyrene and B = polybutadiene. From Meier.[20]

As already indicated (Figure 23), phase separation of the polymeric species occurs. The phase-separated blend is in effect a self-assembled composite but of a different origin than that in the semicrystalline polymers mentioned earlier. This phase separation is of a most unusual type because one part of a given giant molecule is in one phase and the other part is in a second phase. The phase domains are thus of molecular dimensions, typically 10 to 30 nm in diameter. This is a curious situation, but thermodynamics is not violated.

TABLE 2   Influence of Molecular Architecture on Tensile Strength

Type	Molecular Architecture	Tensile Strength (kg/cm²)
Random (SB)	–S–B–B–S–B–S–S–S–B–B–	≈ 0
Diblock (S-B)	–S–S–S–S–S–B–B–B–B–B–	≈ 0
Triblock (S-B-S)	–S–S–S–[B–B . . . B–B]–S–S–S–	300
Triblock (B-S-B)	–B–B–B–[S–S . . . S–S]–B–B–B–	≈ 0
Multiblock (S-B)$_n$	–([S–S . . . S–S] [B–B . . . B–B])$_n$–	≈ 0 ($n > 3$)

NOTE: Polymers: 25 percent styrene (S), 75 percent butadiene (B), molecular weight = 100,000.

SOURCE: D. J. Meier.[20]

Thus, the whole question of phase diagrams becomes as important for polymer blends as it is for metals and ceramics. It is also necessary to know how fast phase separation occurs and whether it is spinodal decomposition or ordinary phase separation. The nature and properties of the interfaces are important.

There is greatly increasing emphasis in both fundamental and applied work in this field. Many commercial applications have arisen with gratifying improvements in properties. Much basic work is going on in studies involving phase diagrams, dynamic mechanical behavior, and attempts to understand impact strengths and the size and nature of interfaces. Progress is already highly significant, but much remains to be done. Some of the needs for new knowledge in the field of blends are

- Theoretical basis of compatibility
- Methods of measuring compatibility
- Establishment of phase diagram
- Theory of kinetics of segregation
- Measurement methods for kinetics of segregation

CHAIN CONFORMATIONS VS. MOLECULAR ARCHITECTURE

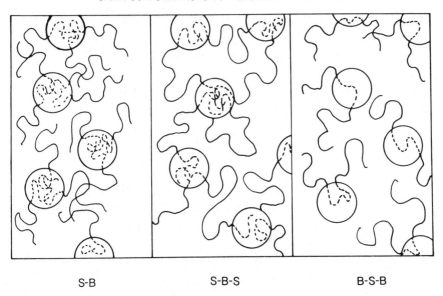

S-B   S-B-S   B-S-B

FIGURE 23 Schematic representation of the structure of styrene-butadiene diblock (S-B) and triblock (S-B-S and B-S-B) copolymers: solid line, polybutadiene; dashed line, polystyrene. Only in the S-B-S triblock copolymer do the polystyrene domains "tie" the structure together over the entire sample. From Meier.[20]

• Theory of interfacial zones
• Mechanism of compatibilizers
• Dependence of properties on segregation
• Durability of properties
• Morphology and structure in segregated phases

Composites

The second area in which much is being done is composites. Nature invented composites—wood (cellulose and lignin) and bone (the polymer collagen and the mineral hydroxyapatite) are specific examples. A composite can and often does have much more desirable properties than do the individual "pure" or "virgin" materials from which it was made. Man-made composites have also been successful, as in the case of the "rubber" tire, which in its most common modern form is a composite of vulcanized rubber (the synthetic or natural polymer), carbon filler, and steel or polymeric fibers. One reason for interest in other man-made composites is indicated in Figure 24, which compares specific strengths (tensile strength/density). The high strength-to-weight ratio of composites is more favorable than their ratio of strength to size. The high strengths of the aramid Kevlar and graphite composites justify commercial interest in them. Glass composites combine a slight sacrifice in properties with a significant drop in cost. Current commercial aircraft use substantial amounts of nonstructural composites and about 37 percent by weight of composites in primary structure. Composites are an absolutely essential component in modern military aircraft. The current in-service airplane contains alloy steel in the engines, aluminum over the body, some titanium, and various types of composites. Current commercial aircraft design

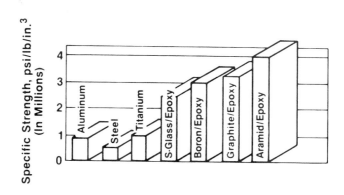

FIGURE 24   Specific strengths of various engineering materials (ultimate tensile strength/density).

contemplates an increased use of composites; for future subsonic (not supersonic) aircraft, the potential composite use in primary structure exceeds 50 percent by weight of the aircraft. The net result will be a considerable weight saving, with a concomitant increase in fuel efficiency, as well as highly satisfactory durability, strength, and corrosion resistance. For many aircraft structural members, composites have become the materials of choice.

In a related field, the body of the popular and impressive Pontiac Fiero automobile is made of composites. Lest one believe that the use of polymers for automobile parts and bodies is entirely new, one of the authors had in his possession a photograph taken in 1942 showing Henry Ford wielding an axe on a plastic trunk door made from soybeans (there is no photograph of the sequel). The science of polymers was in its infancy in those days. The idea, strongly espoused by Staudinger,[37] that polymers were giant molecules had not yet taken full hold. (It now seems almost incredible that Staudinger, rightly deemed the father of polymer science, had an extremely difficult time convincing many of the scientists of his day that giant molecules existed. Some of the resistance undoubtedly arose, apart from the natural conservatism of most scientists, from the then strong presence of influential scientists who refused to believe even in atoms, because thermodynamics, mechanics, and optics had been developed so successfully without them.) The current scientific basis is much improved, and more rapid progress can now be made. The increased use of composites in automobile manufacture is a virtual certainty.

Although not emphasized up to this point, most of the current polymer formulations employed in composites in aircraft and automobiles are three-dimensional networks, the so-called epoxy compounds being typical. These networks are similar to those shown in Figure 23, except that the cross-links involve chemical bonds. These materials (''thermosets'') are converted from the monomer-fiber-filler mixture (which is like a slurry) by the introduction of a chemical catalyst and application of heat in a curing cycle. The result is a tough composite consisting of high-molecular-weight polymer bonded to the fiber and the filler. Voids can be a problem. Because of the time required for the procedure, thought is currently being given to using thermoplastic polymers (i.e., polymers that are softened by heat and thereby rendered rapidly moldable) in composites. Such thermoplastic polymers might be of either the crystallizable or amorphous type; if crystalline, the crystals themselves can act as cross-links between chains. Rapid manufacture of a finished part having uniform high quality and predictable properties is the overall goal.

Current problems and issues for further study concerning composites certainly include their processing and manufacturability and the manner in which they fail. Damage to an object made of metal (such as a car) results in a visible dent, and repair is relatively simple. A composite can be damaged badly and frayed on the inside but show little sign of it on the outside.[38] Repair tends to be difficult. The detection of flaws with nondestructive evaluation is a major issue in composites. A basic scientific understanding of the mechanism of failure and of the lifetime durability of composites is a high-priority subject.

In this regard, a research briefing[39] prepared at the request of the Office of Science and Technology Policy and the National Science Foundation (under the joint chairmanship of D. W. McCall of AT&T Bell Laboratories and R. Pariser of E. I. du Pont de Nemours & Co.) recommended directions for research. Among other concerns, it is necessary to obtain a better understanding of the relationships between molecular structure and physical properties of fibers and how these relationships can be translated into the behavior of a fiber in a composite. Since composites are subject to long-term cyclical loading, an understanding of the fatigue behavior of fibers under such conditions is necessary. Other key issues for further study are the fundamentals of the fiber-polymer interface as related, for example, to adhesion and load bearing; methods for joining or fastening composites to like or different materials; and control of creep under load (desired also for metals). The best way to resolve these issues is not clear. Efforts have been made, with some success, but there remains a great challenge. A common current practice is to pick a specific system and then explore that system in depth. But can broad generalizations be made? The answer, it is hoped, is "yes," but the information must be sought out with vigor.

The issues involved in the processing of polymer composites include the chemistry of the composite itself (what materials are chosen), the chemical interactions at the interfaces with the filler and the fiber, the flow and other problems associated with manufacture, and the nature of the structure finally achieved. Fundamental scientific and applied technological attacks on all aspects are required. It should come as no surprise that some of the flow properties encountered in the "slurries" that make up pre-composites before molding or curing are related to concepts developed by soil scientists, who have studied the behavior of moist earth under stress for a long time.

For both blends and composites there is a clear need to understand chemical, physical, processing, and lifetime behavior. Approaches must be interdisciplinary, based both on theory and on experiments in organic chemistry, physical chemistry, rheology, and solid-state physics. They must include the fields of metals, polymers, ceramics, interfaces, and nondestructive evaluation. This breadth of endeavor itself poses a large and difficult challenge to scientists and engineers. Cooperation and interaction among industrial, academic, nonprofit, and government organizations will be important. Japanese and European competition is already evident, but the future holds sufficient promise to make the effort well worthwhile.

The universities have made a significant response to the need for education and research in composites. Some of the institutions involved are the University of Massachusetts, Washington University, the University of Delaware, Virginia Polytechnic Institute, and the Case Western Reserve–University of Akron dyad. This list is, of course, not exhaustive. Certain universities, such as Michigan State University, Michigan Technological University, and the University of California, Santa Barbara, have serious intentions in the field. Doubtless, there will be more.

The authors' organization, Michigan Molecular Institute, plans to cooperate with universities on both education and research efforts in the areas of blends and composites. We believe that a strong *materials* science base is an absolute prerequisite for such an activity. Industrial research laboratories are also highly active in the area—the aerospace industries heading the list—and it is clear that great interest and activity have also developed in the automotive company laboratories.

Governmental involvement is not lacking either: the highly significant programs at Wright-Patterson Air Force Base and by the National Aeronautics and Space Administration are well known, and recently the National Bureau of Standards developed a response. The National Science Foundation is fully aware of the issues involved and has provided significant support to some of the universities mentioned.

POLYMER SCIENCE

The final topic of this review concerns aspects of the newer theories of polymer science currently stimulating the field: reptation, phase transitions, and some unusual behavior and generalizations concerning polymer melts. Reptation has already been mentioned and will be discussed again shortly.

The "trajectory" of a flexible polymer molecule in the molten state is not unlike the path of an inebriated bumblebee, except that, because the chain atoms occupy space, the chain cannot cross itself. Consequently, the chain is slightly expanded and is called the excluded-volume coil (Figure 25, left). If there were no self-exclusion, the chain would be somewhat smaller (Figure 25, center); certain solvents (called theta solvents) permit the chain to act like this. If the pH or the thermodynamic driving force of the solvent is changed

FIGURE 25 Schematic representation of the trajectory of an "amorphous" polymer molecule under various conditions: (left) with excluded volume; (center) random coil (theta conditions); (right) collapsed. The single molecule may undergo an abrupt phase transition.

(i.e., the "goodness" of the solvent is changed), a collapsed coil can appear abruptly (Figure 25, right). In other words, there is a true phase transition *within a single molecule!* This possibility has been of great interest to theoreticians. This "collapse transition" was originally predicted by Stockmayer,[40] Monte Carlo studies suggested it,[41] and the newer renormalization group and scaling theories[26] have been able to deal with it effectively. The problem is similar—practically identical mathematically in one limit—to the magnetic spin problem in ferromagnets.[42] This for a linear, flexible polymer! Recently, the collapse was observed experimentally.[43] Figure 26 summarizes the theories and observations. The mean-square radius of gyration, $\langle R_g^2 \rangle$, is related to the length, N, of a polymer chain raised to some power, γ, where γ is a measure of the solvent power. The schematic shows an abrupt change in size with solvent character, with the transition actually occurring over a few tenths of a degree. In other words, polymer chains in solution behave differently than do low-molecular-weight compounds. One fascinating side effect of all this is that articles relating to the aforementioned phase transition in polymers are now occasionally found in the *Physical Review,* a journal that has in the past carried very few articles on polymers. It must be pointed out, however, that neither the American Chemical Society nor the American Physical Society ignores the topic of polymers; on the contrary, both strongly support active divisions for polymer science.

Polymer melts also show unusual behavior when compared with normal fluids. For example, an ordinary liquid pumped out of a tube will exhibit the profile left-hand part of Figure 27.[44] A polymer liquid (without confinement) pumped out of a tube swells up on exit, as shown on the right-hand

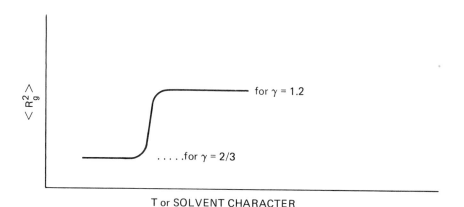

FIGURE 26   Schematic mean-square radius of gyration $\langle R_g^2 \rangle$ of a polymer molecule as a function of temperature, T, or of solvent character. The value of $\langle R_g^2 \rangle^{1/2}$ is a measure of the effective size or "extent" of the polymer molecule.

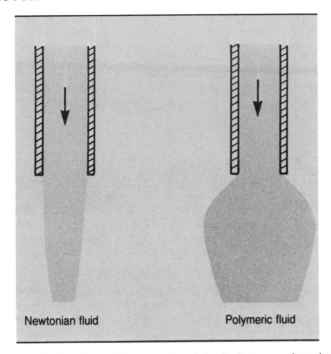

Newtonian fluid   Polymeric fluid

FIGURE 27   Illustration of the difference in flow behavior between polymeric and simple Newtonian liquids. From Bird and Curtiss.[44] Reprinted with permission.

side of Figure 27; i.e., it exhibits "memory." In many systems, such as metals, the deviation from perfect elasticity is usually small. In polymeric systems, by contrast, mechanical behavior is frequently dominated by such viscoelastic behavior with its pervasive memory effects. Bird and Curtiss[44] have illustrated many other differences in the behavior of simple and polymeric liquids. (We have already mentioned one—namely, the behavior of the fluidity ϕ with temperature.) The unusual mechanical behavior of polymer melts is governed in general by nonlinear viscoelastic theory. To understand manufacturability and processing in polymers better, one must understand not only such simple behavior but also many complex phenomena, of which the example of Figure 27 is but a premonitory hint. One wants a molecular view of these effects that could be reduced to practice.

However, the polymer engineers and phenomenologists prefer to think in terms of continuum equations, called constitutive equations. An example of a generalized simple linear constitutive equation is

$$\sigma_{12}(t) \simeq - \int_{-\infty}^{t} m(t - t') \, \gamma_{21}(t, t') dt',$$

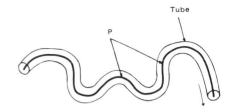

FIGURE 28   A reptation "tube" in which the polymer chain is confined. The arrow indicates the direction of reptation. From de Gennes.[26] Copyright © 1979 by Cornell University. Used by permission of the publisher, Cornell University Press.

where γ_{21} is the shear strain at time t' relative to that at time t. In a sense this approach is similar to thermodynamics in that there is no presence of the molecule in such equations—i.e., no molecular parameters. This equation implies that the shear stress, σ_{12}, is obtained by an integration of the product of some kind of memory function, m, and the shear strain.

This, in a general sense, is the sort of formulation required to understand phenomena such as that illustrated in Figure 27. There is no lack of inspired constitutive-based equations to deal with such situations; an example is the useful Bernstein-Kearsley-Zapas (BKZ) theory.[45] But, as we have said, we would like to know about the role of the molecules.

The reptation model (which is molecular in character) discussed earlier is thought to be applicable here and is shown with the subject molecule and its confining tube in an isolated state in Figure 28.[26] Recently, Doi and Edwards,[27] de Gennes,[46] Curtiss and Bird,[44] and Graessley[47] have begun to modify the reptation model by, for example, letting the tube diffuse around on its end. On the basis of this type of molecular model, in one simplistic form, they have been able to derive an elementary constitutive equation from molecular considerations. It is hoped that such an approach, if it is not mathematically intractable, will lead to a much-improved molecular picture of what is happening when polymers are processed. The ultimate goal is to relate chain (i.e., molecular) properties to stress-strain-time relations in a polymer melt so that processing may be understood in basic terms. A special need is perceived for what may indeed be a new language that will allow scientists and engineers (and project managers) to communicate better concerning polymer properties as they relate to practice. Quoting the modulus is no longer enough, if indeed it ever was. Neither is a computer simulation that slurs over material properties. The need is great enough for polymers in conventional use and surely reaches its zenith when composites of polymers with metals or ceramic bodies are considered.

The field of polymer science is displaying a tremendous vitality and energy, coupled with high-quality science. It now involves basic scientists from seemingly distant fields: theoretical physics (phase transitions); solid-state physics (piezoelectric, conductive, and semiconductive polymers); statistical mechanics; quantum mechanics; continuum mechanics; biophysics; and biochemistry. In addition, rheology and viscoelasticity are its special province. There is plenty of scope for intellectual curiosity and creativity, with many unsolved problems even in the "conventional" parts of the field. In these, as well as in some of the new directions we have noted, there is a high probability that the science will lead to practical results and benefits. However, progress will depend in considerable degree on broad and fundamental knowledge and training in materials science as a whole; as we have illustrated repeatedly, a single type of material no longer stands in total isolation from the others, and the basic disciplines are still fundamental to every aspect of materials science.

ACKNOWLEDGMENTS

In preparing this review the efforts of numerous others were invaluable, specifically C. M. Guttman, G. T. Davis, L. Smith, and D. Huntston of NBS; M. Jaffe and R. M. Mininni of Celanese Corporation (in cooperation with DARPA and Dow Corning); K. Bowen of MIT; DARPA; R. E. Hefner, consultant to Michigan Molecular Institute; D. J. Meier of MMI; D. W. McCall of AT&T Bell Laboratories; J. T. Quinlivan of Boeing Company; R. S. Porter of the University of Massachusetts; and R. K. Eby of the Johns Hopkins University.

NOTES

1. H.-G. Elias, *New Commercial Polymers 1969–1975* (Gordon and Breach, New York, 1977); H.-G. Elias and F. Vohwinkel, *Neue polymere Werkstoffe für die industrielle Anwendung,* 2nd ed. (Hanser, Munich, 1983).
2. A. Keller, Philos. Mag. **2**, 1171 (1957).
3. D. C. Bassett, F. C. Frank, and A. Keller, Philos. Mag. **8**, 1753 (1963).
4. J. D. Hoffman, G. T. Davis, and J. I. Lauritzen, Jr., in *Treatise on Solid State Chemistry,* edited by N. B. Hannay (Plenum, New York, 1976), Vol. 3, Chap. 7.
5. T. C. Chean and S. Krimm, J. Polym. Sci., Polym. Phys. Ed. **19**, 423 (1981); X. Jing and S. Krimm, *ibid.* **20**, 1155 (1982).
6. C. M. Guttman, E. A. DiMarzio, and J. D. Hoffman, Polymer **22**, 597 (1981).
7. D. M. Sadler, "Neutron scattering by crystalline polymers: Molecular conformations and their interpretation," in *Structure of Crystalline Polymers,* edited by I. H. Hall (Elsevier, London, 1984), p. 125.
8. J. D. Hoffman, L. J. Frolen, G. S. Ross, and J. I. Lauritzen, Jr., J. Res. Natl. Bur. Stand., Sect. A **79**, 671 (1975).
9. R. Eppe, E. W. Fischer, and H. A. Stuart, J. Polym. Sci. **34**, 721 (1959).
10. H. D. Keith and F. J. Padden, Jr., Polymer **25**, 28 (1984).
11. A. Keller, University of Bristol (private communication).
12. G. C. Claver, Jr., R. Buchdahl, and R. L. Miller, J. Polym. Sci. **20**, 202 (1956).
13. H. D. Keith and F. J. Padden, Jr., J. Appl. Phys. **35**, 1270, 1286 (1964).
14. E. J. Clark, National Bureau of Standards (unpublished).
15. A. J. Pennings and A. M. Kiel, Kolloid Z. Z. Polym. **205**, 160 (1965).
16. A. J. Pennings, J. M. A. A. van der Mark, and A. M. Kiel, Kolloid Z. Z. Polym. **237**, 336 (1970).

17. I. M. Ward, Adv. Polym. Sci. **70**, 1 (1985).
18. R. S. Porter (private communication). See also R. S. Porter, in *Cutting Edge Technologies* (National Academy Press, Washington, D.C., 1984), pp. 109–116.
19. A. E. Zachariades and R. S. Porter, in *The Strength and Stiffness of Polymers,* edited by A. E. Zachariades and R. S. Porter (Marcel Dekker, New York, 1983).
20. D. J. Meier, Michigan Molecular Institute (private communication).
21. K. Ziegler, E. Holzkamp, H. Breil, and H. Martin, Angew. Chem. **67**, 426, 541 (1955).
22. G. Natta, P. Pino, P. Corradini, F. Danusso, E. Mantica, G. Mazzanti, and G. Moraglio, J. Am. Chem. Soc. **77**, 1708 (1955).
23. W. F. Graessley, Adv. Polym. Sci. **47**, 67 (1982).
24. P. J. Flory, *Principles of Polymer Chemistry* (Cornell University Press, Ithaca, N.Y., 1953).
25. E. A. DiMarzio, National Bureau of Standards (unpublished).
26. P. G. de Gennes, *Scaling Concepts in Polymer Physics* (Cornell University Press, Ithaca, N.Y., 1979).
27. M. Doi and S. F. Edwards, J. Chem. Soc., Faraday Trans. 2, **74**, 1789, 1802, 1818 (1978).
28. J. D. Hoffman, "Golden jubilee conference polyethylene, 1933–1983," Proceedings of the Plastics and Rubber Institute (June 1983), p. D3.1.
29. J. D. Hoffman, SPE Trans. **4**, 315 (1964).
30. J. H. Gibbs and E. A. DiMarzio, J. Chem. Phys. **28**, 373 (1958).
31. J. H. Gibbs (private communication).
32. M. L. Williams, R. F. Landel, and J. D. Ferry, J. Am. Chem. Soc. **77**, 3701 (1955).
33. G. T. Davis, J. E. McKinney, M. G. Broadhurst, and S. C. Roth, J. Appl. Phys. **49**, 4998 (1978).
34. A. J. Lovinger, Science **24**, 3 (1983).
35. R. L. Miller, in *Polymer Handbook,* 2nd ed., edited by J. Brandrup and E. H. Immergut (Wiley, New York, 1975).
36. W. J. Bailey, R. L. Sun, H. Katsuki, T. Endo, H. Iwama, R. Tsushima, K. Saigo, and M. M. Bitritto, in *Ring-Opening Polymerization,* ACS Symposium Series No. 59), edited by T. Saegusa and E. Goethals (American Chemical Society, Washington, D.C., 1977), p. 38.
37. H. Staudinger, Chem. Ber. **53**, 1073 (1920).
38. M. D. Rhodes and J. G. Williams, "Concept for improving the damage tolerance of composite compression panels," presented at DOD/NASA Conference on Fibrous Composite Structures, New Orleans, La., 27–29 June 1981.
39. "Report of the research briefing panel on high-performance polymer composites," in *Research Briefings 1984* (National Academy Press, Washington, D.C., 1984), pp. 45–56.
40. W. H. Stockmayer, Makromol. Chem. **35**, 54 (1960).
41. F. L. McCracken, J. Mazur, and C. M. Guttman, Macromolecules **6**, 859 (1973); A. T. Clark and M. Lal, Br. Polym. J. **9**, 92 (1977).
42. P. G. de Gennes, J. Phys. (Paris) **36**, L-55 (1975).
43. I. Nishio, S.-T. Sun, G. Swislow, and T. Tanaka, Nature (London) **281**, 208 (1979); S.-T. Sun, I. Nishio, G. Swislow, and T. Tanaka, J. Chem. Phys. **73**, 5971 (1980).
44. R. B. Bird and C. F. Curtiss, Phys. Today (January 1984), p. 36.
45. B. Bernstein, E. A. Kearsley, and L. J. Zapas, Trans. Soc. Rheol. **7**, 391 (1963); **9**, 27 (1965).
46. P. G. de Gennes and L. Léger, Ann. Rev. Phys. Chem. **33**, 49 (1982).
47. W. W. Graessley, J. Polym. Sci., Polym. Phys. Ed., **18**, 27 (1980).

New Ways of Looking at Surfaces

E. WARD PLUMMER, TORGNY GUSTAFSSON,
DONALD R. HAMANN, INGOLF LINDAU, DOUGLAS L. MILLS,
CALVIN F. QUATE, and Y. RONALD SHEN

The tremendous progress in surface science in the last 10 to 15 years is due primarily to the development of new theoretical and experimental techniques capable of probing the surface of materials in microscopic detail. The scanning tunneling microscope now shows the surface in near-atomic detail, revealing the surface order, steps, and defects. In the near future this instrument will be advanced to the stage where high-resolution inelastic tunneling spectra can be obtained for each atomic site, giving chemical as well as structural information. Experiments based on scattering of electrons, photons, and ions to determine structure have shown significant progress in the last few years. It is nearly correct to say that the static structure of any ordered surface can now be determined, thus placing emphasis on understanding why a given structure occurs. Recent experiments have examined changes in surface structure as a function of temperature or the presence of foreign impurities. X-ray scattering from adsorbate layers is used to explore the nature of two-dimensional melting for both physisorbed and chemisorbed layers. Recent ion-scattering experiments have shed light on the nature of surface melting of a lead crystal. The use of insertion devices on high-energy synchrotron sources will produce orders of magnitude more intensity for surface x-ray scattering experiments, making them nearly routine.

This next generation of insertion devices also opens up the possibility of doing magnetic x-ray scattering experiments from surfaces. The development of the double alignment technique for medium-energy ion scattering shows great promise for routine surface structural analysis even on multicomponent systems.

Synchrotron radiation facilities have become the workhorse of all forms of surface electron spectroscopy. The coupling of this light source with angle-resolved photoemission has given the community a detailed picture of the electronic states at a surface. For clean surfaces, almost every form of surface state imaginable has been identified and understood theoretically. Dangling-bond or back-bond surface states on semiconductor surfaces, free-electron surface states on metals as well as magnetic surface states have been documented. Studies of adsorbed atoms or molecules, or impurities segregated to the surface, have revealed the nature of the adsorbate-adsorbate and adsorbate-substrate interaction.

Simple symmetry rules that exploit the polarized nature of the light source are used routinely to determine bonding geometry. The new insertion devices on the synchrotron, coupled with much more efficient detectors, will produce a sufficiently strong signal that spin-polarized angle-resolved photoemission will become common, enabling the experimentalist to observe with unprecedented detail the magnetic properties of the surface. The new sources will also enable experiments to be conducted with much higher energy and momentum resolution.

One of the most exciting applications of synchrotron radiation sources to surface science has been to the area of core-level spectroscopy. Conventional core-level photoelectron spectroscopy measures the binding energy shifts of a specific element in different environments. The intensity from undulator sources, coupled with the resolution from specially designed monochromators, will give a hundred to a thousand times more signal with less than 0.1 eV resolution. For the first time the inherent line shape of core excitations from chemisorbed atoms or molecules will be accessible, yielding valuable information about the dynamics of the excitation process. The tunability of the synchrotron has allowed experimentalists to probe the near edge or threshold region, as well as monitoring the extended x-ray absorption fine structure (EXAFS) oscillations above threshold. This technique has yielded important new information about the geometry and chemical nature of atoms and molecules bound to the surface. The next generation of undulator source, coupled with new monochromator designs, promises to make this type of spectroscopy even more useful. With better resolution and more intensity, the dynamics of the excitation and decay process can be monitored.

Recent experiments on an undulator have demonstrated the feasibility of coincidence experiments between electronic decay and ion fragmentation. The use of fluorescent detection will also provide a depth perception into the solid.

Inverse photoemission has, in the last few years, begun to yield as detailed a picture of the unoccupied surface states as photoemission has for the occupied states. The series of Rydberg-like surface states trapped in the image potential have been observed for many metals, presenting a more detailed picture of the nature of this long-range surface potential. The future will see higher-resolution spectra as well as the use of spin-polarized sources. The characteristics of the unoccupied states are important for a complete understanding of chemical bonding at the surface.

The development of high-resolution inelastic electron scattering has led the way in the study of surface vibrational modes. Simple selection rules that have been predicted theoretically and confirmed experimentally allow the experimentalist to determine the directionality of a given adsorbate vibrational mode and consequently the bonding geometry. Angle-dependent measurements are now mapping out the dispersion of intrinsic surface phonon modes as well as adsorbate-induced extrinsic phonon bands. It will not be long before direct correlations are seen between the surface phonon dispersion and reconstruction. The development of inelastic atom scattering will give a much higher resolution picture of surface phonons than can be achieved using inelastic electron scattering. Recent experiments have shown that time-resolved inelastic electron scattering can be used to monitor the time evolution of surface species.

One of the most exciting prospects for the future is the marriage of laser technology to surface science. The development of tunable, intense, and ultrafast lasers will have a significant impact on surface science.

Experiments that have already been completed demonstrate that tunable continuous-wave lasers can be used to measure vibrational modes on the surface with high resolution, monitor the vibrational or rotational states of desorbed molecules, measure the neutral desorption products following high-energy electron or photon excitation, or produce second harmonic generation from clean or adsorbate-covered surfaces.

It is already apparent that there will be many more pump- and probe-type experiments in which, for example, a tunable infrared laser is used to preferentially excite an adsorbate molecule and a time-delayed visible laser pulse is used to monitor the second harmonic generation as a function of time after the initial excitation. These types of experiments will measure desorption times and identify intermediates on a picosecond time scale. The combination of a laser to excite and the synchrotron to probe matter holds great potential.

Finally, the development of surface science has relied heavily on advances in theory. Unfortunately, most experimental probes must be strongly interactive to achieve surface sensitivity. This makes analysis of the data more complicated, requiring considerable theoretical support, and has produced a close collaboration between theorists and experimentalists. For example, advances in theory have been instrumental in the development of both inelastic electron scattering and photoemission.

The new developments in atom scattering and nonlinear optical phenomena will also require considerable theoretical effort. The surface theorist must wear two hats, one for doing calculations related to a measurement technique and the other for conceptually oriented theory. Armed with an increasing data base and the progress that has been made in numerical calculations of the surface, the modern surface theorist is capable of actually predicting surface properties such as structure and phonon dispersion. The future will surely see a reversal of roles between the surface theorist and the experimentalist as many more theoretical predictions lead to experiments.

This chapter shows the current state of techniques for "seeing" a surface. Many important and interesting areas of science will use these techniques to advance basic understanding and improve technology. The following sections present in more detail the current situation and future developments in the specific areas of surface theory, scanning tunneling microscopy, scattering experiments, electronic spectroscopy, vibrational spectroscopy, and laser-surface interactions.

SURFACE THEORY

Total Energies

This section touches upon some of the most active areas of theoretical surface science. Certain active areas, such as the statistical mechanics of phase transitions on surfaces, have been omitted because the questions addressed are generally outside the mainstream of surface science. Much of the research described is heavily computational and aimed at specific systems. This situation should be regarded as a phase in the development of a young field and as the laying of foundations for a future period of generalization and conceptual advance.

The most rapidly growing area in the theory of surfaces is the calculation of total energies. Given a geometric arrangement of atoms at a surface, the electronic energy of the system can now be calculated with an accuracy sufficient to determine preferred equilibrium structures, chemisorption bonding sites, and stiffness with respect to small displacements. The major breakthrough here came from the development of new methods to apply theory to extended systems. Parallel contributions have come from the introduction of better empirical models for extended surfaces, and from the incremental refinement of traditional quantum chemical methods for cluster models of surfaces.

Local-density functional theory is an approximation to a rigorous theory of many-electron interactions, and is particularly applicable to extended systems. Early work had led to the belief that it was not sufficiently accurate for useful determinations of total energy. The development of norm-conserving pseudopotentials, a new and more accurate way of representing electron-ion interactions, led to the first mathematically converged solutions of the local-density equations. These results, for the structural energies of bulk semiconductors, gave remarkably accurate values for lattice constants, cohesive energies, high-pressure phase transitions, and phonon frequencies.

The generalization of these total-energy calculations to slab representations of extended semiconductor surfaces is straightforward, and a number of groups now have these capabilities. The pseudopotential method is an efficient way of solving for the quantum-mechanical states of semiconductors and simple metals, but not of transition metals. The linear augmented plane-wave method, which is well suited for these materials, has also now been adapted to provide mathematically converged total energies within local-density functional theory. Although these are the most developed methods, variants using localized basis functions are being explored and should be capable of comparable accuracy.

A parallel development has been the introduction of new empirical methods for total-energy calculations. So far limited to semiconductors, this approach entails a highly simplified quantum-mechanical contribution to the energy and a near-neighbor classical pair potential. Parameters are fitted to experimental data or results. These methods can be applied to far more complex surface structures than can other methods. Caution must be exercised, however, in situations where the bonding arrangements differ greatly from the fitted reference configurations.

The above methods are all limited to the study of periodic surface structures. Isolated chemisorbed atoms or molecules as well as surface point defects have so far been treated by the application of quantum chemical molecular theory to clusters of atoms. The major difficulty with this approach is that the computational complexity grows rapidly with the size of the cluster, and it is seldom possible to establish convergence to the desired limit of an isolated entity on an extended surface. Recently, the first successful application of a direct approach to this class of problems was reported. It is based on local-density functional theory and uses a Green's function method similar to one recently developed to treat point defects in bulk solids. Only a cluster consisting of the adsorbate and substrate atoms within a few screening lengths of the defect need be treated explicitly in this approach. Nevertheless, the effects of the rest of the substrate atoms are properly included.

Total-energy calculations have already made substantial contributions to the solution of surface problems. One example concerns the reconstruction of the cleaved (111) surface of silicon. Calculations have shown that an old and widely accepted model for the atomic structure of this surface was unfavorable with respect to energy. A radically different arrangement, with its bonding topology altered from that of the bulk crystal, was found to result in a significant reduction in total energy. A further calculation has answered some strenuous objections to the new model by demonstrating that the energy barrier to be overcome in reaching this structure is in fact very small.

Another recent success of these methods is the low-temperature reconstruction of tungsten, which involves small energies since it is destroyed by thermal motion at room temperature. The calculation showed that there was an arrangement of surface atoms with a slightly lower energy than the ideal arrangement of the bulk solid, and that it involved displacements of the atoms consistent with experimental results. A third example concerns the first stages of the epitaxial growth of nickel silicide on silicon. Calculations indicated that a proposed intermediate site for the nickel atoms was much less favorable than a site corresponding to the final configuration at the fully reacted interface.

It can be anticipated that there will be substantial further growth in the number of groups engaged in total-energy calculations and in the variety of systems to which their results are applied. Although improvement in the basic physical approximations inherent in local-density theory is a long-term goal, the benefits of this method are far from being exhausted. Incremental improvement in computational efficiency can be expected, but trade-offs between accuracy and speed are inescapable. Substantial progress should be made in the new area of isolated adsorbates. The required numerical calculations nearly always consume large amounts of supercomputer time, and it is extremely important that such resources become more widely available. The variety and complexity of the mathematics involved make it improbable that special-purpose computers will be useful in these computations.

These methods are expected to have a growing impact on all areas of surface science and related areas of technology, ranging from semiconductor device processing to catalyst design. There are many more materials for which studies of reconstruction and interface energies will be of value. These calculations can be expected to contribute to the solution of a large number of fundamental problems, such as adsorbate reactions, surface modification, and surface vibrations. Well-designed investigations should lead to a qualitative understanding of mechanisms and chemical trends and not just to the case at hand.

Experimental Probes

It is an unfortunate truism of surface science that surface-sensitive probes must interact strongly with matter and therefore require nontrivial theoretical effort to extract the desired information. One such area that has experienced rapid recent growth is the diffraction of monoenergetic atomic helium beams from surfaces. Though the utility of this method as a structural probe had been limited by the inability to relate the helium-surface interaction potential to surface atom positions, an approximately linear relationship between the repulsive potential acting on the helium atom and the surface charge density has been demonstrated. This quantity can be calculated from surface atom positions by employing simple approximation techniques or by methods related to total-energy calculations. Progress has also been made in the development of better ways to calculate diffraction intensities, which is itself a computationally intensive problem. Although advances have been impressive, better models of the weak attractive part of the potential and of the effects of the thermal motion of surface atoms on diffraction are needed. These same theoretical advances will also support a new experimental field— high-resolution inelastic helium scattering. Although surface phonon spectra can be extracted by kinematic analysis of such data, more complex calculations are required to extract the information contained in intensities and line shapes.

Scanning tunneling microscopy is an exciting new development that yields real-space topographic images of surfaces at near-atomic resolution. A qualitative interpretation of these images can be made independent of theory, but theory is required to understand the interplay of atomic positions and electronic effects in determining the detailed shape of the topograph. A recently developed basic theory of low-voltage topographs also describes the effective resolution. There are many unexplored possibilities for these instruments, such as localized tunneling spectroscopy of electronic states and vibrational excitations. At high voltages the microscope tip strongly perturbs the electronic structure of the surface, and theoretical advances will be needed to unscramble such spectra. As tunneling tip preparation becomes reproducible and the atomic structure of high-resolution tips becomes known, a new level of the theory of the resolution will be possible.

With the increased availability of synchrotron radiation sources, angle-resolved photoemission spectra measuring bulk- and surface-energy bands proliferate. Theoretical methods for calculating such bands have been developing since the early 1970s. All are essentially based on the local-density functional approximation and form a part of total-energy calculations. Local-density theory is not as accurate for excitations as for total energies, but reasonable agreement with measured bands has been found in many cases. Recently, the first fully systematic study of the energy bands of a real solid, based on a more sophisticated many-body approximation, was reported for silicon. The improvement in agreement with experiment was striking. The task of bringing this level of theory to bear on surface problems will certainly be addressed in the near future. Limitations of even the largest supercomputers appear to preclude a straightforward extension at present.

Another class of related problems is that of localized electronic excitations, such as atomic core levels or internal valence states of adsorbed molecules. The spectra of electrons emitted following such excitations contain complex structure, which is strongly dependent upon the energy of the exciting photon. Many-body effects are often dominant in such processes. Desorption of atoms by incident photons or electrons is believed to involve related complexities. There is considerable theoretical activity in these areas, and future progress can be expected.

It is obvious that considerable theoretical effort will be required to fully understand the new class of nonlinear optical experiments being conducted on single-crystal surfaces. The local fields at the surface must be calculated as a function of the laser frequency and electronic properties of the surface. The mechanism for second-harmonic generation from a clean or adsorbate-covered surface is not fully understood at the present time.

The experimental tools for determining surface atomic geometry have impact on all areas, as discussed in connection with theoretical determination of surface structure. Spectroscopic tools can go further in that the electronic states they probe provide the mechanism of bonding at the surface. More information about surface chemical activity is potentially available from the interpretation of such data. The technique of "fingerprinting," using a spectroscopic signature to identify a particular surface species such as a molecular fragment, is of value in both applied and basic surface research. The reliability of this technique depends on a thorough understanding of many-body effects on spectra.

Kinetics

Considerable recent progress has been made in understanding the dynamics of gas-surface interactions. The cases for which the theory is well in hand involve nonreactive situations in which the gas consists of either inert atoms or diatomic molecules that do not dissociate on the surface considered. These problems have been treated principally by molecular dynamics computer simulations using empirical classical interatomic potentials. The results have provided a fairly complete picture of energy exchange among translational, vibrational, and rotational energies of the gas and vibrational energy of the solid. They are in substantial agreement with the results of molecular-beam laser-probe experiments that measure such energy exchanges. Other theoretical approaches have recently shown that coupling to electronic excitations in metal substrates is a dominant energy-exchange mechanism only for high-frequency molecular vibrations. The long-standing puzzle of the so-called precursor state, a weakly bound state believed to precede the chemisorbed state of some molecules, may in the future be within the grasp of theorists in this field.

An understanding of the kinetics of chemical reactions at surfaces is a considerably longer-term goal. The chief limitation here is the lack of knowledge of the so-called potential function, the total energy as it depends continuously on the coordinates of all the active atoms. Although pair-potential models are not realistic for dissociative reactions, it is hoped that total-energy calculations of the sort described in the first section can provide needed insight toward describing this quantity. Progress is expected to come through an interplay between preliminary calculations and progressively refined model potentials.

Recent progress has been made in understanding the kinetics of charge transfer at surfaces. The results obtained explain ion yields in sputtering experiments and their dependence on such surface properties as work function. The new methods may provide a key to understanding ion yield in other experiments such as induced desorption and, in the longer term, the dynamics of charge transfer as it occurs in many surface chemical reactions.

Static characterization of the surface provides important clues to dynamic behavior but cannot provide rate constants for surface processes. Fundamental research on surface kinetics has the potential to provide valuable directions in applied areas ranging from catalyst design to the growth of exotic materials. Competing rates determine what product will dominate or what structure will grow, and whether the yields will be of practical value.

Interfaces

A surface may be considered a solid-vacuum or solid-gas interface. Solid-solid interfaces are an active area of study that involves many of the same theoretical issues. Theory is stimulated by the large experimental effort in interfaces, which involves many of the same techniques and even some of the same experimentalists as surface research. Semiconductor electronic devices are essentially collections of solid-solid interfaces, and basic advances in this area are directly relevant to applied research for the electronics industry.

The class of systems that has received the greatest amount of theoretical study is the semiconductor-metal interface, or Schottky barrier. Detailed local-density functional calculations have been carried out for semiconductors in contact with a simple model of a metal in which the metal ions are smeared into a uniform positive background charge. Although these theories produce correct trends for the barrier heights, they cannot be directly compared with experiment, and alternative models in which interface defects determine the barrier height have a large following. The existence of new systems in which metallic silicon compounds are grown in perfect epitaxial registry on silicon may be sufficiently ideal that they can provide a meeting ground for theory and experiment leading to the resolution of key issues. Many theoretical questions such as electron transport through metal-semiconductor interfaces remain to be addressed. The ability of the local-density functional method to give accurate band positions may be a more important factor in the theory of interfaces than in the theory of surfaces. Semiconductor energy gaps are often in error by as much as 50 percent, yet interface behavior is determined by differences in energy level that are small in relation to the gaps. Advances in generalizing more sophisticated many-body formulations to surfaces may have their biggest impact on the understanding of interfaces.

Semiconductor-semiconductor interfaces, known as heterojunctions, have received attention since it became possible to grow them as ideal abrupt structures by molecular beam epitaxy. Such structures offer a tremendous range of possibilities for novel semiconductor device designs. Multilayered collections of these interfaces form artificial materials that can be tailored to have exotic properties. Of key interest is the alignment of the energy bands of the two materials across such interfaces. Several theoretical models for calculating this alignment exist, but they are based on conflicting mechanisms. Detailed calculations are hampered by the gap problems already discussed. Recent progress has been made in formulating improved theories of electron confinement and transport in heterojunction structures, but many important questions in this area remain to be pursued.

Existing theoretical methods can do little with incommensurate interfaces or crystal interfaces with disordered materials. Passivating layers on semiconductor devices fall in this category and are of extreme technological importance. Solid-liquid interfaces are an even broader example, encompassing all of electrochemistry. It is premature to predict bold steps forward in these areas, but it is clear that they will receive increasing attention.

SCANNING TUNNELING MICROSCOPE

The possibility of seeing atoms has always had a romantic attraction for both scientists and nonscientists.* The scanning tunneling microscope, pushed to its ultimate capability, appears to give a real-space picture of the atomic structure at the surface. This section describes briefly how this new instrument works, presents a few research highlights, and looks to its prospects for the future.

The principal tools employed in the study of surface atomic structure have made use of elastic scattering experiments, which use incident beams of photons, electrons, atoms, or ions (see the following section). While these experiments give a picture of the atomic positions at a surface, almost everyone would agree that the experiments do not ''see'' surface atoms. The experiments require many atoms arranged in a given structure.

Imaging techniques allow one to see the surface directly. Historically the first images of atoms were obtained with the field-ion microscope. A second means by which images of atoms can be obtained is with the electron microscope. Recent experiments have obtained the images of atomic planes near a surface. The newest development in this area is the tunneling microscope.

As the name suggests, this microscope operates by the mechanism of

---

*This section draws on an article by J. A. Golovchenko, Science **232**, 48 (1986).

tunneling. Electrons tunnel from a small metallic tip held above the surface, across a vacuum barrier, into the surface if the tip is biased negatively with respect to the surface or vice versa if the bias is changed. The vertical resolution is achieved by the exponential dependence of the tunneling current on the tip-to-surface separation. A typical variation in current is an order of magnitude for every angstrom of separation. An image in the lateral direction is achieved by scanning the tip across the surface. The lateral resolution is determined primarily by the size and shape of the "probe" or tip. Ultimately, experimentally realizable resolution in the vertical direction is dictated by the electronic and vibrational stability of the individual instrument, typically 0.1 angstrom. The horizontal or lateral resolution (2 to 3 angstroms) depends not only on the stability but upon the size and shape of the tip. An "image" is usually obtained by moving the tip across the surface with a piezoelectric *x-y* scan while maintaining a constant current (fixed height) with a third piezoelectric device. The many experimental difficulties associated with vibrations, electronic stability, and tip shape will not be discussed here.

A fundamental problem of this technique is one of interpretation: How does one translate tunneling images into pictures that reflect the identity and position of individual atoms of an unsolved structure? Solutions tend to be part science, part art, and the subject of continuous discussion. Both an advantage and a disadvantage of scanning tunneling microscopy is that the pictures obtained are in general a mixture of spectroscopy and microscopy. It is tempting to say that the tunneling microscope sees atoms, but, in fact, electrons tunneling from the Fermi energy of the tip see the spatial characteristics of the local density of states of the surface at an energy level equal to the bias voltage, which is higher than the Fermi energy. Therefore, the image is a function of bias voltage. This cross between microscopy and spectroscopy has tremendous advantages if we can learn to use it properly.

Keeping in mind the caveats listed above, the following few paragraphs describe experimental observations, beginning with structural studies where the reconstruction of clean metal and semiconductor surfaces has been observed. These observations include images of gold, silicon, germanium, and gallium arsenide. The steps on a Si(111) surface have been imaged and show how the surface defects causing the surface reconstruction are incorporated into the step edge. Images of germanium-silicon alloys indicate that at the surface there is an ordered GeSi alloy. These structural studies are just beginning to present a picture of the role of defects such as step edges and vacancies on such surface processes as epitaxial growth and catalysis. Preliminary steps are being taken to image foreign atoms on surfaces, including large molecules such as DNA or viruses.

The tunneling microscope can also provide images of the change in the electronic distribution at the surface. Two recent examples hint at future possibilities. The periodicity of charge-density waves (approximately 10 angstroms) has been imaged, and liquid-helium-cooled Nb_3Sn has been imaged to show spatial variations in the superconducting gap.

The general use of the scanning tunneling microscope will benefit from experimental development of better tips and from advances in tunneling spectroscopy. Ideally, the tip would be terminated by a single atom. This situation now may occur in practice only once in a while by luck. The use of field-ion microscopy to monitor and prepare tips may make it possible to prepare this "one-atom" probe. At present there is no way to identify the kind of atoms being imaged. This potentially serious problem can in principle be overcome by using the spectroscopic nature of the process. Measurement of the probe current as a function of bias voltage surveys the unoccupied density of states of the imaged atom. If the density of states of an impurity is known either experimentally or theoretically, the bias voltage can be set to "image" this atom or molecule. If the temperature is reduced, resonances in the inelastic tunneling current reflect vibrational losses that are highly characteristic of the specific adsorbate.

It is easy to imagine that in the immediate future the scanning tunneling microscope will be used to locate the binding site of an impurity or adsorbate and then home in to measure the local electronic states and vibrational modes.

SCATTERING EXPERIMENTS

Knowledge of the structure of surfaces is clearly a prerequisite for an understanding of many of the surface properties of materials. However, current understanding of the structure of surfaces lags behind, say, knowledge of the electronic properties. In fact, instead of probing the structure directly, much effort in recent years has proceeded in the direction of theoretically exploring how various trial models of the geometric structure affect the electronic structure of materials, in the hope of isolating some feature that is unique to one particular model. Electronic-structure experiments are then performed to prove or disprove this model. Over the last few years, however, new theoretical techniques have made it possible to predict the geometric structure directly. These techniques have been accompanied by (1) a technical revitalization of existing experimental probes, such as low-energy electron diffraction (LEED) and atom diffraction, so that more complex problems can be tackled; and (2) the development of three new techniques that promise to open up new fields. One of these techniques is tunneling microscopy. The exciting feature of the other two techniques (ion scattering and x-ray diffraction) is that unlike almost all other surface-sensitive techniques, their results can be interpreted using simple and well-understood laws of probe-surface interaction. The challenge in applying them is of an experimental nature. Synchrotron radiation may well have its most powerful impact on surface science in the field of structural determinations through the availability of intense, tunable hard x-rays from "wigglers" and "undulators," periodic magnetic arrays inserted into the straight sections of electron storage rings.

Techniques

There are many advantages of LEED as a tool for surface structural work. It is well established, technically simple, and inexpensive. Its principal disadvantage is that the interpretation of the spectra is not very intuitive. The diffracted electron intensity as a function of energy depends in a nontransparent fashion on the details of the scattering process. Although the diffraction patterns themselves contain much useful information, the intensities cannot be analyzed without theoretical aid. Such an analysis involves calculating the diffraction pattern for a number of trial structures and finding the one that best fits the experimental spectrum. Such experiments will continue to be important as computational algorithms are being refined so that much more complicated structures can be treated. Instead of collecting data for one reflection at a time, new hardware allows data collection for many beams simultaneously. This effort is complemented by an increased use of image intensifiers, which allow the use of much lower electron beam doses. This is important in studies of hydrocarbons on metal surfaces, for example, which easily decompose under the influence of the electron beam.

A novel direction is the analysis of the angular profile of the diffracted beam, which enables the experimentalist to extract information about the nature of the defects. These defects could be simply steps on the surface, or they could be nucleation centers for dislocations as a surface phase transition is approached. To study such phenomena, electron sources with much larger coherence lengths have been developed. The lack of simplicity in data interpretation has led some investigators to criticize LEED. This criticism is largely unjustified, however, since hundreds of structures have been determined by LEED, whereas high-resolution results with other techniques are counted in the dozens. For the problems to which it can be applied, LEED serves as a standard by which other techniques can be measured. Where quantitative disagreements have occurred, LEED has most frequently been correct.

A fundamental advantage of ion scattering is that the law governing ion-solid interaction is extremely well known—the basic principle is simply Rutherford scattering, which has been understood since 1913 (this discussion is limited to high- and medium-energy scattering, excluding low-energy ion scattering, which, although important and useful, is a more qualitative tool). As long as the ion velocity is much larger than the velocity of the conduction electrons in the target, the sea of conduction electrons does not have time to adjust to the presence of the projectile. These conditions are fulfilled when using protons with an energy above, say, 25 keV. The technique becomes surface specific through appropriate alignment of the ion beam with the target. The magnitude of the backscattered flux will therefore be proportional to the number of surface atoms visible to the ion beam, assuming that the atoms are frozen in their rigid lattice positions. For nonzero vibrational amplitudes, the number of visible atoms (and hence the backscattered flux) will increase as the shadowing of near-surface atoms becomes less effective. A measurement of the backscattered flux will therefore provide information about displacements in the surface in the direction perpendicular to the beam. If, for example, the atoms in the surface have moved laterally, they will shadow the atoms in the second layer less completely. This will result in an increase of the backscattered flux, and the magnitude of the increase will depend on the relative movements of the atoms.

A particularly useful variant of ion scattering is the measurement of the angular distribution of the backscattered flux: in the directions joining second-layer atoms with those in the first layer, the flux from the second layer will be blocked by that from the first layer, resulting in a reduced flux ("blocking dip") at those particular directions. The positions of these blocking dips are therefore, to a first-order approximation, a direct measure of the relative positions of these two atoms. To quantify such data, the scattering process can be simulated on a computer using Monte Carlo techniques. To perform these types of experiments, a new class of high-resolution ion energy analyzers were constructed. The principal advantage of these new instruments is that they enable quantitative depth analysis of Rutherford backscattering with unprecedented resolution (3–5 angstroms). Another advantage of the technique is that of mass dispersion. For example, in studies of binary systems, it is useful to have a separate signal from each of the two constituents rather than a superposition of the two signals.

Ion scattering is a local probe, as the interaction is kinematic. X-ray scattering, on the other hand, is a diffraction phenomenon and yields information about the long-range order. It is only recently that x-ray scattering has been applied to surface structural problems. The difficulty is that x rays are deeply penetrating and that the surface signal is therefore only a small part of the total diffracted intensity. This technique is therefore particularly suitable for studies of systems where the bulk and the surface have different periodicities. However, only with intense sources is it possible to obtain an acceptable signal-to-noise ratio. Even the strongest laboratory source available today (60-kW rotating anode) gives, from the (7×7) structure on $Si(111)$, only 10^{-4} diffracted photons per second in a typical reflex, making analysis impossible. However, wigglers now under construction at various synchrotron radiation sources, will increase this flux by 5 orders of magnitude, yielding approximately 10 counts per second (cps). For heavier materials like the (1 × 2) reconstruction of Au(110), the intensity will increase to 10^6 cps. There are few fields of science where such enormous intensity enhancements have taken place in such a short time. Though few mainstream surface systems have yet been studied with x-ray diffraction, these early experiments have provided valuable symmetry information. Additionally, unique information has been obtained about step densities on surfaces. Structural determinations, however, must rely rather heavily on measurements of the diffracted intensity as a function of momentum transfer. Considering these problems, it is not surprising that the actual atomic positions derived from x-ray data are being refined with other structural techniques, a situation that will change dramatically within a few years.

Results

Surface structural investigations are at a stage where different investigators, in different laboratories, using different techniques, studying the same system, can obtain the same results. The multilayer relaxations on Cu(110) and Ni(110) discussed below have been determined with LEED and with ion scattering, and the two experiments agree with respect to all structural parameters to better than 0.01 angstrom. This length scale is useful for discussing structural changes in chemical reactions in the gas phase. It therefore appears likely that within the next several years we will be investigating the geometrical adsorbate-substrate response to a chemical reaction with the accuracy necessary to have an impact on problems of this kind.

Another class of systems where ion scattering and LEED agree extremely well includes the (110) faces of GaSb, InAs, and GaAs. These surfaces consist of equal numbers of anions and cations located in an ideal crystal in the plane of the surface. It has been known for several years that, at the surface, the anion moves out and the cation moves in. It is now known that the axis joining the two forms an angle of 29 degrees with the surface plane and the agreement between the two techniques is 1 degree or better. The two techniques have different strengths, nevertheless: ion scattering has excellent sensitivity to lateral movements, and LEED is sensitive to normal displacements.

The surface structure of metals was long considered a relatively uninteresting field. Metallic screening at the surface, it was argued, is so short ranged that only minor rearrangements of the atoms would be expected at the surface. This view has changed tremendously over the last few years with the observation of phase transitions on clean metal surfaces as well as those induced by adsorbates. Surface melting has been observed at a temperature far below the bulk melting temperature. Even the structure of ideal surfaces has shown some unexpected features.

It has been found, for example, that on clean metal surfaces the separation of the outermost layer is smaller than the average bulk value, while the separation between layers two and three is expanded, and so on in an oscillatory fashion. These results, which (as mentioned above) have been obtained on several surfaces by different groups using both LEED and ion scattering, are in qualitative agreement with theoretical predictions and are caused by the rearrangement of the electronic charge density at the surface. More dramatically, on high-index surfaces such as certain iron faces, the entire first layer of atoms is displaced horizontally while the bulk periodicity is maintained, again as predicted theoretically. Several metal surfaces— W(100), Mo(100), Pd(110), Au(110)—change their two-dimensional superstructure as a function of temperature. Intense theoretical and experimental work is being performed to characterize these new structures. Adsorbates have also been found to induce reconstructions. A particularly interesting case is the (110) face of copper, where oxygen adsorption doubles the size of the unit cell in one azimuth and alkali metals or hydrogen double it in another. This therefore suggests that surface structure can to a certain extent be "custom made" by a suitable choice of adsorbates.

The advance of the next decade will be due largely to the more widespread use of ion scattering and the coming revolution in x-ray diffraction. This coming of age is very timely: electron and vibrational spectroscopy are at a stage where all three techniques can be used to attack problems in surface phase transitions on an unprecedented scale. These techniques will make possible new approaches to the study of structural phenomena in surface chemistry and much greater detail in the investigation of surface structure of multicomponent systems, including silicides and alloys.

ELECTRONIC SPECTROSCOPIES

Spectroscopic tools for measuring the energies of electronic transitions fall into two classes depending upon the excitation source—monochromatic photons or electrons. Since any discussion of surface experiments involving incident photons must focus on synchrotron radiation sources, the following discussion is divided into two parts: synchrotron radiation experiments and all others. With the exceptions of inverse photoemission and laser-induced absorption or multiphoton ionization, the sources of excitation in these two classes of surface experiments are, respectively, photons and electrons.

Synchrotron Radiation Experiments

For convenience, synchrotron radiation experiments are divided into two categories—valence-band and core-level spectroscopy.

Valence-band angle-resolved photoemission has become to electronic structure what x-ray scattering is to crystallography and neutron scattering is to phonon structure. In general, given a single crystal, the three-dimensional bulk or the two-dimensional surface band structure can be determined. The unique capabilities of a polarized, tunable, and intense radiation source enable the experimenter to tune to any portion of the two- or three-dimensional band structure and to determine the orbital symmetry of each state. Intrinsic surface states or resonance of almost every conceivable type have been identified: dangling-bond or back-bond surface states on semiconductors, free-electron or d-band surface states on metals, exchange split surface states on ferromagnetic metals. Obviously the surface electronic properties are intimately related to the surface structure. Photoemission data first led to the proposal of the chain model of the Si(111) surface. Recent high-resolution angle-resolved experiments showed that a metal-insulator transition accompanied the order-disorder transition on Ge(001).

In general, angle-resolved photoemission has become an established tool for probing the occupied electronic states of the surface. It has recently been used also in the study of many materials phenomena, including intermetallic surfaces, rare-earth compounds, intercalated compounds, thin metallic layers on metals or semiconductors, coadsorption systems, two-dimensional phases of physisorbed molecules, segregated bulk impurities, and alkali-promoted adsorption. Yet several important improvements can and will be made. First, the energy and momentum resolution should be improved through the use of better monochromators and analyzers. The most important improvement in angle-resolved photoemission will come when more efficient spin-polarized detectors are incorporated into the electron analyzers. The new undulator insertion devices on electron storage rings, which will produce a sufficient number of photons to offset the lower efficiency of the spin detector, should make spin-polarized photoemission as routine in a couple of years as photoemission is now.

The next-generation insertion device source coupled with developments in monochromator design and soft x-ray optics will have a dramatic effect on core-level spectroscopy. It is reasonable to expect enhancements in signal strength for x-ray photoelectron spectroscopy, usually called electron spectroscopy for chemical analysis (ESCA), by 10^2 to 10^3 as well as significant improvements in energy resolution. The resolution of ESCA systems is limited to approximately 0.2 eV by the inherent properties of the crystal monochromator. Design studies demonstrate that new soft x-ray monochromators should operate in the energy range of 100 to 1000 eV with better than 0.1 eV resolution. This increase in intensity and resolution will make it easier to observe low surface concentrations or to study samples that are rapidly contaminated. But the newfound resolution will also open up the possibility of studying the dynamics of core-hole ionization by measuring the inherent line shape. Recent data indicate that the width of the peak in the core-level photoelectron spectra from an adsorbed molecule is not due to lifetime broadening. Therefore, a line-shape analysis will make visible phonon and electron excitation sidebands.

The tunability of the synchrotron source has enabled experimentalists to use the core-level absorption spectra of adsorbed atoms and molecules to study the bonding configuration on the surface. Core-to-bound excitations have a specific symmetry, which can be probed by a specific polarization direction. The direction of the polarization vector with respect to the surface when the core-to-bound excitation is allowed (or forbidden) transparently fixes the orientation of the molecule. Changes in the energy position of the core-to-bound excitation have been used to measure changes in the intermolecular bond length. The small oscillations in the absorption cross section far above the threshold—EXAFS—is used to determine distances to the nearest and the next-nearest neighbor. Polarization dependence of the surface EXAFS signal can define the directions of the bonds. More intense sources will improve the signal-to-noise ratio for these experiments, thus allowing the study of moieties of lower surface concentrations. The use of fluorescence detection and of higher-energy monochromators will give these types of experiments a depth perception into the bulk.

It is now possible to study the dynamics of core-hole decay and ion fragmentation (photostimulated desorption) following the absorption of a soft x-ray photon. Consider the situation in which the photon energy is tuned to a core-to-bound excitation of either an adsorbed molecule or of the solid (exiton). If the lifetime of the core hole is shorter than the time required for the excited electron to move away from the hole, then the excited electron can participate in the decay process. When this happens the final state is a single hole on the atom or molecule originally excited. This single-hole final state is exactly the same as created by the direct photoionization of a valence electron. However, the direct photoemission process samples the global nature of the wave function, and the deexcitation process views the valence states through the window of the localized core hole. Because there have been only a few experiments of this type, it is too early to evaluate the true potential of this technique. One may conclude, however, that this deexcitation spectroscopy may be used to probe the local electronic configuration. The details of the deexcitation spectra are already yielding new information about the dynamics of core-hole decay.

The second new development is the ability to measure the ion fragmentation products in coincidence with the energy-resolved electron deexcitation spectra. These measurements can make a unique identification of the hole configuration with the fragmentation products.

Laboratory Sources

Inverse photoemission occurs when an incident electron loses energy as it interacts with the surface, a process resulting in an emitted photon. This spectroscopy probes the unoccupied states in a region between the Fermi energy and the vacuum level that is not accessible by other techniques. Just as in the case of photoemission, angle-dependent inverse photoemission has been used to map the two- and three-dimensional unoccupied bands of the surface and bulk, respectively. The greatest potential in surface science for inverse photoemission appears to be in the area of surface chemistry, where the position and dispersion of unoccupied energy levels are as important as the occupied levels. The coupling of these types of studies with the ability to use spin-polarized sources to investigate magnetic changes induced by chemisorption yields a powerful and complementary surface tool.

Inelastic electron scattering (electronic excitations) was one of the earliest probes used in studies of surfaces. Yet, it has not developed into a commonly used surface technique. Several recent developments indicate that this technique may become more important in the future. Measurements of the valence-band losses for an adsorbed molecule as a function of the incident electron energy and scattering angle indicate that surface losses may be separable from bulk losses and that dipole and nondipole excitation can be identified. New theoretical interest in the inelastic-scattering cross sections from oriented molecules may help unravel the data. It is now obvious that core-level loss spectra can be used in conjunction with photoabsorption data, with the advantage that the electron-loss experiment can detect optically forbidden transitions.

It is also clear that $3e$-e or $3e$-ion coincident experiments will soon be conducted on a surface. The first coincidence experiment between the energy-resolved Auger decay and the photostimulated desorption products was just reported. As described in the foregoing discussion of synchrotron radiation, these coincidence experiments will determine the hole configuration responsible for desorption. New technology will make it possible to do gas-phase e-$2e$ experiments on the surface such that the energy-resolved, scattered, and emitted electrons are detected in coincidence. This e-$2e$ experiment is capable of measuring the momentum distribution of a specific energy level or, used in a different mode, capable of measuring the surface EXAFS signal.

The improvements in source intensity and detector efficiency will bring on line more coincidence or two-probe experiments. Unoccupied surface states could be probed with a two-photon process in which molecules can be vibrationally excited and then ionized.

VIBRATIONAL SPECTROSCOPY OF THE CRYSTAL SURFACES

In molecular physics, as well as condensed-matter physics, access to data on the frequencies and nature of the vibrational modes of molecules or crystals has led to major new insights into their geometry, the nature of their chemical bonds, and the dynamic properties of, or energy transfer between, the basic constituents. Various forms of vibrational spectroscopy have been applied to the study of adsorbates on surfaces (and, in some instances, atoms within the surface itself) for nearly two decades. However, the information that could be extracted from the data has been limited, and compromised by the limited resolution of probes used for this purpose.

In the past five years qualitative advances in experimental method have led to an explosive expansion in the data available, and we are in a position to explore many new questions that simply could not be addressed in the recent past. The near future looks exciting indeed.

For the first time, it has proved possible to perform detailed studies of the dispersion curves of surface phonons on clean and adsorbate-covered surfaces. This is done through the use of particle probes in energy-loss experiments that are a surface analogue of the neutron-scattering experiments that have proved so powerful in studying crystals. Two complementary methods may be used to study surface phonons. One method makes use of highly monoenergetic, well-collimated beams of neutral helium atoms directed at the surface. Their kinetic energy is in the thermal range, and energy resolutions of a few tenths of a millivolt (three or four wave numbers) can be realized. Surface phonons have already been studied for a range of materials, from insulators to metals.

Shortly after helium beams were used in the first studies of surface phonons, a second method was demonstrated. Electron energy-loss spectroscopy as a function of scattering angle was used to study clean and adsorbate-covered nickel surfaces. The key experimental development was the use of much higher energies (50 eV–300 eV) than are used in the more traditional spectrometer. One must use such high energies to probe well out into the Brillouin zone, and the experimental challenge is to produce high-energy beams, sufficiently monoenergetic to allow resolution of the low-energy losses associated with scattering from surface phonons.

The two methods are complementary in that the helium beams may be used to study rather low-frequency surface phonons whose excitation energy is far too small to be resolved by the electron energy-loss method. One such example is the study of vibrational modes of rare-gas monolayers, bilayers, and trilayers adsorbed on Ag(111) by using helium beams. Here dispersion curves are studied in the frequency range from 10 cm^{-1} (1.2 meV) to 30 cm^{-1} (3.7 meV). The electron energy-loss method can detect modes as "soft" as 30 cm^{-1} (3.7 meV), but is best suited to the study of the spectral range above 100 cm^{-1} (12 meV). There is no upper bound to the frequency range that may be explored with electrons, whereas multiphonon scattering obscures single phonon features in spectra taken with helium beams above roughly 250 cm^{-1} (30 meV). Electrons can also resolve modes in which the atomic motion is predominantly parallel to the surface, and the extraction of useful information from the spectra will be assisted by the appearance of a quantitative theory of the excitation process, which can be used to predict energy regimes within which excitation cross sections are enhanced.

In the near future we may expect these two methods to be applied to the study of areas of surface dynamics where little information is available at present. The dynamics of the surface may be studied as its temperature is raised to the point where melting begins. A modest improvement in the resolution of the helium-beam method will allow the magnitude and temperature variation of the surface-phonon line width to be studied at various points in the two-dimensional Brillouin zone. This will provide fundamental insights into the nature of vibrational energy transfer between adsorbed layers and the underlying substrate. Many new questions such as these will be addressed in the coming years.

Infrared spectroscopy offers, in principle, much higher resolution than either of the particle probes discussed above. The line width of narrow high-frequency adsorbate modes may thus be studied, along with subtle splittings that contain important information about the symmetry of the adsorption site. This technique has also developed impressively in recent years; there have been high-resolution studies of hydrogen adsorbed on silicon surfaces, and subtle line-shape anomalies have been resolved in recent work. Thermal emission studies of adsorbate-covered surfaces have led to the quantitative study of the low-frequency vibration of carbon monoxide on the Ni(100) surface. The development of tunable continuous-wave infrared lasers will have a large impact on the infrared spectroscopy of surfaces.

The appearance of particle probes that can explore the dispersion of surface phonons (and surface resonances) throughout the Brillouin zone and the dramatic improvement in the infrared technique have created a new era of surface-vibrational spectroscopy. The field is evolving rapidly at this point, and the next five years will see numerous important results emerge from the laboratory. The time scale for collecting an inelastic loss spectrum from a surface can be reduced considerably by using multichannel detection and dispersion compensation allowing real-time data collection. This technique has already been used with temperature pulsing to study the kinetics of decomposition versus desorption of an adsorbed molecule. Since electron-loss spectroscopy (ELS) is site and molecular specific, the time evolution of the molecular orientation, binding site, and intermediates on the surface can be followed. The single-shot time resolution at present is approximately 5 ms, whereas a reversible process can be resolved at the 1-ms level. Future experiments will use pulsed gas beams, higher pressure, and laser excitations and will probably improve the time resolution by at least one order of magnitude.

Light scattering (Raman and Brillouin) has been a mainstay of vibrational spectroscopy in solid-state physics and can also be applied to surface and interface studies. Under conditions outlined in the literature, the signals can be enhanced enormously, though appreciable roughness of a surface or interface is a key requirement. Thus, at least in this mode, light-scattering spectroscopy is not used to study the clean, carefully prepared surface structures that are the backbone of modern surface science. However, on clean, high-quality surfaces, Raman spectroscopy has been used to study a small number of adsorbed monolayers, and in some cases signals from a single monolayer have been reported. There is still an unresolved question concerning the possibility of tuning the laser into an electronic excitation to do resonant Raman spectroscopy. If it is possible to do resonant Raman spectroscopy on adsorbed atoms or molecules, then Raman spectroscopy will become useful for surface science. If this is not possible, then Raman spectroscopy is likely to emerge as a useful probe of systems that contain a few monolayers of adsorbates in molecular form.

Brillouin spectroscopy offers promise in the study of the liquid-solid interface, as do certain sophisticated forms of modern multibeam nonlinear spectroscopy (coherent antistokes Raman spectroscopy, for example). During the next decade, light-scattering and nonlinear laser spectroscopies may be expected to play an increasingly important role in the study of the "ideal" surface or interface environment, though at present the amount of unambiguous information derived from those methods is limited.

LASER-SURFACE INTERACTION

The last decade saw tremendous growth of interest in the area of laser interaction with surfaces. The high-intensity, coherent, and directional nature of laser beams provides unique possibilities for studying, controlling, and modifying surfaces. The advances are generally on two fronts: development of laser techniques for probing surfaces, and development of laser techniques for processing the surfaces of materials.

Numerous methods of laser surface probing have been invented in the past five years, and most of them are spectroscopic. Photoacoustic and photothermal spectroscopies rely on surface resonant absorption of laser photons and subsequent conversion of these photons into acoustic waves or heat, which are then detected. These techniques have been used to obtain vibrational spectra of adsorbed molecules and to probe the surface states of reconstructed semiconductor surfaces.

Photodesorption spectroscopy is based on resonant excitation of adsorbed molecules and subsequent desorption of the molecules from the surface. If the desorption is a resonant process, then this technique can also be used to obtain vibrational spectra of adsorbed molecules. Furthermore, valuable information about the laser desorption process, which is essential to an understanding of laser material processing, can be obtained from laser-stimulated desorption.

Raman scattering and fluorescence spectroscopies have also been applied to surface studies. The recent development of detectors and computer-assisted detection technology has dramatically improved the sensitivity of such measurements. With but a marginal improvement in the technique, it will become easy to obtain a Raman spectrum from a monolayer of adsorbed molecules on a smooth surface. This is very exciting, as one would then have a relatively simple optical technique that could yield the vibrational spectrum of adsorbed molecules in a single scan.

These laser techniques have, at least in principle, the advantages over other surface tools in that they possess a high spectral resolution, can probe an interface between two dense media as long as one of them is transparent, and are applicable to time-resolving studies if a pulsed laser is used. The spectrum of adsorbed molecules provides direct information about the geometry and strength of the molecule-substrate interaction, which is the basis of all surface reactions, including catalysis, corrosion, and adhesion.

Another effective method for studying molecule-surface interaction is to measure the redistribution of energy in various degrees of freedom resulting from collisions of molecules with a surface. The highly sensitive laser spectroscopic techniques are ideal for such measurements. The state-selective detection ability of these techniques makes it possible to measure not only the translational energy distribution of the molecules before and after collisions but also their internal energy distribution. Thus, the exchange of rotational, vibrational, and electronic energy states of the molecule resulting from surface collision can be probed directly. Such information is important for the understanding of surface reactions and is difficult to obtain by conventional means.

Nonlinear optical effects can also be used to probe surfaces. Among the few possibilities that have been explored, second-harmonic generation appears to be the most sensitive and versatile. Its surface specificity is based on the fact that this process is generally forbidden in a bulk with inversion symmetry but always allowed at a surface or interface. This technique has numerous proven advantages over other surface tools. It is nondestructive, capable of *in situ* remote sensing with subpicosecond time resolution, and applicable to all types of interfaces. This technique can be used to measure the adsorption isotherm; the symmetry of surface structure and molecular arrangement; the spectrum and orientation of adsorbed molecules; the time development of adsorption, desorption, and epitaxial growth; and many other properties. In addition, this technique provides the prospect of probing real-time surface dynamics and reactions with ultrafast time resolution on a wide range of interfaces. Applications of this technique to science and technology are limited only by the imagination. Examples include studies of electrochemistry at a liquid-solid interface, surfactants at liquid-liquid and liquid-solid interfaces, biological membranes, oxidation of silicon surfaces, and surface corrosion and catalysis. All these problems are intimately related to the future progress of modern science and technology.

Laser surface techniques provide new ways to probe surfaces and molecule-surface interactions. They can yield valuable information complementary to that obtained by other means. The field is still in the beginning stage: the existing techniques need further development, and many other possible techniques are yet to be explored. The practical importance of this research area is evidenced by the recent entrance of many industrial and national laboratories into the field.

Lasers already play a significant role in the area of surface processing. Although most of the laser techniques are still in the developmental stage, a few have reached the production line. Laser annealing is probably the best-known process: the recrystallization of the surface after laser-induced melting can yield high-quality crystalline films. With a pulsed laser, it is even possible to obtain selectively a crystalline or amorphous film depending on the duration of the pulse. Laser heating of surfaces is also the basis of a number of other laser surface-processing techniques. These include laser-enhanced etching, laser-enhanced electroplating, and laser alloying. In the former two cases, a continuous-wave laser beam can enhance the processing speed by orders of magnitude. In the latter, pulsed laser alloying with extremely rapid quenching can yield alloy films obtainable by ordinary methods. In all these cases, laser heating has the advantage of being able to heat a local spatial region selectively to a very high temperature. The spatial resolution of such laser processing techniques would be limited only by the degree to which the laser can be focused. Aside from laser heating, laser-induced chemical reactions can also be used to modify surfaces. Photochemical surface etching or deposition is one example. Micron-size metal or nonmetal structure can be inscribed on a surface at high speed using such a process. Laser ablation can also be an effective method for surface processing. With ultraviolet lasers, the technique can carve extremely sharp surface patterns on polymers or biological materials. This is believed to be the result of laser-induced bond breaking rather than thermal evaporation.

All of these laser processing techniques hold considerable promise as practical tools for surface treatment. Many industrial labs have already invested heavily in the development of these techniques. One might think that the basic physics underlying these laser processes must be well understood. This is not true, however, and universities in collaboration with industrial laboratories can expect to make significant contributions.

Materials Synthesis and Processing

WILLIAM F. BRINKMAN

As the research discipline of materials science has matured, its theoretical base has broadened and become more rigorous. This progression has led to the development of new materials whose performance is vastly superior to that of only a few years ago. New techniques for materials synthesis draw on knowledge from physics, chemistry, and other disciplines to create entirely new materials. In addition, better theoretical understanding of established processes allows materials scientists to control materials properties to a degree previously unachievable. The following examples illustrate how better understanding of the fundamentals of materials synthesis and processing has led to improved, and in some cases new, materials.

These examples are (1) strained-layer superlattices—a new concept in semiconductor structures; (2) glass-ceramic materials—an older materials technology that has not been understood but holds promise for structural ceramics; and (3) gel-derived, controlled-porosity materials—solution-to-gelation chemical processing applied to antireflective coatings with tremendous potential for high-technology applications.

STRAINED-LAYER SUPERLATTICES

The strained-layer superlattice (SLS) is an important new field of semiconductor materials research. The SLS consists of many thin (a few tens of angstroms) layers of alternating, strained single-crystal semiconductor types (for example, GaAsP and GaAs). In structures of this type the lattice mismatch is accommodated totally by uniform lattice strain, and no misfit dislocations are generated at the interfaces (see Figure 1). This remains true as long as the layers are sufficiently thin (up to 250 angstroms for a 1.8 percent

307

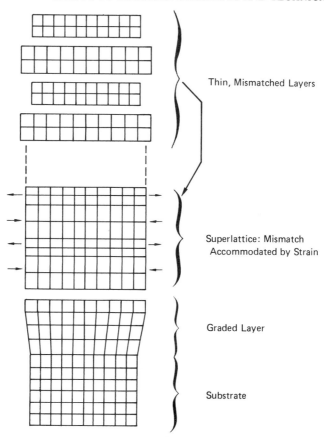

FIGURE 1   Strained-layer superlattice (SLS): schematic cross section showing substrate, buffer layer, and superlattice.

mismatch). SLSs are typically made from the more common Group III–V compound semiconductors such as InAsSb, GaAsP, or InGaAs.

The multiple thin layers may be viewed macroscopically as a new semi-conductor material (material X). The combination of the thin layers and lattice strain allow flexibility in tailoring the properties of material X. The properties that may be controlled include the energy bandgap, direct-indirect bandgap, effective mass-velocity field characteristics, and average lattice constant.

The energy bandgap of an SLS can be controlled by changing either the type of material or the thickness of the layers or both. The effect is akin to the behavior of the particle-in-box solution to the Schrödinger wave equation, that is, thin layers increase the energy ground state.

The multiple thin layers also change the periodicity of the Brillouin zones. In some cases this can cause the valence band maximum and conduction band minimum to have the same crystal momentum in the SLS when they do not in the bulk crystal.

The lattice constant of the SLS depends on the stiffness and thickness of the individual layers of the material. Hence, it is also possible to adjust the average lattice constant of this material. This greatly increases the number of choices for host substrates on which to grow these materials.

The number of new semiconducting materials that can be made is almost infinite. Variations can be made in material type, layer thickness, and doping over a wide range. This tremendous variety dictates that researchers be able to synthesize their own SLSs to achieve significant progress in this field. Crystal growth by molecular beam epitaxy (MBE) is one technique that allows control of the growth of these materials to essentially monolayer levels.

These new SLS materials can be synthesized to optimize material properties for a given device type, such as microwave, optoelectronic, and infrared (IR). An example of this is InAsSb SLS 8–12-micron IR detector material. None of the common Group III–V compound semiconductors has a bandgap small enough to reach the important 8–12-micron IR band. This has forced the development of HgCdTe detectors for this wavelength range. This material system has several undesirable material properties. Theoretical calculations have shown that the strains in an SLS can produce sufficient lattice dilatation in InAsSb to shift the absorption edge from 9 microns in the bulk alloy to greater than 12 microns in the SLS.[1] This SLS is therefore an alternative to HgCdTe. Figure 2 shows a transmission electron micrograph of a typical InAsSb SLS.

Another example of special semiconductors that can be synthesized only from SLSs is light-hole material. Many Group III–V compound semiconductors have electron effective masses much smaller than silicon. This results in n-type devices that are faster than similar silicon devices. However, the holes in most Group III–V semiconductors are degenerate, that is, the valence band contains both heavy and light holes. Hence, p-type devices made from Group III–V semiconductors are no faster than silicon devices. It has been shown both theoretically and experimentally that the strain and quantum well effect in specially designed SLSs in the InGaAs/GaAs system can cause a favorable splitting of this degeneracy and produce light-hole material for p-type devices.[2] This development is important to high-speed, low-power logic circuits.

Finally, it has been shown that the SLS can produce high-quality materials on lattice-mismatched substrates (defects are blocked by the SLS). This feature, coupled with the tunability of lattice constant and bandgap in SLSs, makes it possible to synthesize SLSs from ternaries (such as InGaAs) that can perform the same function as bulk quaternaries (such as InGaAsP). This

$$\frac{190 \text{ A InAs}_{.2}\text{Sb}_{.8}}{190\text{A InSb}} \text{ SLS}$$

1000 A

FIGURE 2   Transmission electron micrograph of $InAs_{0.2}Sb_{0.8}/InSb$ strained-layer super-lattice for infrared detector applications.

is important because it reduces the difficulty in fabricating devices such as semiconductor lasers at 1.5 microns.

GLASS-CERAMIC MATERIALS

A glass-ceramic is an inorganic material that is formed from molten glass and is subsequently transformed to a polycrystalline ceramic object by controlled crystallization. Glass-ceramics are used in applications as diverse as dinnerware, telescope mirrors, radomes, and semiconductor substrates because frequently they are more economical to produce and because they possess special properties that cannot be achieved by other means. Control of the crystallization process is the key to obtaining desirable properties in those materials. Most glass-ceramic formulations contain small amounts of special additives, called nucleating agents, that initiate the crystallization process and influence the particular mix of phases that develops. Platinum, TiO_2, ZrO_2, and P_2O_5 in concentrations from 0.01 to 10 percent are commonly used nucleating agents in silicate-based glass-ceramics.

Although the nucleation and growth process in glass-ceramics has been extensively studied in the 25 years since it was discovered, at present there is no general theory that explains how the nucleating agents operate. Most available models are specific to a given system, and they commonly postulate the formation of some sort of heterogeneity by the nucleating agent that catalyzes the subsequent crystallization.[3]

Recently, the nucleation and crystal growth mechanism in a P_2O_5-doped lithium silicate glass-ceramic has been explained in detail.[4] Transmission electron microscopy, x-ray diffraction, and differential thermal analysis showed that at the nucleation temperature, the P_2O_5 reacts with the glass constituents to precipitate small Li_3PO_4 crystallites throughout the molten glass. The size and degree of faceting of the Li_3PO_4 crystallites increases with time at the nucleation temperature (Figure 3). During crystallization, desired phases of lithium metasilicate, lithium disilicate, and cristobalite grow epitaxially on preferred {120} and {010} faces of the Li_3PO_4. There is a definite crystallographic orientation relationship between the Li_3PO_4 substrate and the different crystal phases, with a *d*-space mismatch of less than 5 percent (Figure 4). Further research revealed that the Li_3PO_4 crystallites must grow to some critical size before their {120} faces are sufficiently faceted to serve as the substrates for the epitaxial growth (Figure 3). The concentrations of the different crystalline phases can be varied reproducibly using different nucleation times to change the size of {120} faces on the Li_3PO_4 crystallites.

This work is important because it is the first direct observation of a nucleation mechanism that was hypothesized more than 20 years ago. Further, the specific orientation relationships that are observed may allow the existing qualitative theory to be made quantitative. The discovery that the phase concentration is controlled by the size of preferred faces in the nucleant is unprecedented. That fact, and our understanding of the nucleation mechanism, allows us to vary the expansion coefficient of the resulting glass-ceramic reproducibly from 100 to $160 \times 10^{-7}/°C$. One glass-ceramic in that family that has an expansion coefficient of $145 \times 10^{-7}/°C$ is now used to make high-strength glass-ceramic-to-metal seals with Inconel 718 for pyrotechnic actuators, connectors, and other electrical components. The under-

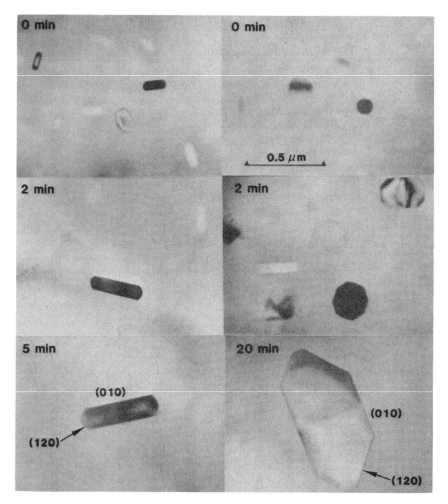

FIGURE 3   Growth of lithium phosphate crystallites at 1,000°C, in which {120} faces develop.

standing of the crystallization mechanism permits close control of the glass-ceramic expansion coefficient (Figure 5), which in turn minimizes materials stresses so that the resulting components are more than three times stronger than those they replaced.

GEL-DERIVED, CONTROLLED-POROSITY MATERIALS: ANTIREFLECTIVE COATINGS

Chemical syntheses and powder processing in solution are used at Sandia National Laboratories to produce a variety of technologically important in-

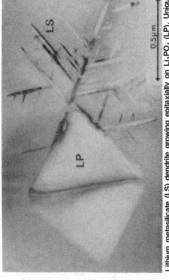

Cristobalite (CR) crystals growing epitaxially on Li₃PO₄ (LP). Unique orientation relationship: $(111)_{CR} \| (120)_{LP} : [1\bar{1}0]_{CR} \| [001]_{LP}$.

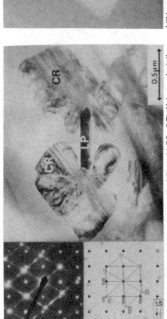

Cristobalite (CR), lithium metasilicate (LS), and lithium disilicate (LS₂) crystals growing epitaxially on Li₃PO₄ (LP). Two orientation relationships for LS₂:

(1) $(150)_{LS_2} \| (1\bar{1}0)_{LP} ; [001]_{LS_2} \| [001]_{LP}$
(2) $(150)_{LS_2} \| (010)_{LP} ; [001]_{LS_2} \| [001]_{LP}$.

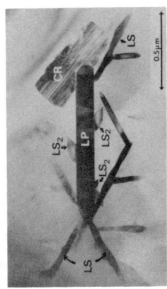

Lithium metasilicate (LS) dendrite growing epitaxially on Li₃PO₄ (LP). Unique orientation relationship: $(010)_{LS} \| (010)_{LP} ; [001]_{LS} \| [001]_{LP}$.

These electron micrographs prove that glass-ceramics can crystallize by epitaxial growth on heterogeneous nuclei formed from an added nucleating agent. Here, the parent glass is a modified Li₂O-Al₂O₃-SiO₂ glass containing P₂O₅ nucleating agent. The heterogeneous nuclei are Li₃PO₄ crystallites that precipitate during an initial high-temperature (1000°C) treatment. Subsequent crystallization at lower temperatures occurs entirely by epitaxial growth of cristobalite, lithium metasilicate, and lithium disilicate on favored facets of the Li₃PO₄ crystallites.

FIGURE 4 Crystallization of a glass-ceramic by epitaxial growth. From: T. J. Headley and R. E. Loehman, Sandia National Laboratories.

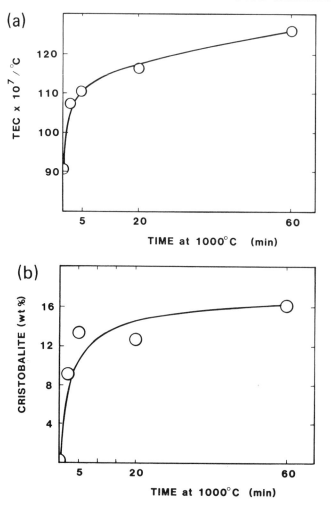

FIGURE 5   (a) Thermal expansion coefficient as a function of time at 1,000°C; (b) cristobalite concentration as a function of time at 1,000°C.

organic materials—for example, electronic and photoelectronic ceramics, catalyst substrates, and refractory glasses. One area of intense interest that has developed in the last five years is the solution-to-gelation route to inorganic glasses—the sol-gel process. Sandia has an extensive R&D program to understand and exploit this important technology.

The sol-gel process uses monomeric compounds (normally alkoxides) of network-forming elements (for example, silicon, aluminum, titanium, and boron) as glass precursors. In alcoholic solutions catalyzed by the addition of acids or bases, the alkoxides are hydrolyzed and condensed to form inorganic oxide networks composed of —M—O—M— linkages as follows:

$$Si(OR)_4 + xH_2O \rightarrow Si(OH)_x(OR)_{4-x} + xROH \qquad (1)$$

$$n[Si(OH)_x(OR)_{4-x}] \rightarrow nSiO_2 + n(x - 2)H_2O + n(4 - x)ROH. \qquad (2)$$

By control of growth conditions or precursor chemistry, the topology of the condensed species can be varied from dense balls of anhydrous oxide to wispy, ramified structures (random fractals). This control makes it possible to tailor the microstructure to a particular application,[5] as seen in Figure 6.

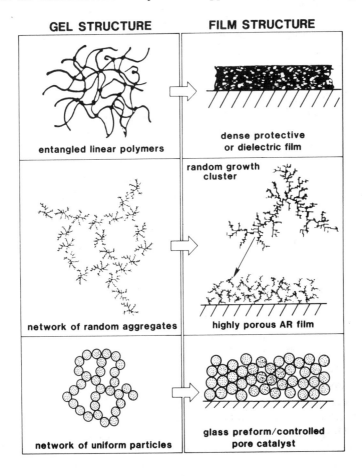

FIGURE 6   Various ways of controlling structural properties of materials during growth in solution.

Inorganic oxides exhibiting controlled pore size, pore volume, refractive index, and chemistry (for example, acidity/basicity) are of interest in high-technology applications such as catalysts, sensors, and photonics. We describe here one application of sol-gel-derived controlled-porosity materials: quarter-wave interference films used to make glasses and plastics antireflective for solar and inertial confinement fusion applications.[6]

In work at Sandia, controlled growth in solution has been used to tailor the refractive index of gel-derived SiO_2 thin films. Working in a pH and concentration regime where growth occurs by a process analogous to random agglomeration, we observe that the hydrodynamic radius of the scattering species increases with $t^{1/2}$ and the refractive index of the corresponding deposited films decreases with $t^{1/2}$ (Figure 7). For a single-layer antireflective film, the reflectance at a specific wavelength will be zero when the refractive index of that film, n_f, is given by

$$n_f = (n_g n_a)^{1/2}, \tag{3}$$

where n_g is the refractive index of the substrate and n_a is the refractive index of the ambient atmosphere.

The very low refractive indices required in antireflective films for vitreous silica, lucite, and polycarbonates ($n_f \cong 1.22-1.25$) are easily achieved by this controlled-growth method.

To understand this process, it is necessary to consider the structures of solution-grown polymers and aggregates. In dilute solution near the isoelectric point of SiO_2 (neutral charge), growth occurs as primary species randomly diffuse in a growing embryo.[7] As shown in Figure 6 this results in fractal structures, that is, structures in which the density decreases radially from the center of mass (incremental pore volume increases radially from the center of mass). The refractive index of thin films is an inverse function of pore volume. The fact that the refractive index of deposited films decreases (pore volume increases) with the hydrodynamic radius is due to the fractal nature of the solution-grown polymers. Whereas dense or uniformly porous species should randomly close-pack to the same pore volume regardless of size, packing of fractal objects that do not interpenetrate causes the pore volume to increase (refractive index decreases) with the size of the primary aggregate (Figure 6).

This concept allows us to deposit a quarter-wave interference film on lucite using a one-step process requiring no heat treatment or acid etching. Single-layer interference films exhibit discrete minima in reflectance as a function of wavelength. This minimum occurs when the optical thickness, $n_f d$, is an odd multiple of one-quarter of the wavelength of the incident light. Thus, by adjustment of the film thickness, d, we are able to minimize reflectance at any desired wavelength, for example, at the solar spectrum maximum, 580 nm.

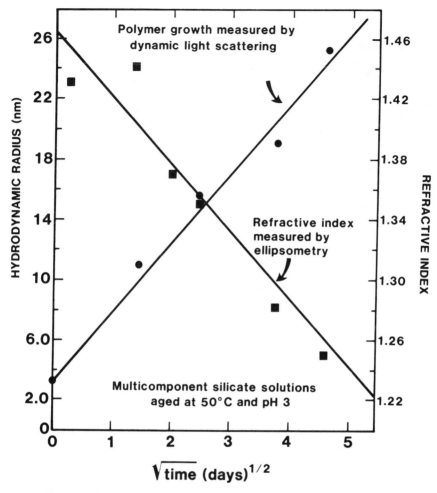

FIGURE 7   Interrelationship between polymer growth and refractive index.

The process of controlled growth in solution to obtain controlled-porosity materials is a general technique adaptable to numerous applications. Sandia has applied for a patent covering these concepts.

ACKNOWLEDGMENT

The author would like to acknowledge the help of R. Chafin, R. Quinn, and T. J. Headley in preparing this chapter.

NOTES

1. G. C. Osbourn, J. Vac. Sci. Technol. **B2** (3), 176 (1984).
2. J. E. Schirber, I. J. Fritz, and L. R. Dawson, Appl. Phys. Lett. **46** (2), 187 (1985).
3. P. W. McMillan, *Glass Ceramics*, 2nd ed. (Academic Press, New York, 1979).
4. T. J. Headley and R. E. Loehman, J. Am. Ceram. Soc. **67** (9), 620–625 (1984).
5. C. J. Brinker, G. W. Scherer, and E. P. Roth, J. Non-Cryst. Solids **70**, 301 (1985); **72**, 345, 369 (1985).
6. R. B. Pettit and C. J. Brinker, Soc. Photo-opt. Instrum. Eng., **562**, paper no. 33 (1985).
7. A. J. Hurd, in *Proceedings of the International Symposium on Physics of Complex and Super-Molecular Fluids: Colloids, Micelles and Micro-Emulsions*, Exxon Monograph Series, edited by S. Safron and N. Clark (Wiley, New York, in press).

Part 3

CURRENT TOPICS IN MATERIALS RESEARCH

Ensuring Contributions to Materials Science from Small-, Intermediate-, and Large-Scale Science

Introduction

HERBERT H. JOHNSON

Materials is not to be thought of as a single discipline, but rather as a broad and vital field of knowledge and techniques that constitute an essential foundation stone of modern technological societies. In that respect, materials resembles other sprawling fields such as energy, communications, and medical science, each of which encompasses several disciplines and is characterized by intellectual ferment and enormous impact on society.

The several cultures of materials research are a distinguishing feature of the field, a primary source of its intellectual richness and organizational diversity. In contrast to many disciplines the materials field in its present form is relatively new. The materials community has evolved rapidly from separate disciplinary bases in the past quarter century. This process of integration has brought a welcome, but still partial, coherence to the field. It is unlikely, however, that the materials community will ever coalesce into a single discipline. The intellectual and factual breadth of the field is simply too great to be confined within the boundaries of a single disciplinary structure.

It is inevitable, then, that the materials field will on occasion appear disorganized, even turbulent, when compared with more tightly focused and hierarchical fields such as high-energy physics.

Materials also differs from high-energy physics and astronomy, again to use them as examples, in the scale of instrumentation required for experimental research. Advances in fundamental problems in high-energy physics and astronomy require complicated and expensive instruments such as accelerators, storage rings, and telescopes (optical, radio, and orbiting). It is intrinsic to these fields that many experiments require large teams of researchers and a scale of coordinated effort that is absent in most other areas, including materials.

Frontier materials research is, in fact, at present carried out in several modes. Small group research is prominent throughout the materials spectrum in universities as well as in industrial and government laboratories, and small group research continues as a vital source of forefront discoveries. In recent years interdisciplinary research directed toward specific goals, as pioneered by the Materials Research Laboratories (MRL) program, has become increasingly important, as complex materials problems have required the coordinated talents of several investigators. The MRL program has demonstrated the impressive results that can ensue when interdisciplinary groups work toward specific goals with the support of well-developed central laboratory facilities. Finally, a small but growing number of materials investigators are working at large machines, especially synchrotron radiation facilities, obtaining invaluable results that could not be obtained in any other way. This is small group research carried out in a big-science facility and context.

These multiple research modes have arisen because of the increasing complexity of many frontier research problems in materials. Progress often requires the use of several techniques and the associated instrumentation. Interdisciplinary groups become an effective organizational strategy for tackling multifaceted problems. The development of centralized laboratory facilities is essential to minimize equipment costs and to maximize the use of expensive equipment, which should not and cannot be duplicated in every investigator's laboratory. Each research mode makes a distinctive contribution to the overall strength of the materials field.

Instrumentation will remain a major problem for the universities, not only for research, but for graduate education. The proper training of graduate students requires instrumentation that does not lag in quality and sophistication too far behind the equipment used in industrial and government laboratories. This is essential if new graduates are not to founder in their early professional careers. The cost of the necessary equipment continues to rise rapidly, placing a growing burden on university research groups. Unless present trends can be reversed, the number of universities with comprehensive and high-quality materials research programs will surely decrease in the years ahead.

The conditions for funding of materials research have become increasingly tight and complicated in recent years. There has been a clear trend toward larger grants on more sharply focused topics, at the perceived cost of support to small university groups built around a single professor and his or her graduate students. Agency program managers appear to be under increasing pressure to turn over their programs in shorter time periods. They sometimes assume an active role in local program decisions, apparently again under pressure to produce specified results over a predetermined period.

This perceived micromanagement of research has put the university system of small group research under additional strain. The time scale in which funding agencies expect significant research results is now equal to or less than the time required for a student to carry out a graduate thesis. This situation has made it much more difficult for faculty members to fund and manage their individual research groups. As a consequence, the university small research group appears to many to be an endangered species!

Problems Facing Small-Science Research in Materials

WILLIAM D. NIX

The quality of materials research depends directly on the quality of the people doing it, whether it is done on a small, intermediate, or large scale. Thus, it is most important, and clearly in the national interest, to attract the brightest and the best to the field. The small-science research group is the basic unit around which graduate education programs are built, and from that perspective it is essential to the entire materials research and development area.

Small-scale research groups typically have close contact with students who are not yet involved in research, so these groups carry the primary responsibility for recruiting for the field. The best candidates sometimes look for ways to be unique and to stand out. They are often idealistic and yet want to do something outstanding that will bear their name. Graduate education through the small-science research group route gives them the opportunity not only to develop their research capability, but also, and of equal importance, to develop intellectually and to prepare themselves for leadership in the field. For this reason alone, small group research is of central importance to the entire field.

A major problem facing small research groups is the escalating need for instrumentation and associated support. The need for modern research instrumentation has been much discussed, is now widely recognized, and is being addressed through various instrumentation programs. Nevertheless, formidable problems remain, especially in the smaller universities. Some universities with substantial past accomplishments can no longer compete in top-rank materials research because of inadequate facilities.

An equally formidable, even more expensive, problem is the need for vastly improved laboratory space and facilities to house future materials research programs. This problem is endemic across the science and engineering fields. Many universities are forced to put modern research programs into space that was constructed many years ago, usually for undergraduate instruction.

The need for greatly expanded and improved facilities and the inability to generate the necessary funds through conventional sources have led some universities to approach the Congress directly for specific appropriations. The concomitant end run around the peer review system has generated a storm of controversy, which shows no sign of abating. It has also surely damaged the financial health of the programs approved through the peer review system.

The universities are not well structured to handle the new instrumentation that is essential for advanced research in all fields of engineering and the physical sciences. Funds are generally not available for new or upgraded laboratory space, for service contracts, or for permanent staff to maintain and operate the increasingly complex new equipment. As a consequence, equipment is often operated at neither optimum specifications nor maximum efficiency. Of course, it is the formal responsibility of the universities to provide funds for these purposes, but they have been slow to realize that modern graduate research programs require new administrative and support structures and sources of funds. The problem is not handled well, even at major institutions.

The Materials Research Laboratories program and the Materials Research Group (MRG) program, both administered by the National Science Foundation, have been a great help in this connection at the universities where these programs exist, but they provide only a small fraction of the help that is needed. It is sometimes suggested that principal investigators at universities should voluntarily include support personnel in their individual research budgets or apportion their research funds to take care of these needs. However, the system contains strong forces that make this suggestion impractical. Research funds for individual principal investigators are limited. Department heads and deans often expect faculty members to generate as much of their salary as possible from contract funds and also to support as many graduate students as possible. The keen competition for funds causes principal investigators to reserve their research funds for only those things that contribute directly to the scientific output of a given project. It is almost invariably counterproductive to individual programs to allocate funds to general support services.

A generally acceptable solution to this problem is not yet evident. It may eventually be necessary to require major research universities to allocate a reasonable fraction of their funds to research support as a condition for receiving external support.

Strong forces are operating to move university researchers away from the small-science mode and toward a team concept of research. These forces include (1) the need for instrumentation, (2) the necessity for sharing instrumentation, and (3) the increasing complexity of many advanced materials research problems. In addition, the funding agencies appear to be under steady pressure to justify their programs in terms of short answers to application-oriented problems.

This trend has positive features, but it surely has a negative effect on the intellectual development of graduate students. The team concept does prepare students for some forms of industrial research, and it allows them to be associated with high-visibility projects. However, team research also very much restricts the opportunity for intellectual growth during thesis research, as the opportunities for exploratory and original research are usually limited. The planning and goal setting associated with team projects can on occasion reduce a graduate student's role to that of a cog in a large machine.

Prospective employers invariably ask about the originality shown by graduate students in their thesis research. They rarely ask about students' ability to fit into a team, except in the context of their ability to get along with people. Originality is best developed and displayed in an unstructured environment. Students must have the opportunity to explore their own ideas and, on occasion, to fail. All evidence suggests that employers of graduate students are interested in people who have been encouraged to think independently and creatively and who are prepared for independent work.

The MRLs and MRGs provide in their interdisciplinary thrust programs a satisfactory compromise between small-scale and team research. Often it is possible to develop a major thrust in a chosen area by clustering groups that operate in a small-science mode. The success of such groups depends on the personalities and interactive chemistries of the people involved. It is a satisfactory experience when it works well but a disaster when done poorly. The most successful collaborations are those that arise spontaneously.

Continuity of support is becoming an increasingly serious problem for university researchers who work in the small-science mode. The research is conducted primarily by graduate students who take between 4 and 5 years to complete their studies, including the thesis. The time scale for this process has not changed significantly in 40 years and is not likely to change in the foreseeable future. Yet, the availability of grants or contracts that extend beyond 1 or 2 years is rare in today's fast-paced world. It is not uncommon to see graduate students shifted from one project to another several times in the course of their studies. This is inefficient at best, and in some cases even destructive to the student involved. Small-scale research thrives on stable support that extends over the thesis lifetimes of several students. Most university researchers believe strongly that they have been most productive (as judged by significant papers published or doctoral degrees granted per dollar) in research programs for which support was provided over an extended period of time.

It is often suggested in informal discussions that the development of a new idea in materials science takes a minimum of two graduate-student lifetimes. The first student explores the idea or effect, and the second brings it to fruition and develops the application. However, because the second part of the process depends on the success of the first, some projects would be expected to extend over several student lifetimes.

In spite of the need for stable support, many funding agencies are not able to provide support over an extended period. This may be because of limited total funds, or perhaps because of a perceived need for rapid turnover in the subject matter in an agency program. In any event, their attention span is all too often much shorter than the characteristic time constant for small-science research. In some cases this means that the most pressing problems of the agencies are not addressed by the most gifted and productive university research groups.

Academic materials research is supported almost wholly by the federal government; industry has not been a stable source of long-term funding. This may change as a result of rapidly growing interest in university-industry interactions. However, current university research is directed primarily to basic problems that are of interest to the federal government. This may occasionally lead to neglect of areas that are important to national economic strength. For example, the materials community has played a relatively minor role in the area of microelectronic materials. Magnetic materials is another area that has been neglected by the academic community. The increasing industrial interest in academic materials research may in time lead to a more balanced national materials program.

To the university practitioners of small-scale science, it appears that support for small-scale science is being continually eroded in favor of big science. The reasons for this are both political and sociological. First, it must be acknowledged that many exciting problems in science require large facilities for their solution. However, it is also true that major projects and big science come naturally to the attention of policymakers in the top ranks of government, especially when they are presented by a persuasive and prestigious group of scientists. Furthermore, the big-science communities are considerably more cohesive, essentially because their research progress depends critically upon the development and operation of large facilities. Hence, there is a strong internal driving force that leads big-science communities to develop a tightly focused set of priorities and to present a united front in the never-ending quest for funds.

In contrast, small-science communities such as materials are inherently more decentralized, for the availability of large facilities is not the primary determinant of research success. In materials there are many areas where exciting research progress is possible; some require extensive instrumentation and some do not. Consequently, materials programs appear throughout the budgets of the agencies, but only rarely at a level that attracts the attention of top policymakers. Furthermore, there is no single widely acknowledged organization that can speak for the materials field and convey an authoritative sense of its prospects, accomplishments, and needs. Indeed, researchers in small-science communities are more commonly critical of their colleagues than supportive. This is a problem that the materials community must address.

Basic Research Supported by Mission Agencies

MILDRED S. DRESSELHAUS

A problem that affects all of the scientific communities, including materials, is the question of how to maximize the effectiveness of the basic research programs supported by the mission-oriented agencies. Independent and persuasive studies indicate that the cost of research has been increasing consistently by about 65 percent more than the Consumer Price Index, independent of what the Consumer Price Index is doing at any instant in time. When that fact is considered in relation to the budgeting trends in federal agencies, the only conclusion that can be reached is that there will shortly be a decline in the number of people who will have the privilege of pushing the frontiers of materials science forward.

The materials research community for the first 25 years of the Materials Research Laboratory program has operated on the premise that the federal establishment would continue to provide support on a more-or-less one-way basis. There is of course a different approach, one in which the research community takes the initiative and provides a much more comprehensive rationale for supporting basic research. The following suggestion has less to do with small science, intermediate science, or big science, individually, than it does with the entire research community and the way in which it should relate to the larger technological enterprise.

The suggestion is to place funding of basic science more on a basis of mutual benefit. The core idea of the proposal comes from an experience that most researchers have had at one time or another—consulting for private industry if they are university faculty members or interacting with university faculty members if they work in industry. Similar relationships hold for staff members of the federal research laboratories.

The proposal is to encourage senior investigators, selected from among the basic research grantees, to visit appropriate groups in the mission agency laboratories for a few days each year to share the experience and expertise gained from years of research in the field. The senior investigators participating in the proposed program would normally be university professors. Many would have significant experience as consultants to private industry; their interaction with the R&D groups in the mission agency would be similar to that of consultants. Participation in this program would of course be voluntary, although in the aggregate it might be expected that about 40 percent of the qualified investigators would participate after receiving research funds from the mission agency for an extended time, perhaps 5 years. Young investigators with less than 10 years of professional experience would normally not be expected to participate. The program might be especially attractive to "elder statesmen" of science, or people who have gone far enough in their careers that they can afford to spend a week or more per year in this kind of activity.

The proposed program has essentially three objectives. The first is to enhance the cost-effectiveness of all programs—the university programs and the programs at the government laboratories, whether they be DOD, DOE, or other federally funded laboratories. There would be a clear gain if this program would enhance the cost-effectiveness of the R&D activities of the laboratories where most of the expenditures of the mission agencies are directed. In this way the basic research programs would gain leverage, and there would be a stronger justification for the expenditures necessary to maintain an effective basic research program in each agency. An expanded justification is desirable, as the cost of research continues to increase, while rapid scientific and technological breakthroughs continue to expand the opportunities for exciting basic research.

The second objective is to develop much stronger bridges of communication between the basic research community and the mission agencies. The benefits of the proposed program would flow in both directions. The results of basic research would be brought in a timely and effective way to the development efforts. At the same time, contact with applied programs often leads to a recognition of new and exciting areas of basic research that are ripe for exploitation. An important additional benefit is that research scientists would be much more aware of the activities in the mission laboratories. This knowledge is important and useful in providing advice to students about the scientific challenges and opportunities that careers in the mission agencies can provide.

The third objective is to broaden understanding and appreciation of the role of basic research, and in this way to accomplish two things: the first is simply to increase the total amount of resources going into basic research by making it more cost-effective; the second is to buttress the role of basic research so that it can provide even more effective contributions to the technological strength of the nation.

To implement this proposal a pilot program with a small number of participants should be established to evaluate the concept and to learn from early experience. If that evaluation shows that the program would be viable on a national scale and of mutual benefit to enough members of the research and development community, then the program should be enlarged and extended to all who wish to participate.

The Two Domains of Materials Science

ALBERT M. CLOGSTON

Materials science is a highly interdisciplinary field consisting of diverse specialties, including physical metallurgy, solid-state physics, solid-state chemistry, ceramic science, polymer science, materials preparation, and materials analysis. Other individuals would no doubt construct somewhat different lists, depending on their perspective, but that is an indicator of the richness and diversity of the field.

However, these specialties tend to divide into two separate domains, the microscopic and the macroscopic. The microscopic view is concerned mainly with atoms and molecules and the electromagnetic forces that bind them. There is a strong emphasis on such topics as electronic structure, lattice vibrations, and the many interactions of radiation and particles with condensed matter. The macroscopic point of view focuses on the properties of matter in bulk, with typical topics such as microstructure, phase transitions, continuum behavior, and mechanical properties.

These two ways of thinking about materials tend to be vertically integrated with respect to measurements performed, instrumentation used, phenomena studied, and the technologies to which they lead. It is also true that few researchers cross the boundary between these two domains, although those who do often make strong contributions.

In the microscopic domain, which includes solid-state physics, the materials and phenomena studied, and the kinds of instrumentation and measurements required, tend to be associated with what are often described as high-technology industries and materials. With some exceptions these materials are used for their electronic, magnetic, or optical properties. In contrast, research at the microstructure or continuum level leads to technologies that use high-performance materials, developed primarily for their mechanical properties, often under a wide variety of rigorous operating conditions.

There are tremendous opportunities to advance the science of materials by horizontally integrating studies of the phenomena that are of interest in the microscopic and macroscopic domains. The integration that has occurred over the past quarter century is impressive, but the full potential of the field has not yet been realized. For example, physical metallurgy and solid-state physics have much to say to each other about such topics as interactions at surfaces, fracture, dislocation physics, and electronic materials. Many other examples could be cited. Both physical metallurgy and solid-state physics would derive vast benefits from closer interaction with solid-state chemistry.

As the previous discussion indicates, there is a close connection between materials science and basic materials technology. This tight coupling is one of the striking characteristics of materials science, and certainly one of its greatest strengths. It is the reason why materials science has been the source of major contributions to other sciences and, perhaps even more importantly, to industrial innovation, and why it has such potential for future contributions.

The strong coupling of materials science and technology leads to a second major point, which is the critical role played by basic technology as a link between research and development. This somewhat unconventional view of the research and development process is nevertheless the view of research and development held, at least implicitly, by most of the major industrial laboratories, and also in a formal way by the Department of Defense and the Department of Energy. Basic research as defined by those agencies, for example, can be read to include not only the increase of basic knowledge, but also the increase and enlargement of the technology base for exploratory and advanced development. Basic technology should be recognized as an important research activity, and as the critical link between research and development.

This leads to the proper place for materials research in the overall research and development process. Basic materials science and basic materials technology should both be regarded as research activities in the research and development process. They couple to basic science and basic technologies coming from other sources to make possible the exploratory and advanced development of systems of all kinds, including systems for communications, energy, national security, and transportation.

It is important that basic technology be recognized as a legitimate research activity. It is carried out by the same kinds of people who do basic research for new knowledge. They use the same kinds of instrumentation and the same research methodologies. They are the people who, in industry, do basic research one day and basic technology the next.

New Demands on Materials Science

PRAVEEN CHAUDHARI

Materials science, drawn from studies at the scale of atoms to macroscopic bodies, encompasses much of what we know about the physical world. To cite two examples: the laws of thermodynamics have proved useful not only in designing engines but also in understanding chemical reactions, and quantum mechanics is essential to understanding many scientific phenomena as well as the operation of the silicon transistor.

Materials science is characterized further by the role of empiricism in the practical use of knowledge. It is sometimes believed that if perfect understanding were available, then and only then could a perfect device, or mechanism, or structure be built. However, as those who are knowledgeable about industry know, technology is often at the same level of advancement as science, and occasionally is ahead of it. Thus, scientific understanding and the building of new devices may go hand in hand, with a substantial assist from empiricism.

The interdisciplinary nature of materials science gives rise to the broad scope of its activities and to its importance. This is also true of other interdisciplinary fields such as medical science and computer science. There are also differences between these fields that must be recognized.

In medical science the issues of purpose are well recognized by society. For instance, no one would dispute that to find a cure for cancer is a worthy goal. There is broad and intense interest in knowing how the brain or the human body functions. There is also a sense of immediacy in the medical sciences: a cure for cancer or AIDS is an urgent need.

Computer science differs from medical and materials sciences. It stands in relation to its future much as materials science did before the laws of thermodynamics were discovered. The laws for computer science are still being discovered. It is a nascent, exciting science that will evolve with all of the complexity that is found in materials science.

Materials science is sufficiently complex that to one unfamiliar with the field it appears diffuse and aimless. There are no specific goals and no sense of urgency. Materials researchers need to articulate their role in society. We at the Research Division in IBM have attempted to do this. In so doing we have found it useful to divide scientific work into two categories, called area science and general science.

In area science, scientists and technologists jointly study a particular technology and extract the key technical issues for today and for the future. Those key technical issues are then examined to extract what is called essential, or generic, science—the knowledge that is needed to develop or evolve technology. Thus, there are two key elements in the process: first, to identify the technical issues and, second, to identify the generic science.

Using this approach, we have found that continuing progress in electronic devices—from data storage to the central processing unit of a computer—depends crucially upon materials and processing sciences. By processing of materials we mean, for example, adding or removing atoms where and when desired. There are many ways to add atoms, including crystal growth, chemical vapor deposition, vacuum deposition, molecular beam epitaxy, sputtering, and electroplating.

There are also many processes by which atoms can be removed. Let us use an etching process as an example of how generic science issues are developed in a given area of science. In the electronics industry, reactive ion etching, an emerging process that is attracting much attention, illustrates the complex demands placed on materials science by advanced technology. Reactive ion etching consists of applying a voltage across charged species in a plasma to accelerate ions, which hit the surface of a substrate. By shielding various areas of the substrate with a "resist," the substrate can be etched in a directional fashion. Structures can then be constructed by selective deposition of materials into the cavities formed by the original etching treatment.

The density of the plasma used in reactive ion etching lies between the density of matter in intergalactic space and that in nuclear fusion. The chemical and physical properties of the plasma of interest in reactive ion etching are not well known. Moreover, the radicals that exist in these plasmas are not well identified. Until recently, techniques for identifying the chemical species both spatially and temporally were not available.

After the radicals have been identified, the next problem is to investigate the mechanism by which they interact with the substrate. Why is a particular material etched more efficiently than another? Why do polymers behave differently from metals? Why does p-type silicon behave differently from n-type silicon?

The etching reaction occurs not only on the surface of the substrate but also beneath the surface. In fact, the atoms penetrate below the surface. They can be found tens to hundreds of angstroms deep, depending on how the process is carried out. It is important to understand this process in detail, for not only is it desirable to have very clean substrates on which to deposit a substance in a controlled way, but it is also important to be able to produce damage-free regions near the surface of a semiconductor material.

One can ask the following question: If an atom or molecule hits a surface, how does it lose its energy? This question leads to many more detailed questions. What are the modes of energy transfer that apply here? Is there chemisorption or physisorption? How do atoms diffuse near a surface when a charge is present? Such questions transform a mundane, practical process into a series of questions of fundamental scientific interest.

To go a step further, there are many processes other than reactive ion etching that require understanding a great deal about surfaces and about particle interactions with them. Such understanding is important not only to the computer and electronics industries but also to processes ranging from electroplating, to catalysis, to the evolution of hydrogen in the universe from the atomic to the molecular state.

The study of complex phenomena and processes in industrial technology suggests two important points. The first is that within a given area of science there must be a spectrum of activities that proceed from science to technology. These activities should be evaluated on the basis of their value to society, not on the basis of some arbitrary criterion by which "basic science" is deemed more acceptable than "applied science." Moreover, distinctions between big science and small science are irrelevant when studying a problem as complex and important as reactive ion etching. Both kinds of science are frequently needed in modern industrial research. In the case of reactive ion etching, many of the modern techniques of materials research are necessary. These include Rutherford backscattering, ion scattering, synchrotron radiation, various surface spectroscopies, nuclear resonance, and transmission electron microscopy.

An important point that cannot be taken for granted or emphasized enough is that the research enterprise of the nation requires an infrastructure that nurtures general science, or science that cannot be identified at present with any particular area of application. This provides the freedom to move freely in a spectrum of specific activity according to the merit of the question being pursued. In materials science three recent developments illustrate the importance of such freedom. The first is the scanning tunneling microscope, which evolved from a desire to improve understanding of the uniformity of dielectrics. When it was shown, however, that atomic resolution could be achieved, the research was redirected into much broader areas of atomic and electronic structure of surfaces. The second example is the quantum Hall effect, which is leading to a better understanding of the behavior of electrons in matter, especially in lower-dimensional systems with various degrees of disorder. The third is the discovery of quasicrystals, which may or may not represent a new structural state of matter but must surely be studied and understood.

Perspectives on Facilities and Instrumentation for Materials Research

Introduction

DEAN E. EASTMAN

In the past few decades, materials research in the United States has emerged as a large national effort vital to our technological and economic welfare. Materials research is interdisciplinary and is carried out through important programs in the university, government, and industrial sectors. Facilities and instrumentation, an essential element of these research programs, are becoming more sophisticated and costly. This chapter presents several perspectives on that element of materials research programs.

Large-Scale Facilities for Materials Research

MARTIN BLUME

Many of the large facilities and the large-scale aspects of materials research originated at Department of Energy (DOE) national laboratories many years ago. The quintessential large facilities are, of course, the high-energy physics facilities. In materials research and in other areas with a strong tradition of small science, these large-scale laboratories evolved gradually; in fact, the first were not built as materials research facilities. They were supported with funds designated for neutron scattering research, for example, from reactor programs.

As a result, there was no problem with funding arrangements until a decade ago, when such facilities started to turn up in materials research budgets. The national laboratories, of course, had their own problems and research programs connected with atomic energy in the days of the Atomic Energy Commission. Thus, DOE not only had these internal programs, but became an agency that also provided large research facilities to universities and, more recently, to the industrial community as well.

The synchrotron light source at the Brookhaven National Laboratory is an example of the large facilities available for materials research. The research carried out at these facilities, as opposed to the high-energy physics facilities, remains basically in the small-science mode and in effect provides research opportunities similar to those in the small laboratories.

For neutron scattering, a fair number of research facilities are available: the intense pulsed neutron source at Argonne, the pulsed source at Los Alamos, and the reactors at Brookhaven and Oak Ridge. In synchrotron radiation the DOE-supported facilities are at Stanford and Brookhaven, with National Science Foundation (NSF)-supported facilities at the University of Wisconsin, Cornell University, and elsewhere. In addition, an electron microscope facility is available at the Lawrence Berkeley Laboratory, a high-magnetic-field facility is available at the Massachusetts Institute of Technology, and there are others.

All of these large research facilities are open to users, and pressures for their use have grown in the last decade. These pressures have had to be responded to by the agencies that fund research in materials science, as opposed to other areas. In the past, materials scientists were accustomed to working parasitically on either a high-energy physics facility or a reactor facility.

The pressures for increased use of synchrotron radiation sources arise from the relatively simple fact that for many generations, x-ray tubes provided more or less the same intensity. With the advent of synchrotron radiation sources, however, came an exponential increase in the intensity of electromagnetic radiation available for research.

Brookhaven has two synchrotron radiation storage rings—an ultraviolet ring that runs at 750 million electron volts (MeV) and provides radiation up to the soft x-ray part of the spectrum, and a high-brightness x-ray ring that runs at 2.5 billion electron volts (GeV) and provides the harder part of the radiation. There are 16 ports for radiation on the ultraviolet ring, each of which is capable of providing up to four experimental beam lines. Similarly, there are 28 ports with perhaps three experimental beam lines possible on each of those ports.

Thus, it is possible to carry out many experiments simultaneously. This provides important advantages, social as well as scientific, but at the same time produces tremendous problems.

The operation of a facility like this differs considerably from that of a high-energy physics facility (where there is only one primary user of the beam) in that two or three experiments may be going on at one time. How is such a facility organized? How are all of those beam lines built? One way is for the laboratory itself to provide all of the experimental beam lines and then take proposals from each of the users. A difficulty with this approach is that it engenders a large bureaucracy and is counter to the way in which materials science researchers as well as biologists, chemists, and others who use the facility are accustomed to working. The bureaucracy also tends to eliminate spontaneity in the conduct of research. (This is one of the major advantages of having an x-ray source in your basement laboratory. You can go down there without having to ask a committee to use it at a particular time; you can make mistakes and try new things.)

The management of concurrent research at Brookhaven is of interest because it involves a different organizational method—having users build and operate the beam lines. The compromise adopted at Brookhaven is to ask for the organization of participating research teams. These are groups that propose to place instruments at the facility. If a team's proposal is accepted, the instruments are installed and the Department of Energy provides the photons for research. In return for those photons, the research team makes this instrumentation available one quarter of the time to small users who just want to come in and do a single experiment.

This mode of operation has worked very well. The participating research teams are left to themselves to organize and to carry out their own experiments. A further advantage is that industry is investing in this instrumentation—something that is strongly encouraged. Thus, a system that amounts to time-sharing has succeeded in attracting a fair amount of money and instrumentation expertise.

Many institutions, including governmental laboratories, corporations, and universities, have taken part in this system through the participating research teams. All of them are involved in beam lines at various places. Many of these are beam lines that have been installed by Materials Research Laboratories (MRLs) and are used as parts of the MRLs. Many of the MRLs located near to one another, including those at the University of Pennsylvania, Cornell University, Massachusetts Institute of Technology, and Harvard University, have been actively involved in this way.

Some corporations participating in the Brookhaven system are not known for basic research. Indeed, assistance had to be provided to researchers at some of these corporate research laboratories to enable them to make even a relatively small investment in this equipment outside their own institutions. Thus, some of the corporate research centers have been opened up to basic research. There has also been a good deal of "marriage brokering" to bring together joint university and corporation programs.

Despite the large number of participants in research at Brookhaven, the facility still functions like a small-science facility. It is as if all of the experiments that required electric power had to be done right at the power plant. Thus, from a research activity viewpoint, facilities like Brookhaven should be viewed not as extremely large single units, but as impressive concatenations of many different facilities and many different types of science. At Brookhaven, for instance, chemists and biologists sit together as members of participating research teams at that early stage. It is important, however, not to overlook the large core cost associated with such a large facility.

Despite the size and complexity of the facility, the operating cost for individual experiments is relatively low. The cost of a shift on one of the beam lines is $80 an hour just for the photons. Although overall operating costs of $14 million per year are not particularly low, the number of beam lines in use is relatively high.

In addition to the participating research teams, many small groups use the facility. For instance, it is not uncommon to see a single professor and a graduate student using one of the beam lines. These small groups can come in at a relatively low initial cost and do this kind of research. Brookhaven has the possibility of providing for travel grants, although this presents one important difficulty—such grants are very useful for small groups, but they can distort the research agenda. They create the possibility that a small group with a good idea but unable to get a research grant will push its efforts in directions dictated by the availability of these facilities.

This important question needs careful attention. This is one reason why it is important to avoid what might be described as "giving away lollipops" with each of the experiments that is funded. It is important not to make research at large facilities (such as Brookhaven) so desirable that people will distort their research in this direction. Balance must be maintained overall in the research program.

It is unfortunate that the funds that are necessary to operate these large facilities often are not fully realized. Consequently, there often is strong pressure to cut back on internal small-science programs at the host laboratory and to use that money for the operation of the large facility. As a consequence of this, at Brookhaven virtually all of the internal research is now based on large facilities.

National Commitment to Facilities and Instrumentation for Materials Research

C. PETER FLYNN

Most university and national laboratory materials research is supported by the National Science Foundation (NSF) through its Division of Materials Research (DMR) and by the Department of Energy (DOE) through the Division of Materials Sciences (DMS) in Basic Energy Sciences. These two agencies have "grown up" as the field of materials science has come into being over the past two decades. Together they are responsible for about $300 million of yearly materials science funding. This approaches half the annual total in materials research funding for the nation, including that provided from the Department of Defense, industry, the National Bureau of Standards, and so on.

The relevant point for present purposes is that both DMR and DMS commit roughly 25 to 30 percent of their yearly resources to the support of various types of facilities. The details differ in the two cases. Most DOE facility support passes into major Centers for Collaborative Research in such areas as neutron scattering, synchrotron radiation, and electron microscopy, which are established at institutions (both university and governmental) in the DOE Laboratories Program. NSF also supports major centers for synchrotron radiation, microscopy, and so on. Through its Materials Research Laboratories (MRLs), Materials Research Groups (MRGs), and Instrumentation programs, it also funds smaller-scale facilities on a number of university campuses. While the details differ, a massive commitment to the support of facilities is evident in both agencies. Still further facilities for materials research are operated by other organizations, including the National Bureau of Standards and the weapons laboratories at Livermore, Los Alamos, and Sandia.

It is a contemporary phenomenon that such a large portion of research funds is directed to facilities. At the time the MRLs were founded in the early 1960s, there were far fewer facilities, of which neutron sources operated by the Atomic Energy Commission constituted the major part. Without question, the current prominence of facilities funding is in direct recognition of the important role that research facilities play in modern materials science and of the unique research avenues that they open to the enterprising researcher.

Such growth in difficult times has naturally caused tension in funding decisions at both NSF and DOE. A further growth of facilities expenditures by a factor of two to 50 to 60 percent of the total appears unlikely, at least without major new resources, because facilities only contribute to a portion of the entire materials field. To help judge whether the present balance is appropriate, one must be familiar with the level of marginal declinations of research proposals in non-facility-related areas and with the level of marginal research supported by facilities-related programs. The decisions are complex and involve many considerations. These include the fact that facilities are justified in part by the finest work to which they give rise, the long time scales required to establish facilities, the cumulative distortion of the research field and the funding patterns they produce downstream, and many others. These are complex issues on which opinions differ.

Despite the current large investment in materials research, the United States lacks desirable research facilities in a number of areas. At the same time, the marginal rejections of research proposals at both NSF and DOE are alarmingly high in the materials sciences, and the ability to fund new proposals from the brightest young scientists entering the field is dangerously low. The competition between these factors presents a critical dilemma in the disposition of available resources.

In the following brief commentary on the roles that research facilities play, the different types of facilities are referred to as *infrastructure, research facilities,* and *collaborative research centers.*

The term *infrastructure* refers to durable, shareable equipment established in a given research environment for use by several or many researchers to whose work the equipment is, to some degree, beneficial. Examples of such environments might be a campus or department. Equipment typically costs between $100,000 and $300,000. It might consist of a VAX computer, mechanical testing equipment, fairly simple x-ray systems, or a robust scanning electron microscope. Such equipment can be kept up and used to mutual benefit by a number of scientists whose main research directions differ, provided that means for maintenance and occasional expert consultation are available.

To be well used, infrastructure equipment must nevertheless exist inside an organizational framework. If there is an MRL or similar organization on campus, these matters are easily handled. The MRGs—surely a much-needed funding initiative—can bring a leadership structure to many other campuses. Organization is required for maintenance and replacement of infrastructure equipment. A maintenance contract on a computer costs perhaps 10 percent of its purchase price per year, and on an electron microscope perhaps 3 percent. These and other operating costs must generally be defrayed by a system of usage charges. In general, few research universities lack instrumentation of this type, although what exists may not be optimal.

The term *research facilities* refers to instrumentation that is more specialized, more fragile, and much more expensive than infrastructure equipment. Often these are commercial systems that perform the primary research itself. Examples are high-resolution transmission electron microscopes, surface science systems, machines for advanced materials synthesis, as in molecular beam epitaxy or microfabrication, and complexes of laser equipment. One machine may cost a million dollars. The facility may consist of a single instrument or several. It may be operated by an organization, such as an MRL, or it may be separately funded. Examples of larger complexes are the electron microscopy facilities operated by DOE at Argonne, the University of California at Berkeley, the University of Illinois, and Oak Ridge, and by NSF at Arizona State University, and the NSF surface science facility at Montana State University. These are generally identified with user programs that draw investigators from an extended geographical region.

Research facilities face a number of organizational difficulties. Local expertise at an advanced research level is generally needed to justify the expense. Costs for maintenance, operating, and technical assistance may be considerable. Again, the need to have experts maintain fragile equipment for nonexpert users raises obvious problems. Yet, these questions must be faced. In electron microscopy, for example, the United States still is not self-sustaining in the training of research talent, despite the major role these instruments have played in revealing the structure of solids on the scales of 1 micron to a few angstroms.

Social factors enter into the operation of a research facility and can influence its effectiveness. Because an expert's involvement is essential, the instruments tend to become captive rather than appropriately accessible. To maintain such equipment at the state of the art can become a funding burden that inhibits other new initiatives. The peer review system has not easily adapted to decisions about organizations with the complexity of MRLs or surface science facilities. The task of handling research facility funding in the best interest of the nation is both delicate and vital.

The third category of facilities is *collaborative research centers*. These facilities include neutron sources for spectroscopy and synchrotron radiation sources (one or two electron microscope centers with uniquely engineered instruments could possibly be included). Research centers involve large-scale, complex engineering and have price tags of at least $50 million for synchrotron radiation and an order of magnitude more for neutrons. When instrumented, the facilities accommodate 10 to 100 independent projects simultaneously, often operating around the clock.

Collaborative research centers provide the nation with research opportunities that would otherwise be inaccessible. Neutron scattering, for example, has revealed much that is known about phonons in crystals and about magnetic structure. Synchrotron radiation is heir to both x-ray and ultraviolet spectroscopies and has played a key role in the contemporary development of surface science. Existing U.S. neutron reactors at Brookhaven, the National Bureau of Standards, and Oak Ridge are powerful and well used but aging; new facilities are needed. Institut Laue-Langevin in Europe has become a center of activity. The past decade has seen new synchrotron radiation centers built at Brookhaven, Stanford, and Madison to join existing sources. None is yet fully developed. At least two more are planned for special production of hard x rays and high-intensity ultraviolet. Although recent U.S. investment in these areas is more evident than in neutron reactors, these developments only keep us abreast of comparable advances abroad.

Materials science has emerged as a field only over the past two and a half decades—the same period over which the MRLs have existed. A significant part of this self-identification in the United States has occurred in concert with the Division of Materials Research at NSF and the Division of Materials Sciences at DOE. These agencies and the field now face a critical problem:

How can we channel more funds into new research facilities when the funding criteria in other areas of the field are already unrealistically high? Either choice will damage existing programs and cause major research opportunities to be lost.

There are two points to be made. First, the field of materials science is not yet organized so that decisions of this type can be made in the context of the overall national program. Second, the field is not well organized to present its needs appropriately in the national arena.

One major deficiency of the field is the lack of a forum for national consensus. This is not a surprising problem for a field that has drawn itself together from the diverse disciplines of metallurgy, ceramics and polymers, solid-state physics, and chemistry. The National Academy of Engineering and National Academy of Sciences have sponsored symposia on materials science topics and organized bodies such as the Solid State Sciences Committee of the National Research Council. These efforts contribute to the broad exchange of information at a level at least comparable with that of the professional societies in the several areas of materials science. It seems clear, however, that a further ingredient is needed to ensure that representational factors in this diverse field are correctly balanced in the consensus. The funding agencies have charted these difficult waters for a decade or more and have operated representative committees. Their experience is now needed in pulling together an appropriate forum in which national issues in materials science can be discussed and collective decisions can be made in the best interests of the field as a whole.

A representative body of this type would not, of course, eliminate the difficulties mentioned above. The debate over major facility developments would still have charismatic leaders urging decisions that are to their own benefit, and laboratories would still seek to have their own machine concepts funded. Small science would still feel threatened by the encroachment of large machines onto the funding base. The advantage lies in having the debate focused in an arena of continuing, rational discussion. Recommendations could be fitted into a logical pattern in which commitments and priorities evolve hand in hand. It would be possible to consider the way infrastructure, research facility, and collaborative research center funds balance with each other and with science issues unrelated to facilities; whether facilities are in fact paid for substantially with "extra" funds that would not otherwise be available to the field; and whether DOD, industry, and others should contribute more to facility costs to ease the burden on the NSF and DOE materials sciences programs. The best interests of the field are not served by having different bodies recommending solutions to each problem separately.

Materials science could reap a final major benefit from organizing a representational body. By doing so it would identify its own voice in the public debate over funding priorities. Authoritative statements could be made about the needs of materials science and about the consequences of their neglect. After all, materials science plays as critical a role in national defense and in improving the quality of life as it does in the nation's industrial well-being and its intellectual progress. The problems of the field are not so much in the division of funds between science and facilities as in the fact that $600 million annually is much too small a national investment in this ubiquitous and still youthful branch of science. Materials scientists need to organize so that this viewpoint becomes recognized and accepted in the national debate.

Instrumentation for Materials Research

J. DAVID LITSTER

Questions of instrumentation for materials research are addressed in the recent report *Financing and Managing University Research Equipment,* a study carried out under the supervision of the Association of American Universities, the National Association of State Universities and Land-Grant Colleges, and the Council on Governmental Relations. With support from six government funding agencies and the Research Corporation, a three-member field research team, of which I was a member, visited 23 universities, government laboratories, and industrial research laboratories and spoke with approximately 500 people. Recognizing that the existence of a problem in research instrumentation in universities had been well documented by previous studies, we asked the following questions: What changes in federal and state regulations and policies would help solve the problem? What changes should universities make? What changes in tax and other laws might help? What can be accomplished by alternative or creative methods of financing?

Changes can be made in all of these areas to improve the efficiency of university acquisition and management of research equipment. The problem is so large, however, that its solution requires substantial and sustained investment from all available sources.

Let me begin by reviewing the nature of the problem, drawing heavily upon work carried out by the National Science Foundation in its survey of academic research instrumentation in 1982 and 1983.

More than 70 percent of the departments surveyed reported that lack of equipment prevented crucial experiments. About 20 percent of the equipment in their inventory was obsolete. Of the equipment in use, about 22 percent was more than 10 years old; only about 50 percent of the equipment in use is in excellent condition. The report stresses that maintenance and operation of equipment is as serious a problem as getting the money for its initial

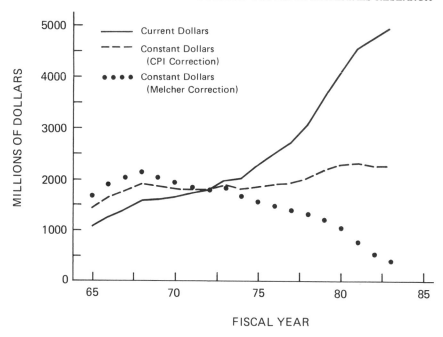

Federal expenditures for R&D in universities and colleges from 1965 to 1983. The solid line shows expenditures in current dollars, and the dashed line is corrected to current dollars using the Consumer Price Index relative to 1972. The dotted line shows expenditures in current dollars corrected for inflation in the cost of scientific equipment.

purchase. With respect to infrastructure, about 50 percent of the departments reported inadequate or nonexistent support facilities.

A further, important ingredient in the problem is the high start-up cost for new projects and for new faculty members. There has been a 78 percent decline in bricks-and-mortar expenditures in real dollars since 1968. This decline also affects instrumentation, since new facilities generally come equipped with instrumentation. Finally, there is the increased sophistication and cost of research equipment in all fields, not just in materials science.

Data in the figure (see above) from the report give a quantitative picture of the research equipment problem. The figure shows the total federal R&D spending in colleges and universities from 1965 to 1983 in current dollars and corrected to constant dollars using the Consumer Price Index. The best data I could find on the proper rate of inflation for costs of research equipment come from an unpublished study by Robert Melcher, a scientist and manager at IBM's Thomas J. Watson Research Center, Yorktown Heights, New York. Melcher examined the costs of the type of research equipment purchased by

IBM between 1976 and 1981 and found a rate of inflation 1.7 times that of the Consumer Price Index. I have applied Melcher's correction for inflation and show the results as the dotted line in the figure. This gives an overly pessimistic view of the overall support of research, since most research costs probably increase at a rate closer to the Consumer Price Index. However, it underestimates the seriousness of the problem for research instrumentation, because over most of the period represented in the figure the federal agencies and the universities were reducing the fraction of research dollars that were spent on equipment.

What can be done about this problem? It is important to keep in mind where the resources come from—well over 50 percent of funding for research equipment in materials science is provided by federal agencies; industrial support, which has never been large, accounts for 3 to 5 percent; the universities themselves have been the second major funder of research equipment and have paid for approximately 30 percent of the cost of equipment in use.

What can these various parties do to ease the problem? Federal agencies, for instance, could interpret their regulations, rules, and policies in a consistent way. The present situation tends to make universities unnecessarily conservative in their management practices. It is sometimes difficult to spread the costs of major equipment across Fiscal Year boundaries and certainly across grant boundaries, but frequently this would help. Numerous administrative barriers increase the viscosity of the systems: for example, excessive inventory requirements and the Defense Industry Plant Equipment Center screening for DOD contracts.

In many cases, realistic depreciation allowances for equipment would help, providing that the funds so generated were put toward the purchase of new equipment. This is not a cure-all, of course, because universities can depreciate only the share of equipment that they paid for themselves.

The policies of state agencies raise similar problems because state regulations are frequently more troublesome than those of the federal government. State agencies can help by improving or removing burdensome regulations. In addition, they can help with tax-exempt financing, although it is not clear whether this will be possible if the current proposed federal legislation goes through. In fact, many universities are now seeking to float tax-exempt bonds just to put money in the bank so they will have it in a year or two. Finally, the states could set up agencies to promote science and industry, as North Carolina has already done.

What can the universities do? First, they should recognize that university research differs from that in industry or government laboratories. University research tends to be much more decentralized than it is in industry or government, and significant funding originates from individual principal investigators within the university. However, it is important that, if universities use creative forms of debt financing to acquire equipment, they must not go into debt in a decentralized fashion. Therefore, it seems likely that resource allocation and planning will become more centralized in universities. Of course, this has its undesirable side effects, and universities will have to make some hard decisions.

Universities will have to cut back on some programs to provide the increased support necessary to maintain the health of others. Each university must investigate its individual potential for university-supported maintenance and repair facilities and perhaps limited inventories of research equipment that could be shared. Iowa State University, for example, has an excellent equipment-sharing program called REAP, elements of which could perhaps be adopted by other universities. In our survey, the field research team investigated carefully the issue of sharing research equipment: Is there enough sharing going on? Should there be more? Are instruments sitting unused? A considerable amount of sharing is already going on in universities, much of which is made possible by the Materials Research Laboratories.

We did find, however, that not in all cases did the universities properly prepare for the realistic costs of operation and maintenance when they were buying research equipment. The universities should try harder to recover realistic depreciation costs. These will, of course, either increase the indirect cost base or increase the direct costs of doing research. Nevertheless, these are real costs that must be met in some way.

We found a further need to work with funding agencies to find an incentive for investigators to transfer equipment to other investigators who might make good use of it, perhaps in other universities. There is little incentive to do that now.

Our overall conclusion was that in the last 10 or 15 years, universities have supported research by supporting people, not instrumentation. Funding by the National Institutes of Health for permanent equipment declined from about 12 percent in 1966 to about 3 percent in 1985, which is clearly too low. Similarly, NSF support for equipment went through a minimum in the period between 1969 and 1976 and has since come back up as the agency recognized the problem.

In summary, an effective and balanced national research program requires that a larger percentage—probably greater than 20 percent—of our resources be devoted to instrumentation, and this must be done on a sustained basis. It will probably be necessary also to increase the size of grants in order to provide this support and to meet the increased costs of operating and maintaining this more sophisticated equipment. If there is no increase in total funding, it may be necessary to reduce the number of grants and the number of investigators supported.

Materials Research and the Corporate Sector

Introduction

ARDEN L. BEMENT, JR.

Many of us have been witness to the increasingly vital force of materials science in the enhancement of U.S. industrial technological potential over the past 25 years. The emergence of new technologies over this period has created demands for advanced materials. Likewise, the development of new materials systems has accelerated advances in new technologies.

This synergistic process has occurred throughout history but never with the intensity apparent today. The major reason for this intensity is our growing ability to devise entirely new materials systems of engineering significance. Examples include the synthesis of diamond and other ultrahard compounds, semiconductor lasers, ultrapure optical wave guides, high-energy-density magnetic materials, high figure-of-merit piezoelectrics, high-modulus fibers, high-purity ultrafine ceramic powders, semiconductor superconductor superlattice and supermatrix devices, polymer blends, and so on.

The establishment of the Materials Research Laboratories (MRLs) was an inspired achievement. The problems faced by the Coordinating Committee for Materials Research and Development 25 years ago are the same problems facing universities today, namely, how to acquire modern research facilities and how to foster cross-disciplinary research efforts to address the more complex problems in materials science. However, the MRLs have achieved much more over the years than the solution to these problems. These labo-

347

ratories have demonstrated that peer interactions among graduate students brought together from different disciplines to share facilities can intensify the environment for creativity and greatly broaden the learning experience.

Unfortunately, industry's exposure to the work of the MRLs has been, by and large, indirect, partly because the focus of the MRLs has been considerably upstream conceptually from that of industry. With the exception of a handful of outstanding industrial research laboratories, most companies do not seek out common interfaces with the MRLs. Moreover, interaction with industry was not designed into the MRL model at the outset, certainly not to the extent that it has been included in more recent NSF programs such as the Engineering Research Centers and the Presidential Young Investigators programs.

However, the existing NSF models for industry-university interaction are still far more concerned with leveraging the funding inputs than with leveraging the technology transfer outputs. Since technology transfer is best achieved through personal interactions, the potential for improving the effectiveness of these interactions through collaborative research, scientist exchanges, internships, and the like is far greater than has been realized to date.

Finally, although the United States enjoys a comparative advantage over the rest of the world because of its strong materials science base, this is not enough in the face of growing worldwide competition. We must also be comparatively effective in strengthening our science base and in exploiting it to add greater value to our industrial products. We all share a vital interest in the success of this enterprise because future investment in the national science and technology base will depend directly upon a strong and growing economy. We must find ways to increase the dividends from such investment if we are to build the university research infrastructure that we believe is needed.

While the key to global industrial competitiveness is not science and technology alone, nations that have a strong science and technology base will have a decided advantage in providing new products and services at the highest quality and lowest cost.

This chapter addresses these and other issues centering on the role of materials research in relation to current and future needs, opportunities, and threats in selected industries.

An Automotive Industry
Viewpoint of Materials Research

JULIUS J. HARWOOD

The Materials Research Laboratories and the many associated events that have taken place in the materials field since 1960 are in large part responsible for our recognition today that advanced materials are key to many future industrial innovations and growth in advanced propulsion systems, micro-electronics, energy conversion, and a broad range of engineered and manufactured products. Accordingly, advanced materials technology has emerged as one of the major thrusts of national policy planning and programs throughout the industrial world, and particularly in the United States and Japan. Materials technology shares the spotlight with next-generation computers, biotechnology, very-large-scale integrated circuits, robotics, automation, and artificial intelligence.

In the past several years, there has been a shift not only in technological thrust in the United States, but also in the debate and philosophical discussion related to national materials policy. Our concerns have changed from vulnerability of strategic materials and mineral resources to issues related to industrial innovations in advanced materials and research and development priorities associated with these issues.

The debate between high-technology and smokestack industries is over. New technology and knowledge-based industrial activities have emerged as the keys for the future—new technology serving both the core of new entrepreneurial high-technology industries and rejuvenating established industrial sectors. There is a growing awareness that the United States' materials competitiveness and industrial innovation potential in transportation, communication and information systems, and manufacturing rest more upon the development and application of advanced materials and less critically upon the problems besetting the traditional minerals and commodity industries.

All of this has led to a remarkable intensity of research and development activity and technological developments in advanced materials (worldwide) and the emergence of new materials industries. Also, it is becoming clear that traditional patterns and segmentation of industrial production are not so readily compatible with accelerated and aggressive industrial exploitation of these new materials technologies. New, innovative industrial coalitions, fresh organizational structures, intercompany cooperation, and information sharing in R&D are becoming more and more evident in this country, as are new modes of industry financing and investment, e.g., R&D limited partnerships. These changes hold profound implications for the development of future industrial infrastructures.

This may be particularly true in the commodity materials industries, in which traditional strength in a single or limited range of materials product classes is giving way to a diversified materials character. This transition is markedly evident in the changing industrial scope and activity of several of our large, formerly single-commodity-oriented companies. One sees a growing integration trend in these companies in becoming, as well, producers and suppliers of fabricated end-item components and consumer products for the higher value-added of engineered products in the marketplace.

In like manner, far-reaching changes are taking place in the automotive industry in its all-out attempt to survive the onslaught of foreign competition. New technology has been pinpointed as one of the industry's keys to survival, and materials technology has been assigned a paramount role in this enterprise. The automotive industry is a voracious consumer of materials and increasingly, unlike in the past, the industry is becoming a key arena in which new high-technology materials and manufacturing methods are being translated into large-scale industrial practice.

In the near term, say by 1990, the automobile may outwardly resemble what is on our roads today, but how that car is manufactured and assembled, the materials from which it is manufactured, and how its functions are controlled are undergoing remarkable changes.

The basic technologies that used to be indigenous to the automotive industry also are changing. Not too many years ago, Ford research was aggressively pushing the development of onboard computers for feedback loop control systems to control engine operations and emissions. In retrospect, it is interesting to recall the debates with the conventional engineering community who preferred to opt for electromechanical hardware, rather than electronic devices, for reliable control systems. Yet, probably the most aggressive in-house training program under way today in the automotive industry is the conversion of mechanical engineers into electronic and electrical engineers to meet the new challenges to the industry. Obviously, as is the case almost throughout the U.S. industrial system, computer scientists and engineers, software analysts, information systems specialists, electronic engineers, and computer personnel of all types are the most sought-after technologists to support design, engineering, development, and manufacturing operations across the board.

Following are a few examples of the newer materials technologies that will exert important influences on the automobile and on the industry.

ELECTRONIC AND INFORMATION MATERIALS

The automobile in a true sense is becoming a communication center on wheels. The impact of electronics and information control systems on driving, engine, braking, suspension and ride quality, transmission, accident avoidance, and driver information operations is only in its infancy. While the automotive industry may not take a leadership role in developing advanced electronic materials, microelectronics, fiber optics, and electro-optical and memory devices, we certainly can expect to see their fast translation and exploitation for automotive vehicle use. In a real sense, the automotive industry will be right on the heels of the electronics and information materials industries, eager to adapt the benefits of photonics, fiber optics, better semiconductor chips, smart sensors, and the like. Semiconductor materials, sensor materials, and information (electro-optical) materials will become as basic to the automotive industry as were conventional structural materials.

STRUCTURES PLASTICS AND FIBER-REINFORCED PLASTIC COMPONENTS

Over the next 10 years there will be a remarkable change in the use of basic materials in motor vehicles. As is already evident from some of the recent announcements, plastics will play a more and more important role. While the current emphasis still is focused on their use for non-load-bearing exterior panel applications, aggressive application programs are under way to prove out their potential as structural materials candidates. There are experimental vehicles "on the road" that are predominantly plastic cars, with rather exciting performance characteristics.

Even though weight saving will probably always be an important objective, the primary impetus for the use of structural plastics and fiber-reinforced composites does not lie in their weight-saving and fuel-economy potential. Rather, it is the opportunities they provide for low manufacturing investment, lower manufacturing costs, and the ability to be flexible and responsive to changing market conditions and more rapid entry into the marketplace with differentiated and diversified vehicles.

CERAMICS

A third technology, which has emerged as a potentially important automotive class of materials, is advanced ceramics. Much is heard today about "ceramics fever," denoting the intense efforts and national programs both in the United States and in Japan. Depending upon the sources one prefers, it has been claimed that the total advanced ceramics effort constitutes between $50 million and $100 million per year. Although the predominant current use and projected near-term markets for the new advanced ceramics lie in electronic applications (such as integrated circuit substrates, packages, capacitors, sensors, and dielectrics), the real driving force for the national focus on structural ceramics both in the United States and in Japan, and more recently in Western Europe, is their potential application in advanced automotive heat engines or power plants. It is the potential automotive engine market that drives the large national investments and the remarkable degree of industrial activity that is evident, particularly in companies that heretofore were not involved in traditional ceramic sectors. Dramatic progress has been made in the engineering of new ceramic materials classes and in fabrication processing for shape making.

It is anticipated that ceramic applications in adiabatic diesels and in associated engine applications will be in production vehicles within the next

5 to 10 years. Nissan has already announced the use of ceramic turbocharger rotors in some of its 1986 vehicles and Isuzu talks about having an all-ceramic engine by the 1990s. Ceramic gas turbines also are in development at Ford and General Motors under contracts with the Department of Energy and the National Aeronautics and Space Administration. There is no question that the application of ceramics for low heat-rejection engines (e.g., the adiabatic diesel) and the implications for superior fuel economy represent a major thrust and a new technology for the automotive industry.

NONEQUILIBRIUM MATERIALS: RAPID SOLIDIFICATION TECHNOLOGY

Most lists of important materials technologies for the future would include rapid solidification technology (RST). It is interesting to note that the largest application of RST in the near term will be in the United States. Iron-neodymium-boron high-performance magnets made by melt spinning for automotive starter motors will represent the first major, truly high-volume application of RST materials. In fact, one of the giants of the automotive industry will become one of the largest producers of rapidly solidified materials in the United States. The use of these new high-performance magnets enables a reduction of about 50 percent in motor size and weight compared with conventional wire-wound starter motors. Here, then, is a model example of how an industry that is geared to the exploitation of high technology can rapidly adapt itself to the development and application of a new materials technology and become a leader in the field.

MANUFACTURING TECHNOLOGY AND NEAR NET-SHAPE FABRICATION PROCESSING

A radical transformation is taking place in the design, manufacture, and assembly of automotive vehicles. Manufacturing technology and, in particular, near net-shape fabrication processing are a key underpinning of advanced materials technology in the automotive industry.

The automotive industry frequently has been called a chip-making operation because of the large volume of machining operations. Any innovation that minimizes or eliminates machining operations and finishing steps has an obvious impact upon production cost and productivity increase. The development of near net-shape fabrication processing has become a major thrust of manufacturing R&D programs. A strong linkage has emerged between materials technology and manufacturing technology, with the knowledge that the success of a new material, device, or hardware concept depends inherently upon a processing innovation or improvement that did not exist previously.

Information technologies obviously are driving the recognition that manufacturing, in essence, is data technology and information flow. Computer-aided manufacturing (CAM) and computer-integrated manufacturing (CIM) have already demonstrated greater potential for improving manufacturing capability and productivity than has been shown by all other types of advanced manufacturing technologies combined.

SURFACE-MODIFICATION TECHNOLOGY

The ability to transform and control the surface composition, surface structure, and surface properties of materials is emerging as a powerful technological tool. The use of plasma processes such as chemical vapor deposition, physical vapor deposition, sputtering, ion implantation, and laser processing has already demonstrated their inherent power. Fifty percent of all carbide cutting tools are now coated to improve life and performance, and it has been predicted that more than half of all machine tools for cutting and forming will be surface coated before the end of the decade. Surface-modification technology involves highly sophisticated equipment. Our better understanding of surface behavior during the deposition and transformation of non-equilibrium and disordered surface structures, which include gradient, layered, and composite films, offers exciting new approaches for the development of novel materials in addition to more efficient uses of materials.

Clearly, other thrusts in materials science and technology could be cited, but the above half dozen are indicative of the new thrusts in automotive materials technology.

CONCLUSIONS

Since this volume celebrates a quarter century of contributions by the Materials Research Laboratories and their predecessors, a few observations about the Materials Research Laboratories are in order. From a research viewpoint—and the automotive industry is a major employer of researchers—the Materials Research Laboratories and associated faculty research activities have contributed to the industry a major intellectual resource and the people to carry out research. They have fostered new attitudes and new ways of thinking that have spurred the growth of materials technology in the automotive industry.

The Materials Research Laboratories and their cousins on campuses probably will have an even more important future role to play with respect to industrial interaction. As our U.S. industries become more mission oriented and less research oriented because of the pressures of international competition and the constraints of economic and other problems, the next generation of research findings in materials science will probably become the almost exclusive domain of universities and research centers like the Materials Research Laboratories. Except for the few companies that can maintain a respectable scientific research establishment, the industrial structure in the United States increasingly will depend on university research for new scientific ideas. Industrial research and development will concentrate on transforming those ideas into technological progress and applications.

Yet we can note a growing trend in academia, particularly in state-supported colleges and universities, to extend their traditional public service role to become key players in state and regional programs to promote industrial revitalization and technological growth. The new, adaptive industry-oriented mission roles of universities bring some concern about the distribution of university activities and resources between pure research and support for industry technology and growth.

Universities also are developing new, innovative modes of interaction and linkage with industry, including the formation of university sponsored venture capital and entrepreneurial companies. These are providing a new academic proving ground for a new breed of technologists and scientists who can take their place in this coming age of entrepreneurship, as described by Peter Drucker in his recent book *Innovation and Entrepreneurship—Practice and Principles*. For an industry such as the auto industry, this is all to the good. The automotive industry in its changing mode needs not only technologists who know technology, but technologists who have the instincts, attitudes, and drive to use science and technology in an entrepreneurial fashion.

Materials for the Electrical and Electronics Industry

JOHN K. HULM

Materials research and development at the Westinghouse Electric Corporation are a vital part of the corporation's business strategy. Westinghouse probably typifies the needs of the electrical and electronic industries for specialized materials. It manufactures electrical and electronic equipment in three general areas:

1. **Electric Power Systems** Distribution equipment, nuclear plants
2. **Industrial Equipment** Electric motors, controls, instruments, robots, elevators, escalators, electric transportation systems
3. **Defense Equipment** Power systems, space, airborne and ground-based radar systems, sonar, missile launching systems

Most of these products make extensive use of advanced materials. About

40 percent of the total effort of the Westinghouse Research and Development Center is devoted directly to work on materials. This includes not only the development of new materials but also the characterization, testing, and evaluation of materials for specific applications. Also included are new methods of manipulating materials—for example, the cutting, drilling, cladding, and joining of materials using lasers.

In Westinghouse laboratories the pressures of product maintenance and improvement and new product development are such that most materials work is highly applied. Currently only 10 to 15 percent of Westinghouse's effort is devoted to basic or exploratory effort—this mainly constitutes tackling basic problems that stand in the way of advancement of the applied work.

In this climate, Westinghouse relies heavily upon university departments of chemistry, physics, and materials science, as well as the MRLs, for new information on materials, new properties, new methods of preparation and characterization, and so forth. It has joined some cooperative research programs, where the fee is modest. It uses university consultants extensively and bids jointly with various universities on government contracts. Needless to say, many of the materials personnel at Westinghouse were trained in the MRLs or equivalents.

It is not possible to discuss all of the materials research relevant to the diverse group of products that Westinghouse manufactures. Instead, this discussion focuses on two particular questions: (1) What emerging materials will have the greatest effect on our industry in the next 15 years? (2) Which industrial requirements pose the greatest challenge to materials research over the next 15 years?

In my view, the materials affecting Westinghouse to the greatest extent in the next several decades will be those underlying the current revolution in electronics, computers, and communication. Thus, a few of the most important materials functions that directly affect Westinghouse businesses and where there is continuing, rapid change of technology are

- Sensor materials
- Integrated-circuit materials
- Microwave amplifier materials
- Surface acoustic wave materials
- Optical fibers
- Laser materials
- Electro-optic materials
- Acousto-optic materials

This pace probably will not slow down before the turn of the century. Indeed, it will probably accelerate, particularly the evolution of the higher-frequency and optical end of the spectrum.

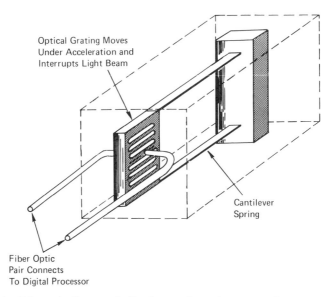

Optical Grating Moves
Under Acceleration and
Interrupts Light Beam

Cantilever
Spring

Fiber Optic
Pair Connects
To Digital Processor

FIGURE 1 Schematic diagram of vibration monitor using a quartz bar to sense movement of the end turns in large turbine generators.

The need for these detection and signal-processing functions for Westinghouse radar and sonar businesses will be obvious. But what do such materials and components have to do with large power plants?

The answer is simply that for the first time in history we have the capability of equipping large machines—such as reactors, turbines, and generators—with first-class nervous systems. We use advanced sensors to detect temperature rise, vibration, electric discharge noise, and chemical emissions. Fiber-optic or acoustic waveguides provide ideal signal output channels where high electrical voltages are present. Data from a variety of sensors can be combined in a probabilistic fashion to diagnose incipient faults. Corrective action can often be taken before the condition becomes serious and forces a plant shutdown, resulting in serious economic loss.

Three examples of new sensors already in experimental use in power systems are vibration monitors that use a quartz bar to sense movement of the end turns in large turbine generators (Figure 1); optical instrument transformers, which measure the current in a high-voltage power line by using the Faraday rotation of polarized light in an optical fiber (Figure 2); and the use of acousto-optic materials to build spectrum analyzers for both military and industrial use. The principle of the third example is that microwave signals from hostile radar sources are converted into acoustic waves in an acousto-optic cell. The key material in the cell has a high photoelastic coupling coefficient, so that the optical refractive index is modulated by the acoustic wave. This sets up a diffraction grating through which monochromatic laser light is passed. The diffracted light represents a Fourier transform of the original radar signal, producing a power-frequency spectrum that is the basis for applying countermeasures.

Essentially this same device is shortly to be used in an industrial application to analyze gases emitted during combustion in power plants, steel mills, and

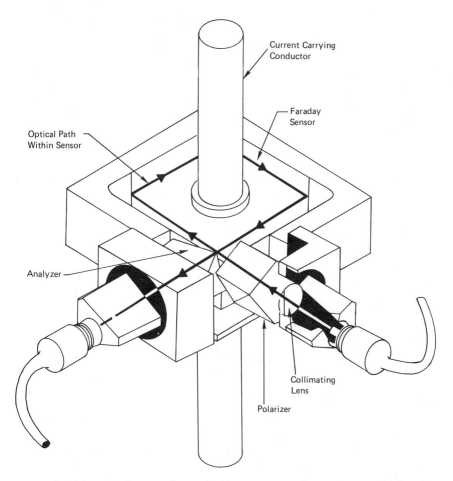

FIGURE 2 Schematic diagram of an optical instrument transformer that uses the Faraday rotation of polarized light in an optical fiber for measuring the current in a high-voltage power line.

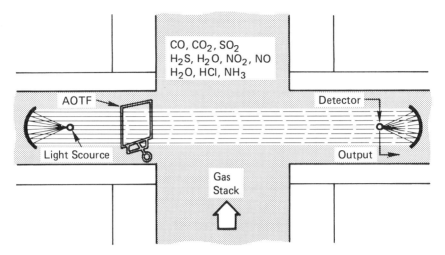

FIGURE 3 Schematic diagram of a spectrum analyzer using an acousto-optic tunable filter (AOTF) to analyze combustion products in industrial applications.

the like (Figure 3). This particular device works in the infrared, and it necessitated development of a new acousto-optical crystal, thallium arsenic selenide.

I see a growing demand for new crystalline materials with special properties as more and more signal conversion and processing are done in the infrared and optical ranges. More complex crystals will have to be grown and new techniques of crystal growth will be needed to better control impurities, stoichiometry, defects, and so on. Even the quality of the electronics workhorse, silicon, is still being improved in the area of device quality, particularly in large power devices for power conversion.

Marching in step with the crystalline explosion is the rapidly growing use of thin films. Improved high-vacuum technology, and techniques such as molecular beam epitaxy (MBE), make it possible to enter a hitherto inaccessible world of new, thin crystalline materials with specially tailored electronic properties.

Westinghouse set up an MBE system that is used to develop thin-film superconductors for Josephson junctions to be applied in high-speed signal processing. The research team has been able to grow single-crystal films of both A15 and B1 superconductors by epitaxial growth on a variety of substrates.

Passive films will play almost as crucial a role as active films, with all gradations in between. New film deposition methods will be needed for glasses, ceramics, and organic materials that will be used as insulators and dielectrics, as well as hermetic encapsulants.

Although the question of where emerging materials will have the greatest impact on Westinghouse has been partially answered, the materials base of electrical energy production and conversion, the so-called energy materials, has not been mentioned. These materials are discussed in relation to the second question, that is, what industrial requirements pose the greatest challenge to materials research over the next 15 years?

Two classes of needs are evident in the materials technology of present-day power plants, reactors, turbines, and generators. The first class includes solutions to long-standing problems of conventional materials—corrosion, stress corrosion, crack growth, insulation aging, and radiation damage. Improvements in this area have been incremental and are likely to remain so. The second class of needs is related to such new materials as amorphous magnetic alloys, fiber-reinforced composites, and superconductors. Here, advances are likely to be more radical but may not be used. For example, U.S. development of superconducting generators is almost at a standstill.

There is always a set of materials problems that are never completely solved. Often these problems are bound up more with plant operation than with basic defects in the materials themselves. In this connection, the extension of plant life has become very important, and nondestructive methods for evaluation of materials are essential.

Defects must be looked for in finished industrial materials. Included are a wide variety of surface and interior defects (Figure 4). Such investigations must often be done under extremely hostile conditions, particularly in nuclear plants, where robotics and remote control are needed.

Various inspection methods have become extremely useful (Figure 5). Most of these have now combined with computer systems to generate complete three-dimensional images of the defect under study. Take, for example, a pitting defect in a tube of a nuclear steam generator—the images may be made from the inside of the tube using two different methods, ultrasonics and eddy currents.

In electric energy technology the turbine generator set is unlikely to be displaced in the next 50 years as the primary method of utility power generation. Coal-fired stations might shift to fluidized bed boilers, and efforts will be made to remove sulfur before it reaches the stack and has to be scrubbed out. One may also view the problem of removing sulfur from coal as a materials problem.

We are likely to see the onset of new auxiliary power sources, even in the next 15 years. The fuel cell, invented around 1820, now seems near industrial deployment because of advances in materials technology. There are several candidates. The phosphoric acid cell has been used in multimegawatt experimental plants. The solid oxide cell is also coming along rapidly.

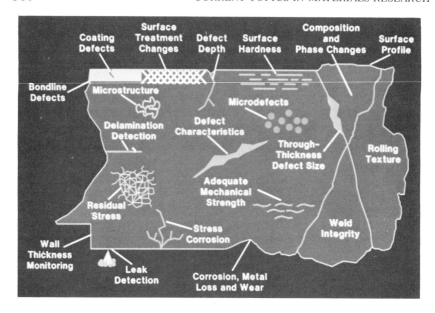

FIGURE 4   Examples of surface and interior defects and conditions affecting the performance of materials. Redrawn, with permission, from New Science Publications, London.

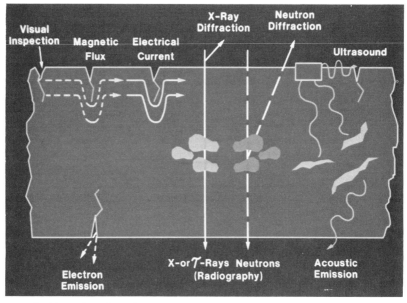

FIGURE 5   Examples of nondestructive testing and inspection methods, many of which are now combined with computer techniques to generate three-dimensional images of defects in materials. Redrawn, with permission, from New Science Publications, London.

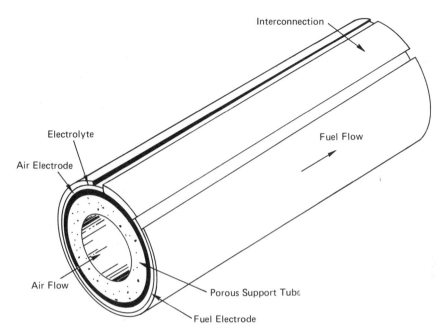

FIGURE 6   Schematic diagram of solid oxide cell, a high-efficiency, all-solid-state power generating device with about 50 percent efficiency.

The solid oxide cell is probably the only high-efficiency, all-solid-state power generating device (Figure 6). The key element is a yttria-zirconia alloy that conducts oxygen ions at 900°C. Gaseous fuel is applied to one side of the tube and air to the other. Oxygen ions migrate through the ceramic and react with the fuel, releasing electrons as they do so. The device thus generates power. It may reach about 50 percent efficiency, exceeding the 42 percent efficiency of a coal-fired plant.

In this area of technology there is a lot of room for research in ionic conduction in solids, and better conductors at lower temperatures would be a great help.

This discussion has focused on the near-term electric energy technologies. Obviously, there are many, more long-term developments, such as fusion, magnetohydrodynamic power, and geothermal power, where the limitations of present high-temperature materials are one of the principal barriers to progress—an area in which future materials research should be concentrated.

Materials Science Research and Industry

HAROLD W. PAXTON

In 1972, when the National Science Foundation (NSF) took over administration of the Materials Research Laboratories (MRLs) from the Advanced Research Projects Agency (ARPA), there were some interesting discussions with the directors, not always totally amicable, on what should be done in the MRLs to differentiate them from the more conventional NSF programs. From those discussions arose the concept of "thrust areas," where emphasis was placed on bringing several different talents to bear on significant problems of a university's own choosing. So, in a recent informal survey of my colleagues in industry, my first question, loosely translated, was what have the MRLs done for you lately?

Unfortunately, the answers that came back stated that they could not think of anything that the MRLs were doing that had sufficiently influenced their present concerns.

The experiment was conducted again at a meeting of the Industrial Research Institute (IRI). The IRI is essentially the vice presidents for research and technology from 270 of the nation's industrial companies. Between them, they spend about 85 percent of the dollars allocated for industrial research.

Members were asked the question approximately as follows: how have the MRLs influenced your research program in the last few years? The question was addressed to representatives from manufacturing companies—ranging from automobile and off-road vehicle manufacturers to chemical companies active in the polymer business, and to others as the occasion arose.

The results were uniform, if not very comforting. MRLs had to be explained to a number of these people, and even after that explanation, no one could be found who could think of any difference the MRLs had made.

I discussed these results with a very respected friend of mine who runs a large materials laboratory at a large corporation. Earlier I had deliberately not asked him or any members of his group because I was sure the MRLs would not only be recognized, but the contributions they could make would be well known to him and his colleagues. He replied, "Not necessarily; I am sure I have a lot of people working for me who have no close association with the MRLs."

Now, what does this tell us or what should we hope to learn from this admittedly imperfect poll? Please note that it does not tell us that the MRL program is not worthwhile or not doing first-class research and turning out new concepts and the people to introduce these concepts into industry.

What it does tell us is that there is a clear gap in communication between the MRLs and at least a substantial and significant number of U.S. industries. In our present set of concerns with industrial competitiveness on a world scale, this is a problem we should address. It cannot be dismissed because many of the industries that were informally surveyed have been in the first wave of international difficulty.

We have seen that a succession of industries of increasing sophistication are now facing heavy weather in being competitive internationally. Thus, we have in the MRL system a national asset that is not having the effect it might have.

Industry has to worry a great deal about markets and providing service to our customers. "Know your customers" is the watchword. It would be interesting to know if MRL members think their real customers are at the National Science Foundation or perhaps in a broader arena, such as industry, where their ideas would be picked up and used.

Good coupling between MRLs and many of the process industries will not be easy. Any time we are dealing in commodities—and these days that means not only sheet steel but also silicon wafers and integrated circuits— the large measure of competitive problems is often developmental engineering and good systems management.

In summary, in no way has it been implied that in any way the programs at the MRLs are other than first class. It is, however, difficult to find out what the programs are, and so, at the very minimum, a "highlights" booklet should be prepared each year to be given broad circulation. The extent of knowledge of MRL programs among many industries in the United States is not what it could be and probably not what it should be. The question is, do we want to do anything about it and, if so, what can we do? As a long-time friend of MRLs, I hope we can find some way of getting even more mileage out of this valuable research program, and I would be willing to work with any group that has ideas on doing something about this.

Materials and the Information Age

ALAN G. CHYNOWETH

The term "Information Age" might sound more abstract, less tangible, than "Industrial Age," more associated with mental processes than physical ones, but it is based just as firmly on materials science and engineering.

True, the Information Age is heavily dependent upon software. But just as sheet music is rather lifeless without the hardware of musical instruments, so also is software useless without integrated circuits for its implementation.

In contrast to the structural, mechanical, and electrical technologies of the Industrial Age, the Information Age makes relatively modest demands on raw material resources and energy and is usually benign in its interaction with the environment. On the other hand, the communications, computer, and control technologies, the "three Cs" of the Information Age, are probably the most complex, sophisticated, and demanding technology systems yet devised by mankind. They are rich in invention and added value resulting from intensive, often very large and expensive research and development programs.

INNOVATION IN COMPLEX TECHNOLOGIES

So complex are the Information Age technologies that, except for the occasional and unpredicted but vital discoveries in pure research, the lone scientist or engineer is usually ineffective or powerless to foster technological advances on his own. Such advances need groupings of scientists and engineers, each person bringing different knowledge, experience, skills, and expertise to bear on a common interest or scientific or technological objective. Much as we might wish to have individual "compleat" scientists and engineers, it simply is not possible. Even teams of individuals in a given discipline are usually insufficient. Overall technological progress and innovation require interdisciplinary endeavors pursuing a systems approach on a mission that captures the imagination of all involved. Indeed, just as scientific progress often occurs primarily as a result of almost chance encounters between individuals from different scientific backgrounds, so technological innovation requires more deliberate interactions between such individuals and groups of individuals. Thus, by encouraging the cross-fertilization and synergy that can come from such encounters, research laboratories and centers in industry or academia can achieve extraordinary discoveries, results, and progress. Perhaps one of the most important contributions of the Materials Research Laboratories on the university campuses has been fostering greater appreciation of the vital importance of effective interdisciplinary collaboration both among those who stay on the university campus and among those who leave it to join mission-oriented laboratories.

In industry, the necessity of relatively large research and development efforts to achieve critical mass and make technological and business progress in risky and competitive industries runs up against the harsh realities of the marketplace. There are two particularly important approaches for helping to achieve this critical mass in research and development. The first is to provide financial incentives to corporations, particularly through such mechanisms as research tax credits. The continuation of these credits is a factor in improving this country's technological prowess and competitive position.

The second is through corporate collaboration in research and development. Thanks to the Cooperative Research Act of 1984, we are seeing more of this. I myself am now employed by what may be the world's largest research and development consortium, Bell Communications Research, or Bellcore, formed by the seven regional fragments of the former Bell System. Another consortium, the Microelectronics and Computer Consortium, started from the opposite condition—traditionally separate corporations sharing a common interest in meeting the challenge from overseas in the push toward super-computers.

These and other consortia may well be critical to ensuring this country's technological progress, but they are not without problems. Perhaps chief among these is when and how to draw the line between shared and proprietary research and development, between cooperation and competition. There are no easy answers to this question. It affects not only research collaboration among industrial companies but also cooperative interaction between universities and industry. The issue needs close attention since its resolution can have a major impact on the prosperity and international competitiveness of this country's industries.

CHALLENGES TO MATERIALS SCIENCE AND ENGINEERING IN INFORMATION TECHNOLOGIES

The seminal event usually regarded as the start of the Information Age was the discovery of the transistor, itself an outcome of intensive studies of the basic electronic properties of semiconducting materials. And ever since, progress in the three C's has been largely paced by the rate of progress in the science and technology of electronic and photonic materials, and this is likely to persist for many years.

A long list of scientific and technical challenges and problems can readily be developed, but the first one that I would emphasize is the continued importance of supporting basic research in materials. On this depends the continued discovery of new materials and processes for synthesis and structure fabrication. Such research has always been at the root of technological progress, and we have surely not explored all the opportunities that nature has waiting for us. Recent examples of such new research opportunities include two-dimensional or layered materials, conducting organic compounds, and magnetic semiconductors. A common theme in this research is putting the process-structure-property relationships on a sound theoretical footing. Perhaps the ultimate proof of the mastery of this science will be the routine use of computer-aided design to discover and create new materials with the necessary properties to meet specific needs.

Second, the Information Age is primarily based on electronic devices and materials. Chief among these is the silicon integrated circuit, which is vital in the areas of signal processing, logic, and short-term storage. We are approaching the limits of what can be achieved in terms of fine lines and component density in two dimensions on a silicon chip. Further advances call for mastering the processes necessary for proceeding to the third dimension, along with finding clever ways to minimize or facilitate the heat removal problem.

Third, for signal transport, the world is turning increasingly to glass fibers instead of copper wires, to photons instead of electrons. But compared with electronic components, photonic components are still in their infancy. The rate at which the universal communications vision of the Information Age can be turned into reality is still largely determined by the rate at which materials problems can be solved. We need advances in the science and technology of various compound semiconductor materials, of nonlinear optical materials and fibers, and of fluoride or other infrared fiber materials for ultralong-distance, repeaterless transmission. We need advances in optical switching devices, in packaging and interconnection techniques for optical components and for mating these with electronic components, and in fabricating high-speed integrated optoelectronic components.

All these potential advances in electronics and photonics portend the era of truly universal wideband communications—voice, data, facsimile, image, and video. In turn, this will put ever-greater demands on information-storage technology. Unfortunately, we still seem to be in the relative dark ages of rotating machinery—involving discs or tapes, magnetic and optical—when it comes to storing enormous amounts of information. With all the wideband transmission and processing technology coming along, mass storage may well become a bottleneck. Thus, the fourth challenge to materials science and engineering in information technologies is the need for advances in the materials aspects and technologies for mass storage.

Fifth, underlying all of the above materials problems is the relentless trend to smallness—cramming more and more information processing and storage capability into a smaller and smaller volume. This trend has various implications. For one, as dimensions get smaller, the processing and diagnostic equipment needed gets larger and more expensive. Whereas a $10 hacksaw and file might have sufficed to prepare a sample in the early days of physical metallurgy, we now need million-dollar molecular beam equipment and electron microscopes to prepare and study samples on the atomic scale. Although these equipment needs are not of the same extent as those in high-energy physics, they are nonetheless real, multiple, and significant, and demand attention, especially at the universities, where the availability of such equipment can have enormous consequences for improving this country's competitive position.

Smallness also usually brings with it more vulnerability to damage, corrosion, and other changes on the atomic scale. Ruggedness and reliability may set practical limits on the component density of integrated circuits. Therefore, study of the physical and chemical stability of surfaces and interfaces becomes more critical than ever.

Though information technology is usually regarded as relatively benign environmentally, one particular facet perhaps needs more emphasis. Many exotic chemicals are used in the manufacturing processes, some of which can be quite hazardous if mishandled. Thus, sixth, toxicity effects, chemical hazards, and ways to avoid or minimize them need more scientific and technical attention.

HUMAN-MACHINE INTERFACE CHALLENGES

The Information Age usually connotes immense information bases on every subject and extensive information transport in various media in all directions before finally contributing to modern society's information overload. We desperately need improved technologies to handle input and output of information, and today's computer terminals have very limited capabilities. We need more touch-sensitive displays and direct voice interaction rather than keyboards for entering data. We need machines with artificial intelligence to digest masses of information and computer graphics and to help us understand it. Other major challenges in this arena include pattern recognition, and encryption to ensure privacy. Another need is for portability and ubiquitous availability of information services; this, in turn, depends on better materials for electric batteries. All these challenges will need to be met before the terminal can really begin to be regarded as convenient and useful for sophisticated applications. In fact, the technologies at the interface between humans and machines may set the pace for the Information Age.

BEYOND THE INFORMATION AGE

Topics such as interactive displays and artificial intelligence are beginning to go hand in hand. This is a particularly noteworthy combination of hardware and software, the synergy between which we have hardly begun to address. It perhaps heralds the beginning of the next age—one that we might think of as the age of the intelligent robot or even the Humanoid Age, in which the brawn expanders of the Industrial Age combine with the brain expanders of the Information Age to begin to simulate simple human abilities. Where this combination will lead is for anyone to imagine, but this vision reminds us of a major challenge that continues to mock our relatively puny achievements—the human body, brain, and nervous system. The functioning of all these aspects of human beings is again based on materials, the properties of which we still understand but little. To understand and emulate nature's success and to develop a robust, often self-healing materials-based system for creating, storing, retrieving, processing, and transmitting information will pose extraordinary challenges to materials scientists and engineers, in collaboration with information scientists and engineers, as far into the future as I, for one, can contemplate.

Contributors

This list includes principal authors of the chapters presented in Parts 1 and 2 of this volume and members of the panels whose remarks appear in Part 3.

WILLIAM O. BAKER retired as chairman of the board of Bell Telephone Laboratories, Inc., in 1980. Dr. Baker received his Ph.D. degree in physical chemistry from Princeton University. He joined Bell Laboratories in 1939 and became head of polymer research and development in 1948. In 1955 he became vice-president of research and for the next 25 years had overall responsibility for research programs at Bell Laboratories. Dr. Baker's extensive service in national science policymaking includes presidential appointments to the President's Science Advisory Committee, the National Science Board, the Regents of the National Library of Medicine, and the President's Intelligence Advisory Board. Dr. Baker is a member of the National Academy of Sciences, the National Academy of Engineering, and the Institute of Medicine.

ARDEN L. BEMENT, JR., is vice-president of technical resources at TRW Inc. Dr. Bement was deputy under secretary of defense for research and engineering from 1979 to 1981 and director of the Materials Science Office of the Defense Advanced Research Projects Agency from 1976 to 1979. He was professor of nuclear materials at the Massachusetts Institute of Technology from 1970 to 1976 and was organizer and principal investigator of the MIT Fusion Technology Program. Dr. Bement is a member of the National Academy of Engineering and has published extensively in materials science and solid-state physics. He received his Ph.D. in metallurgical engineering from the University of Michigan in 1963.

MARTIN BLUME is deputy director at the Brookhaven National Laboratory and part-time professor of physics at the State University of New York at Stony Brook. Dr. Blume received his B.S. degree in physics from Princeton University and his M.S. and Ph.D. degrees in physics from Harvard University. He joined the Brookhaven National Laboratory in 1962. Dr. Blume's research interests include theoretical solid-state physics, theory of magnetism, phase transitions, slow neutron scattering, and synchroton radiation. He is a member of the National Research Council Committee on Materials Science and Engineering, of which he is vice-chairman of the Panel on Research Resources in Materials Science and Engineering.

WILLIAM F. BRINKMAN is vice-president of research, Organization 1000, at Sandia National Laboratories, where he directs research in solid-state physics, pulsed power, engineering, systems, materials science, and process science. Dr. Brinkman joined Bell Telephone Laboratories in 1966 and was director of the Physical Research Laboratory from 1981 to 1984, when he moved to Sandia National Laboratories. Dr. Brinkman has worked on theories of condensed matter and spin fluctuation in metals and other highly correlated Fermi liquids. He is a member of the National Academy of Sciences and has chaired the Solid State Sciences Committee and the Physics Survey Steering Committee of the National Research Council. Dr. Brinkman received his B.S. and Ph.D. degrees in physics from the University of Missouri.

JOHN W. CAHN is Senior NBS Fellow in the Center for Materials Science of the National Bureau of Standards. He was professor of materials science at the Massachusetts Institute of Technology from 1964 to 1978 and a research associate in the General Electric Metallurgy and Ceramics Department Research Laboratory in Schenectady, New York, from 1954 to 1964. Dr. Cahn is a member of the National Academy of Sciences and is on the editorial boards of the *NBS Journal of Research,* the *Journal of Statistical Physics,* and *Phase Transitions.* Dr. Cahn holds a B.S. degree in chemistry from the University of Massachusetts and a Ph.D. degree in physical chemistry from the University of California, Berkeley.

PRAVEEN CHAUDHARI is vice-president for science at the IBM Corporation's Thomas J. Watson Research Center. Dr. Chaudhari received the bachelor of technology degree from the Indian Institute of Technology, Kharagpur, India, in 1961 and the Ph.D. degree in physical metallurgy from the Massachusetts Institute of Technology in 1966. He was a member of the research staff at MIT from 1966 to 1980, before assuming his current position in the IBM Corporation. Dr. Chaudhari's research interests include amorphous solids, defects in crystalline solids, crystal plasticity, and electron localization.

ALAN G. CHYNOWETH is vice-president of applied research at Bell Communications Research, Inc. He is responsible for research in the physical, mathematical, computer, information, and communications sciences and engineering related to new technology and service capabilities of telecommunications networks in the Bell Operating Companies. Dr. Chynoweth received the Ph.D. degree in physics in 1950 from the University of London, King's College. He was on the staff of the National Research Council of Canada from 1950 to 1976 and was director of materials research from 1973 to 1976 when he joined the Bell Laboratories. He was survey director for the National Academy of Sciences Committee on the Survey of Materials Science and Engineering (COSMAT).

ALBERT M. CLOGSTON became chairman of the Center for Materials Science at the Los Alamos National Laboratory in 1982 after retiring from the Bell Telephone Laboratories. Dr. Clogston joined the Bell Laboratories in 1946. His early research interests included the physics of electron tube devices, such as magnetrons and traveling wave tubes. His later work included research in solid-state physics, magnetism, and superconductivity. In 1965 he became director of the Physical Research Laboratory and in 1971 was named vice-president for research at Sandia Laboratories, a subsidiary of Western Electric. He returned to the Bell Laboratories in 1973. Dr. Clogston is a member of the National Academy of Sciences and currently serves on the governing board of the National Research Council. He received his B.S. and Ph.D. degrees in physics from the Massachusetts Institute of Technology.

MORRIS COHEN is Institute Professor Emeritus at the Massachusetts Institute of Technology, where he has been on the faculty since 1937. His fields of interest are materials science and engineering, materials policy, physical metallurgy, phase transformations, and strengthening mechanisms. He is a member of the National Academy of Sciences and the National Academy of Engineering. He chaired the National Academy of Sciences Committee on the Survey of Materials Science and Engineering (COSMAT) and was awarded the National Medal of Science by President Carter. Dr. Cohen received the Ph.D. degree in metallurgy from the Massachusetts Institute of Technology.

FRANCIS J. DI SALVO, JR., is head of Solid State and Physics of Materials Research Department at AT&T Bell Laboratories. After receiving the Ph.D.

degree in applied physics from Stanford University in 1971, Dr. Di Salvo joined Bell Laboratories as a member of the technical staff. He became research head of the Chemical Physics Research Department in 1978 and head of the Solid State Chemistry Research Department in 1981. His primary research interests include electrical and magnetic properties, high-energy-density battery materials, materials synthesis, and physical and chemical properties of solid-state compounds.

MILDRED S. DRESSELHAUS is one of 12 active Institute Professors at the Massachusetts Institute of Technology. Dr. Dresselhaus received her Ph.D. degree from the University of Chicago in 1958. She joined the staff of MIT Lincoln Laboratory in 1960 and was named to the Abby Rockefeller Mauzé Chair in the MIT Department of Electrical Engineering and Computer Science in 1967. Her recent research interests include modification of electronic materials and graphite fibers by intercalation and implantation. Dr. Dresselhaus is a member of both the National Academy of Sciences and the National Academy of Engineering and is a member of the board of directors of the American Association for the Advancement of Science.

DEAN E. EASTMAN is director of development and product assurance for the IBM Corporation's Systems Technology Division. Dr. Eastman joined the IBM Research Division as a research staff member in 1963. His research interests include condensed-matter physics and surface science. He has contributed to the development of new photoemission spectroscopy techniques and their application to study of the electronic structure of solids and surfaces. Dr. Eastman is a member of the National Academy of Sciences. He received B.S., M.S., and Ph.D. degrees in electrical engineering from the Massachusetts Institute of Technology.

C. PETER FLYNN is professor of physics and director of the Materials Research Laboratory at the University of Illinois. Dr. Flynn serves on the oversight committee for the National Science Foundation Division of Materials Research and has served on various National Research Council committees that deal with solid-state physics and materials science. Dr. Flynn is a fellow of the American Physical Society. He received a Ph.D. degree in physics from Leeds University in England.

BERTRAND I. HALPERIN is professor of physics at Harvard University. Dr. Halperin received the Ph.D. degree in physics from the University of California, Berkeley, in 1965. Before coming to his current position in 1976, Dr. Halperin was for 10 years a member of the technical staff at Bell Laboratories. Dr. Halperin serves on numerous scientific committees and panels. He is a member of the National Academy of Sciences and a Fellow of the American Physical Society.

JULIUS J. HARWOOD is vice-president of Energy Conversion Devices, Inc., and president of its subsidiary, Ovonic Synthetic Materials Company. Mr. Harwood retired from a 23-year career with Ford Motor Company in 1983 as director of the Materials Sciences Laboratory. He had served as director of physical sciences, manager of research planning, and assistant director of materials sciences at Ford. He headed the Metallurgy Branch of the Office of Naval Research from 1946 to 1960, and during that period served on a special assignment to the Advanced Research Projects Agency to help establish the Interdisciplinary Materials Sciences University Laboratory Program. Mr. Harwood is a member of the National Academy of Engineering. He holds an M.S. degree in metallurgy from the University of Maryland.

JOHN P. HIRTH is professor of materials science and metallurgical engineering at Ohio State University. Dr. Hirth received his Ph.D. in metallurgy in 1958 from the Carnegie Institute of Technology, where he served as an assistant professor from 1958 to 1961. He joined the faculty at Ohio State in 1961 as Mershon Associate Professor of Materials Science and Metallurgical Engineering. He was named to his present post in 1964. Dr. Hirth's research and teaching interests include nucleation and growth processes, dislocation theory, and physical metallurgy, and he is the author or coauthor of two books and more than 200 articles in these fields. Dr. Hirth is a member of the National Academy of Engineering.

JOHN D. HOFFMAN is director of the Michigan Molecular Institute. After receiving his Ph.D. degree in physical chemistry from Princeton University in 1949, Dr. Hoffman joined the General Electric Company, Schenectady, New York, as a research associate. In 1956 he moved to the National Bureau of Standards as chief of the Dielectrics Section. He was named chief of the Polymers Division in 1964, director of the Institute for Materials Research in 1968, and director of the National Measurement Laboratory in 1978. Dr. Hoffman is a member of the National Academy of Engineering.

JOHN K. HULM is director of corporate research and R&D planning at the Westinghouse Research and Development Center in Pittsburgh. Dr. Hulm received his Ph.D. degree in physics from Cambridge University in 1949. He is also a graduate of the Advanced Management Program, Harvard Business School. Dr. Hulm was a research fellow and professor at the University of Chicago from 1949 until 1954 when he joined Westinghouse. There he has served as director of cryogenics, director of solid-state research, and manager of the Chemistry Research Division. Dr. Hulm has published widely on superconductivity, ferroelectrics, magnetic materials, and semiconductors.

HERBERT H. JOHNSON is professor of materials science and engineering at Cornell University. Dr. Johnson joined the Cornell faculty in 1960 and was director of the Materials Science Center from 1974 to 1984. His research interests include hydrogen in metals, phase stability, thermodynamics of solids, and corrosion. He has served on numerous industry and government advisory committees on materials science issues and consults extensively in the field. Dr. Johnson received his B.S. degree in physics and M.S. and Ph.D. degrees in physical metallurgy from the Case Institute of Technology.

J. DAVID LITSTER is professor of physics at the Massachusetts Institute of Technology and, since 1983, director of the Center for Materials Science and Engineering. Dr. Litster received his Ph.D. degree in physics in 1965 at MIT and joined the faculty in 1966. Prior to his current position, he was head of the Division of Condensed Matter, Atomic and Plasma Physics in the Department of Physics at MIT from 1979 to 1983. He is a Fellow of the American Physical Society and has worked as a consultant to various corporate, governmental, and academic organizations.

WILLIAM D. NIX is professor of materials science at Stanford University. After receiving his Ph.D. degree in materials science from Stanford in 1963, Dr. Nix joined the faculty. He was director of the Center for Materials Research at Stanford from 1968 to 1970 and is currently associate chairman of the Department of Materials Science. Dr. Nix has conducted research on the mechanical properties of solids and is principally concerned with the relation between structure and the mechanical properties of metals and alloys at high temperatures.

HAROLD W. PAXTON recently retired as vice-president for corporate research and technology assessment for the United States Steel Corporation to become United States Steel Professor of Metallurgy and Materials Policy at Carnegie Mellon University. Dr. Paxton received his Ph.D. degree from the University of Birmingham, England, in 1952. He joined the faculty of Carnegie Institute of Technology in 1953, and in 1966 became head of Carnegie Mellon's Department of Metallurgy and Materials Science and director of the Metals Research Laboratory. Between 1971 and 1973 he served as the first director of the Division of Materials Research at the National Science Foundation. Dr. Paxton is a member of the National Academy of Engineering.

E. WARD PLUMMER is professor of physics at the University of Pennsylvania. Prior to his current position he was assistant section chief for surface physics at the National Bureau of Standards. Dr. Plummer's research interests include field emission, angle-resolved photoelectron spectroscopy, and high-resolution inelastic electron scattering applied to surfaces. He is a member of the editorial board of *Physical Review B* and is a consulting editor of *Chemical Physics*. He received his Ph.D. degree in physics from Cornell University in 1968.

CALVIN F. QUATE is professor of applied physics and electrical engineering at Stanford University and a senior research fellow at Xerox Palo Alto Research Center. Dr. Quate received his Ph.D. degree in physics from Stanford University in 1950. He was on the staff of Bell Telephone Laboratories from 1949 to 1958 and of Sandia Corporation from 1959 to 1961, when he joined the faculty of Stanford University. Dr. Quate is a member of the National Academy of Sciences and the National Academy of Engineering. His research interests include linear and nonlinear properties of acoustic waves in the microwave region, imaging, scanning electron microscopy, and new concepts for data storage.

LYLE H. SCHWARTZ is director of the Institute for Materials Science and Engineering, National Bureau of Standards. The Institute carries out research on metals, ceramics, polymers, and composites leading to the development of new measurement techniques and standards. Dr. Schwartz was a member of the faculty of Northwestern University's Materials Science and Engineering Department from 1964 to 1984 and director of the Materials Research Center from 1979 to 1984. Dr. Schwartz has published in physical and mechanical metallurgy, catalysis, x-ray and neutron diffraction, and Mössbauer spectroscopy. Dr. Schwartz received his Ph.D. in materials science in 1963 from Northwestern University.

JOHN H. SINFELT is a senior scientific advisor in the Corporate Research Science Laboratories of Exxon Research and Engineering Company. Dr. Sinfelt joined the scientific staff of the Exxon Research and Engineering Company in 1954 and was named to his current position in 1979. His principal area of research is heterogeneous catalysis, including bimetallic cluster catalysis, and the application of catalysts in petroleum refining. Dr. Sinfelt received the National Medal of Science in 1979 for work that led to the development of new catalyst systems for the efficient production of low-lead gasoline. He is a member of the National Academy of Sciences and the National Academy of Engineering. Dr. Sinfelt received his Ph.D. degree in chemical engineering from the University of Illinois in 1954.

ROBERT L. SPROULL is president emeritus and professor of physics at the University of Rochester. Dr. Sproull received his Ph.D. degree in experimental physics from Cornell University in 1943. He joined the Cornell faculty in 1946 and was named director of the Materials Science Center in 1960. From 1963 to 1965 he directed the Advanced Research Projects Agency. Dr. Sproull moved to the University of Rochester in 1968 and served as president from 1970 to 1975. His research and teaching interests include thermionic electron emission, microwave radar, and experimental solid-state physics.

ALBERT R. C. WESTWOOD is director of the Martin Marietta Laboratories. In 1956, after receiving the Ph.D. degree in physical metallurgy from the University of Birmingham, England, Dr. Westwood joined the research department of Imperial Chemical Industries, Metals Division, in Birmingham. He joined the scientific staff of the Research Institute for Advanced Studies, Martin Marietta Corporation, in 1958 and became associate director and head of the Materials Science Department in 1964. He was named to his current position in 1974. Dr. Westwood is a member of the National Academy of Engineering.

GEORGE M. WHITESIDES is professor of chemistry at Harvard University. Prior to his current position he was Hudson and Dewey Professor at the Massachusetts Institute of Technology. His research interests include reaction mechanisms, organometallic chemistry, applied biochemistry, surface chemistry catalysis, and materials science. He is a member of the National Academy of Sciences. Dr. Whitesides received his Ph.D. degree from the California Institute of Technology in 1964.

Index

National Science Foundation (NSF)
  materials research funding, 338-339, 341-342
  transfer of IDL program to, 37, 40-42, 362
Neutron scattering
  research facilities, 9, 336, 341
  use to study organic polymers, 247
Nicalon fiber, 266-267
Nickel
  in alloys, 11, 74-75, 97, 102, 189-191
  as a catalyst, 181
  crystallization from melt, 157
Nippon Carbon Co., Nicalon fiber process, 266-267
Nondestructive examination, 276, 306, 359-360
Nonequilibrium structures characterized as novel forms of structural order, 138
Nonlinear laser spectroscopy, 304
Nonlinear optical phenomena, study of, 286, 290, 305
Nonlinear viscoelastic theory, 279
Northwestern University, 20, 44-46
Nuclear energy
  ceramics applications in, 242
  materials needs in, 359
Nuclear magnetic resonance
  metal catalyst characterization by, 187-189
  spin echo technique, 187
Nucleation
  autocatalytic, 99-100
  heterogeneous, 99-100
  homogeneous, 96-99
  mechanism in glass-ceramics, 311
  theory, 247

O

Office of Naval Research, role in establishing MRLs, 13, 27, 28
Optical communications, organic materials applied to, 216
Optical instrument transformer, 356-357
Optical waveguides, 229, 240, 356
Optically responsive materials, 216, 219, 356-358
Organic chemistry, strengths of, 206
Organic materials
  disadvantages of, 206
  optically responsive systems applications, 216
Organic metals, accomplishments in, 44-45
Organic polymer chains
  behavior in solution, 277-278

folding in, 247-249, 251-252, 254
regularity, 258
Organic polymers
  amorphous, 257-263
  applications, 15-18, 246, 263-270, 351
  blends, 218, 271-274
  chirality, 257-258
  commercial importance, 248-249, 265
  crystalline, 126, 246-258
  desirable properties of, 206
  doping of, 265
  embrittlement of, 263
  extruded, 253, 255
  fractions, 249
  future uses of, 270, 277
  glass transition in, 257, 259-260, 262-263
  high-strength fibers, 252-255
  impact strength, 257, 271-272
  international advances in, 252
  lamellar spherulitic structures in, 249-252, 254-255
  modulus, 255-256, 259-260
  morphology and properties, 246-263
  piezoelectric, 264-266
  as precursors for ceramics, 210, 214, 266-267
  problems with, 256, 275-276
  processing of, 247, 249, 251-256
  reptations in, 257, 260-262, 280
  shish kebab structures in, 252-255
  in silicon chip technology, 268-269
  single-crystal, 247-248
  spherulites in, 249-252
  tacticity of, 257-258
  thermoplastic, 271-272, 275
  unusual behavior of, 246, 259-260, 270, 278-279
  waste disposal of, 256
  see also Polymers
Orowan-Friedel expression for breakaway of a dislocation from pinning particles, 118
Ostwald ripening, 58, 97
Ostwald, Wilhelm, 177

P

Partially ordered systems, study areas in, 138
Particle-assisted deposition processes, fabrication of microelectronic devices, 213
Pauli paramagnetic susceptibilities, of heavy-electron compounds, 132
Peierls stress and energy, calculation of, 112
Pennsylvania State University, 47
Penrose, Richard A. F., 156